WILDLIFE OF TROPICAL NORTH QUEENSLAND

WILDLIFE OF TROPICAL NORTH QUEENSLAND

Cooktown to Mackay

museum

Published by the
Queensland Museum

with the support of the
Environmental Protection Agency

QUEENSLAND GOVERNMENT
Environmental
Protection
Agency

museum

Requests for this book should be made to:

Queensland Museum
PO Box 3300
SOUTH BRISBANE QLD 4101
AUSTRALIA
Phone: (07) 3840 7555
Fax: (07) 3846 1918
International Fax: +617 3846 1918

National Library of Australia
Cataloguing-in-Publication data:
Wildlife of Tropical North Queensland
Includes index.
ISBN 0-7242-9349-3

1. Animals – Queensland, Northern – Identification
2. Zoology – Queensland, Northern. 3. Queensland, Northern
Guidebooks. I. Queensland Museum

591.99436

General Editor   Scientific Editor
Michelle Ryan   Chris Burwell
With special thanks to Myra Givens
Designed by Janice Watson
With special thanks to Baden Phillips
All Queensland Museum photography by
Bruce Cowell, Jeff Wright and Gary Cranitch
Illustrated by Robert Allen and Bronwyn Searle
Administration Support: Marie Vandenberg and Geraldine de Ruwe

Set in 8.5pt Utopia

Published by the Queensland Museum
First printed 2000
Second printing 2003

PRESTIGE LITHO PTY LTD

Inside front cover: Fan Palms, Bruce Cowell
Inside back cover: Great Dividing Range, north-west of Mount Carbine, Bruce Cowell

FOREWORD

The tropical environments of North Queensland have long attracted explorers, scientists and tourists alike. Today, the rich natural heritage and fascinating wildlife remain one of the region's greatest drawcards.

It is my great pleasure to introduce this fourth volume in the Queensland Museum's *Wild Guide* series. The Museum has been delighted by the high acclaim that has greeted the previous guides — *Wildlife of Greater Brisbane, Wild Places of Greater Brisbane* and *Wild Guide to Moreton Bay*.

This volume introduces the fauna of the area from Cooktown to Mackay, east of the Great Dividing Range. A future volume is planned for the fauna of Outback Queensland, from the Gulf of Carpentaria to the New South Wales border.

Since the Queensland Museum was founded more than 130 years ago, natural history research has been one of its principal strengths. This research continues today, with staff and affiliates continuing to explore and study this wonderful region. Through publication of this volume, it is now possible to communicate some of this accumulated knowledge to a wider audience.

Human impact on the natural environments of Tropical North Queensland is substantial. At this time, the Museum's educational function has never been more important. Despite the pace of development in the region, a rich and diverse wildlife remains to fascinate and educate residents and visitors. In addition, this wildlife is increasingly a major source of income for the region through wildlife tourism, biotechnology and other ecosystem services. It is up to all of us to ensure the wisest use of this irreplaceable resource.

The book is published on the occasion of the opening of the new Museum of Tropical Queensland in Townsville. This major new museum will be a focus for the work of the Queensland Museum in the North. It is another example of the Queensland Museum's commitment to providing its services to the whole of the State, from a network of museums, to advisory services, research, education, publications, Internet resources, educational loans and outreach.

I would particularly like to thank all those involved in the production of this volume: the authors and photographers from both inside and outside the Museum; and the Museum's graphic design team and management, including Dr Peter Jell (Acting Director while this volume was being produced). The Queensland Environmental Protection Agency generously allowed access to its photographic library.

Above all, it is my hope that this book will ensure that all residents and visitors to Tropical North Queensland are alerted to the importance of their natural heritage, and that it will become an essential reference for all those who make decisions about the protection of the State's exceptional biodiversity.

Galloway

Dr Ian Galloway,
Director, Queensland Museum.

ABOUT THIS BOOK

This field guide is designed to help residents and visitors in Tropical North Queensland identify some of the animals they may encounter.

The information presented is intended as a concise, accurate guide to the physical appearance of each animal and includes:

Common Name: The name by which the animal is most widely known.

Scientific Name: The Latin-based name by which the species can be recognised internationally.

Other Names: An animal may have more than one common name.

Identification: Includes body measurements where appropriate; colour details; and any other physical characteristic that distinguishes the animal.

Habitat and Range: Briefly outlines the type of environment in which the animal lives and where it is found: specifically in TNQ, Australia; world.

Similar species: Other species which may closely resemble the particular animal.

Notes: Any other points which make identification easier or brief general information of interest.

Where relevant, the standard descriptions also include several other sub-categories, (e.g. web type and bite for Spiders; traces for Mammals; flight patterns for Bats). The chapter on Land Snakes contains general information on snakes and details the venomous snakes and their bites.

Information considered sensitive in relation to conservation issues has been omitted. For example, details about bird nesting are not given because of the possible problems of egg collecting and nest disturbance.

Every attempt has been made to ensure that this field guide is up to date. However, scientific research is constantly expanding our knowledge of the natural world and there are many animals regarded as 'common' about which little is known because formal studies have not been undertaken.

Users of this guide should also be aware that in the wild, animals may look different to captive or 'domesticated' species. Guppies are common aquarium fish, but in rivers and creeks their bright colouring fades. The reasons for this are unclear. A wild animal's appearance is also affected by its age, breeding condition, and the physical environment in which it is seen.

This field guide is a first step to identification. Readers are encouraged to consult other books or to use the services of the Queensland Museum in Brisbane, (Inquiry Centre 07 3840 7635) or the Museum of Tropical Queensland, Townsville (Inquiry Centre 07 4721 1662) and similar organisations.

Information contained in this book is updated on the Queensland Museum website: www.Qmuseum.qld.gov.au

CONTENTS

INTRODUCTION

Land of weird fauna … Wondrous flora … Land of the Coral Barrier, of coral-girdled green islands, of jungle-covered tropical mountains … Land that shows a diversity and beauty of scenery surpassed by no other on the face of the earth … Meston, Brisbane Courier, 1 January 1901

Archibald Meston, parliamentarian, publicist and promoter was not renowned for reliable reports. He waxed grandiloquently, tantalising readers of his newspaper article on Queensland, the wonder state. If he had been describing the area that is now called 'Tropical North Queensland', his readers might have judged it accurate. Many people today regard Tropical North Queensland as a place of unequalled natural beauty.

In this book, Tropical North Queensland (TNQ) is defined as the narrow, near-coastal strip of land, east of the Great Dividing Range, between Cooktown and Sarina. This area is a paradise on earth for naturalists because of its botanical and zoological diversity.

Tropical North Queensland is in Australia's monsoon belt, where high summer temperatures and heavy, often flooding, summer rain are overriding climatic influences. Summers are enervatingly hot and winters are mild. Each year, anytime between November and early January, thunderstorms herald 'The Wet', a 3–4 month period of torrential rain. The rest of the year tends to be dry, except in two areas where high mountain ranges occur close to the coast. These draw rains from moist sea breezes throughout the year.

The popular perception is that TNQ is all lush rainforests, however there are also significant dry belts of vegetation. Two areas of TNQ are dominated by open forests. In the far north of the region, near Cooktown is a pocket of 'Cape York' with coastal heaths, woodlands and deciduous riverine rainforests. Further south, is a lowland corridor, roughly between Townsville and Proserpine, where dry woodlands occur right to the coast. Here, the only rainforest is found on the summits of a few isolated mountains — Aberdeen, Abbot and Elliott.

Opposite: Near Cape Tribulation, Bruce Cowell
Above: Fan Palms, Bruce Cowell

Extensive rainforests occur in two other areas, which have high, near-coastal mountains. The larger of these is the Wet Tropics, which lies between Big Tableland and Paluma. This is the most mountainous region of northern Australia. The Bellenden Ker Range has two massive peaks (Bartle Frere and Bellenden Ker) of around 1600 m. The Wet Tropics is also the wettest part of Australia. The average annual rainfall on Mt Bellenden Ker is 6500 mm. Both the Wet Tropics and the 'Central Queensland Coast', between species with narrow associations with particular habitats, like boulder outcrops or the tops of mountain peaks. Other species, generalists rather than specialists, range widely in eastern Australia and, in some cases, across the continent or even beyond its shores. The combined result of all these influences is that many groups of animals reach their greatest diversity in Australia in TNQ. Earth-worms, beetles, bugs, microhylid frogs, rainbow skinks, birds, possums and bats, among others, do so. For a

Cycads west of Ingham, Bruce Cowell

Proserpine and Sarina, are lush, green areas with many fast-flowing, crystal clear streams rushing through rugged gorges. The mountains of the Central Queensland Coast, however, are not as high as those in the Wet Tropics and, as a consequence, the area receives less rain.

Tropical North Queensland is an area of ecological complexity, a reflection of its varied landforms and climatic patterns. In its myriad of habitats, live thousands upon thous-ands of native animal species and more than a handful of introduced and very conspicuous feral species. Some native animals are not found outside TNQ. These are the many fairly small part of Australia, this is *the* place to find the maximum number of species of all these groups. It is also a place where many species occur in very great numbers. Insects are a good example. Just about anywhere in TNQ, there would be greater numbers and more varieties of insects flying into a house at night than in most other parts of Australia. Naturalists and specialist researchers alike are drawn to TNQ to collect, observe, photograph and study species, which residents of the area encounter routinely in their homes and gardens, en route to work, or while exploring the bush.

Tropical North Queensland is also the best part of Australia in which to see some of our most dangerous, unusual and rare animals in the wild. Among these are the Coastal Taipan, potentially one of the deadliest snakes in the world and a common inhabitant of cane fields; Tree Kangaroos, secretive canopy dwellers from the rainforests of the Wet Tropics; the Cassowary, the brightly coloured, large, flightless, fruit-eating bird; or insect 'giants' like the world's largest cockroach, heaviest moth or Australia's largest dragonfly.

Many species introduced, either from other parts of Australia or overseas, thrive in and near the region's towns and cities. Most conspicuous and notorious is the Cane Toad, a native of Central and South America. In 1935, Cane Toads were imported into TNQ from Hawaii in the mistaken hope that they would combat insect pests of sugar cane. Other introduced species have 'run wild' in the area and widely beyond it. Pigs, Spotted Turtle Doves and Indian Mynas have, like Cane Toads, taken over areas, particularly cleared and urban spaces. Another introduced species is also in the process of establishing thriving urban populations. The Asian House Gecko probably came here by accident with cargo from south-east Asian ports. This little gecko with a big, distinctive call was first reported in Darwin in the mid-1980s. Since then, it has established healthy populations in most coastal towns and cities from Cooktown to Brisbane. Introduced species are, in many parts of TNQ, the wild animals seen most often by most people.

As in other places, the relationship between humans and wildlife in TNQ is not always easy and balanced. Some species can pose a threat to people. There is a big handful of species which, potentially at least, must be classed as 'dangerous'. Large Saltwater Crocodiles, for instance, 'at home' in

Cluster Fig, Palmerston National Park, Bruce Cowell

any of the estuaries in the area occasionally attack and can kill or injure humans. A Coastal Taipan or a Common Brown Snake, trodden on accidentally, would bite, almost certainly with serious outcome. Standing on a Bullrout lurking among waterweed in a stream backwater, will cause shooting pain. Picking up a catfish without due care will have the same result. A Redback or big Whistling Spider can deliver a painful bite. However, although these and other potential 'nasties' occur in the area, the death rate from encounters with animals is extremely low, because all can almost always be avoided and because very effective protocols for first aid and medical treatment are widely known.

The threats people pose to animals are serious in some parts of TNQ. Several species are at conservation risk, often as a result of human activities. The need for land — for settlement, agriculture, mining and grazing — has resulted in the clearing of hundreds of thousands of hectares of natural vegetation. Such clearing, ever expanding as demands for economic growth rise with population, inevitably creates problems for the protection and conservation of the region's wildlife.

Habitat destruction, either total or partial, has undoubtedly played the major role in the decline of some species, such as the Mahogany Glider, the Northern Bettong and the Star Finch. For other species, the picture is considerably more complicated. A species may be naturally rare within a very small habitat. It can be endangered in other ways, by hunting, road traffic, or feral and domestic animals. For such inherently rare species, even minor habitat change, when combined with accidental or deliberate killing, can be a lethal mix. Habitat destruction, however, has nothing to do with the problem of TNQ's 'disappearing' frogs. This phenomenon has intrigued and dismayed scientists from around the world. In TNQ, nine species of frogs are in decline. All are inhabitants of upland streams in rainforests. The areas from which the frogs have disappeared are relatively pristine and are among the best protected, natural habitats in Queensland. The reason for the demise or possible extinction of populations of these frogs remains a mystery, although there is recent, strong evidence that an introduced pathogen may be responsible.

Continuing conservation losses such as those accelerated by clearing of forests, have been most noticeable in the coastal lowlands. Declines and extinctions cause mounting anxiety in the minds and hearts of naturalists, researchers and managers, but there have also been significant conservation gains. Among the most important has been the gazettal, in 1988, of the bulk of the northern rainforests as a World Heritage Area. This occurred largely through the efforts of the Australian Rainforest Conservation Society. These forests are managed by the Wet Tropics Management Authority. Efforts by the Authority are now hailed internationally as the model for research and management of tropical forests. Other conservation gains include renewed and expanded efforts to conserve the coastal lowlands habitat of the Mahogany Glider; the discovery of a handful of apparently recovering populations of disappearing frogs; and an increased and growing awareness of the need to protect wader habitats, as well as other natural areas.

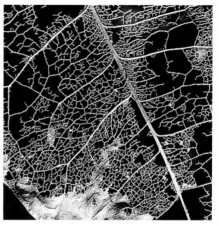

If this book increases awareness of and concern for wildlife in Tropical North Queensland, it will have done its job. If, through concern about conserving the region's biodiversity, some lands that could be cleared, are not; if some bird-killing moggy or wallaby-hunting dog is restrained from such instinctive pursuits; if someone refrains from illegally importing a new plant or fruit or aquarium fish; and if, by example, those of us who care deeply about the values Nature brings to us, influence our successors, this book will have achieved the aims of the Queensland Museum.

Jeanette Covacevich

CAPE FLATTERY TO ROLLINGSTONE

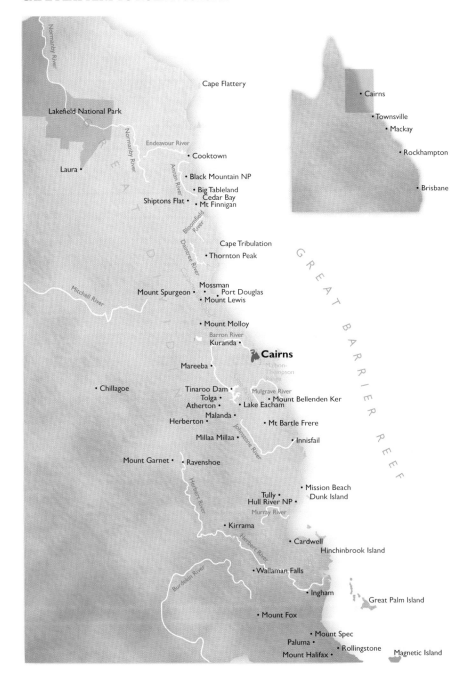

ROLLINGSTONE TO CARMILA

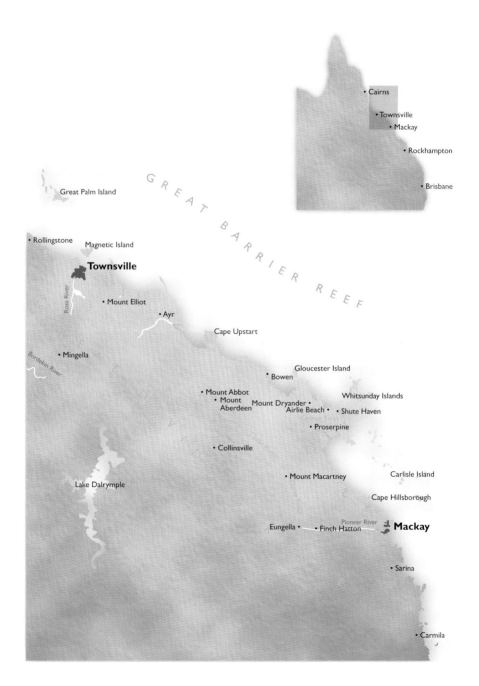

Brown-striped Flatworm, QM, Bruce Cowell

WORMS

Worms actually comprise about 20 groups (phyla) of animals. Indeed, many animals popularly referred to as worms are not worms at all, but the larvae of insects. These include silkworms, glow-worms and mealworms.

The bigger groups of worms we commonly find include the flatworms, earthworms and leeches of forests and freshwaters.

Flatworms (Platyhelminthes) are usually flat and leaf-like. Most are parasitic (e.g. tapeworms), but many are free-living and frequently brightly coloured, particularly those from moist forest habitats. These are covered with glistening mucus to prevent them drying out and to aid their gliding motion. They are hermaphrodites (i.e. containing both male and female reproductive systems) that cross-fertilise and lay cocoons from which adult-like young emerge. Flatworms eat small organisms, but the terrestrial ones may consume large prey such as earthworms or snails.

Earthworms (Annelida) have soft, many-segmented bodies. Contraction of the muscles in each segment along the body and hair-like bristles (setae) move the earthworm through the soil. Earthworms are also hermaphrodites that cross-fertilise. An obvious smooth collar (clitellum) near the head completely surrounds the body and contains reproductive organs. Earthworms produce pale cream cocoons from which 1–2 small juveniles hatch.

Earthworms eat organic matter obtained from the soil. Their burrows enable water and plant roots to penetrate deeper into the soil. Earthworms are often encountered on the surface after heavy rain because the watertable rises and drowning could occur. Up to 400 earthworms per square metre have been recorded in pastures and they can weigh up to 4 tonnes per hectare.

There are about 350 native species in Australia with many more yet to be discovered. Nearly 20 per cent of Queensland's earthworms are introduced and include those sold by worm farms, found in compost and in disturbed forests of the tropics. One species originally from Brazil, the parthenogenetic (self-fertilising) *Pontoscolex corethrurus*, is widespread and frequently encountered in the wet areas around Mackay and the Wet Tropics.

Leeches (Annelida) are related to earthworms, but most have only 34 body segments. A sucker surrounds the mouth and at the other end is a larger sucker. It is just behind the anus that opens on the back. Typically leeches have jaws and sometimes teeth and many secrete fluids to inhibit blood clotting. Some leeches, however, consume their invertebrate prey whole. Leeches are hermaphrodites that cross-fertilise and produce cocoons from which tiny juveniles emerge.

Gordian worms (Nematomorpha) are related to roundworms. They are long and hair-like or wire-like. As juveniles they parasitise insects and when mature they induce the host to go near water; it is then that they break free. The adults are free-living and do not feed, but live for many months on accumulated reserves. During this time the males and females seek a mate. Eggs are laid in strings in water or on wet vegetation and may be ingested accidentally by an insect when it feeds or drinks. Their common name is derived from the Gordian Knot of antiquity because of the complex tangles the worms may form.

Lester Cannon

Flatworms

Leigh Winsor

New Guinea Flatworm
Platydemus manokwari

Identification: Length 4–5 cm. Broad, tapered at each end; upper surface olive-brown with thin cream stripes along middle and sides where brown fades to cream belly. Head greyish, two prominent eyes either side of snout-like tip.

Habitat and Range: Under rotting vegetation, leaf litter, rotting timber and banana leaf bases in gardens, particularly around compost heaps. Human-modified habitats, Lockhart R. (Cape York) to Townsville, Qld; native to New Guinea highlands. Transported around Pacific with cultivated plants, (e.g. bananas, taro, palms).

Notes: Feeds on native and introduced snails, other flatworms. Introduced to some Pacific islands to control Giant African Snail pest (see p. 17). Seen in TNQ gardens after heavy rain when driven out of waterlogged habitat.

QM, Bruce Cowell

Long Wanderer Flatworm
Dolichoplana sp.

Identification: Length 5–10 cm. Long, thin like a shoe lace, grey-black with fine, paired light and dark stripes along back; pale grey belly. Head slightly tapered, two small eyes.

Habitat and Range: Under rotting vegetation, logs, in soil in gardens and open eucalypt woodland of Dry Tropics. Found crawling on driveways late in wet season when driven from waterlogged habitat. Native to Qld Dry Tropics, but transported in soil to other areas.

Notes: Appears to feed only on earthworms; major pest of earthworm farms from northern to south-eastern Qld. Most outbreaks result from introduction of earthworm stock contaminated with flatworms.

Brown-striped Flatworm
Caenoplana sp.

Identification: Length 7–10 cm. Long, thin, tapered at each end; back pale rusty-brown to cream, four fine brown stripes separated by intervals of cream along length; belly creamish-white. Head end pinkish-brown, many fine eye spots around tip and clustered on sides.

Habitat and Range: Common under rotting timber, leaf litter and pot plants in gardens. Suburban areas, Cairns to Bowen, Qld; possibly introduced from New Guinea or New Caledonia.

Notes: Often in large numbers on cool moist early mornings in March–May, especially after heavy rains, climbing walls of houses, in bathrooms, on vegetation and driveways.

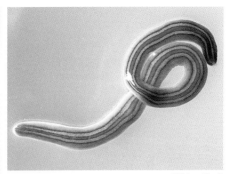

QM, Bruce Cowell

Southern Dugesia Flatworm
Dugesia notogaea

Identification: Up to 15 mm long, 4 mm wide. Back coarsely mottled grey, pale brown or reddish-brown, with pale edges; belly translucent white to pale grey. Head low, triangular, two small eyes in pale patches.

Habitat and Range: Under stones in fast flowing, shallow stretches of rivers and creeks. Native to Townsville–Charters Towers–Burdekin area, Qld.

Notes: Predators of small freshwater animals.

Leigh Winsor

QM

Temnocephala
Temnocephala spp.

Identification: Length about 1–2cm. White, grey, brown to black; five tiny tentacles on head and posterior sucker under tail end. Leech-like looping movements.

Habitat and Range: Symbiotic — found on surface of freshwater shrimps and crayfish. Numerous species associated with different crayfish. Australia has richest fauna, but also found in South America, South-East Asia and Madagascar.

Notes: Opportunistic feeders on microscopic animals; sometimes cannibalistic.

Leeches

QM, Jeff Wright

Elegant Leech
Goddardobdella elegans

Identification: Length 20–60 mm. Three colourful stripes along body. Red-fawn stripe along middle, may be widened into triangular patch at end; two narrow yellow-grey stripes bounded by black on each side of middle stripe. Head end with 5 pairs of eyes, three obvious pairs followed by 4th and 5th between side stripes. Large sucker at tail end.

Habitat and Range: Aquatic, especially in slow streams and ponds. Common, NT, Townsville, Qld, to Grafton, NSW; New Guinea.

Notes: Blood-feeding. Seems unable to bite dry skin. Graceful rapid swimmers, may rest just out of water. Occasionally invade teats of cows and may grow large, white and flaccid.

Earthworms

Queensland Turquoise Earthworm
Terriswalkerius terrareginae

Identification: Length about 60 cm, diameter about 2 cm. Turquoise to grey-blue.

Habitat and Range: Rainforest in soil, found on surface after heavy rain. Upland areas of Wet Tropics, Cape Tribulation to Atherton Tableland, Qld.

M Trenerry

Gordian Worms

Speckled Gordian Worms
Chordodes spp.

Identification: Length 25–30 cm, about 1 mm thick. Brown with dark, rough speckling along length of body. Body stiff, wire-like; coils slowly and seems to get tangled when alive.

Habitat and Range: Aquatic, especially in slow streams and ponds. Worldwide.

Notes: Not commonly seen. Juveniles are parasites of mantids and stick insects.

Similar species: Smooth Gordian Worms (*Gordius* spp.), smooth, golden brown. Juveniles are parasites of grasshoppers and crickets.

QM, Bruce Cowell

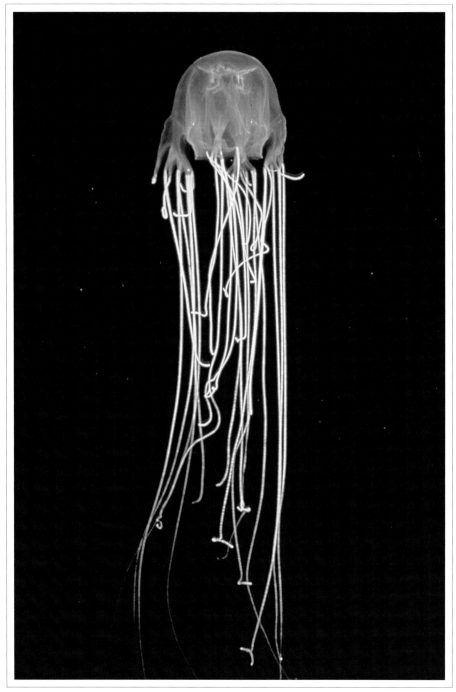

Northern Australian Box Jellyfish, Great Barrier Reef Marine Park Authority

BOX JELLYFISH

Severe marine stings by 'some sort of jellyfish' have been recorded from Tropical North Queensland since 1884, but they were not substantiated until 1955. In that year, a five-year-old boy died in Cardwell from a suspected marine sting. The subsequent effort to find and identify the animal concerned resulted in the identification of a large 'jellyfish', *Chironex fleckeri*. The Northern Australian Box Jellyfish is now recognised as amongst the most venomous creatures known and has caused at least 60 fatalities in Australia. It is not a typical jellyfish (Scyphozoa), but belongs to the Cubozoa, a group characterised by the placement of the tentacles at the four 'corners' of the body.

Northern Australian Box Jellyfish
Chironex fleckeri

Other Names: Sea wasp, Chironex box jellyfish, Big stinger, Sea stinger.

Identification. Body transparent, faintly blue, milky-white, sometimes brownish, box-like bell (2.5 to 25 cm across); up to 60 ribbon-shaped tentacles in four groups at corners of bell; tentacles remarkably contractile, range in size from a few centimetres to many metres long.

Habitat and Range: Mainly shallow coastal waters, estuaries, near mouths of creeks and coastal rivers; especially numerous near river outlets after heavy rains; does not appear to venture far off coast (no more than about 300 m out to sea). Tropical Australia, Dampier, WA, to Agnes Waters, Qld. In coastal waters of TNQ year-round, but dominant during warmer months; most stings October to early June.

Stings: Tentacles dangerous to swimmers; contain millions of microscopic stinging cells that discharge venom on contact with skin. Stings severely painful. Each stinging cell produces single, large, red welt; multiple stings produce series of long, whip-like lines; affected area quickly becomes intensely swollen and red, may be accompanied by 'severe sickness'. Stings may eventually blister and leave permanent scarring. Massive stings (e.g. direct contact with several metres of tentacles) may be fatal.

Protection and Avoidance: Stinging cells only discharge on direct contact with skin. Protective clothing best way to avoid stings (e.g. lycra stinger suits), but even thin full body covering will serve same purpose.

Emergency Treatment: Seek immediate medical assistance. If stung, immediately flood area with vinegar (inactivates stinging cells on tentacles that stick to skin). Do not rub sting with hands, towels or sand. Do not use any other liquid before vinegar. Tentacles may be carefully removed by hand, but may cause further 'firing' of stinging cells. Pain from minor stings may be alleviated using iced water, but only after vinegar is first used. Aspirin may also help relieve pain. **For large stings to limbs, compression will help reduce circulation of venom through body; immobilise limb (as for snake bite, (see p. 237), with vinegar soaked bandage. Victim's survival is dependent on care and monitoring. Do not move victim. Monitor breathing and heartbeat and employ expired air resuscitation (EAR) and cardiopulmonary resuscitation (CPR) as required.** Anti-venom available from Surf Life-saving Patrols on patrolled beaches in TNQ.

John NA Hooper

Rhynchotrochus macgillivrayi, QM

LAND SNAILS

The greatest regional diversity of land snails in Australia occurs in Tropical North Queensland. Here, a dense coverage of moist, lush rainforests has provided ideal conditions for the evolution of a rich land snail fauna.

The rainforests of the Wet Tropics and Conway Range–Eungella region are home to more than 300 species of native land snails. Most are confined to these areas, even to the tops of single mountain peaks. A smaller number have more widespread distributions.

Among the land snails of Tropical North Queensland are some of the smallest and largest species in Australia and some spectacularly coloured slugs and semi-slugs (snails with a small, thin shell). In the Wet Tropics, there are several arboreal or tree snails. Unlike the vast majority of species that live on the forest floor under logs and rocks, tree snails live on the leaves, branches and trunks of trees.

Although most species are native, several have been introduced by humans. Many of these can be found in suburban gardens. The Giant African Snail (an agricultural pest) occurred near Gordon-vale in the mid-1970s, but was successfully eradicated. This species is widespread in the Indo-Pacific region and remains a serious threat to Australian agriculture.

Identification is based on the features of the shell such as size, shape, colour and sculpture. Sculpture can be spiral (in the direction of coiling) or radial (at right angles to the direction of coiling). The measurements and descriptions here are based on adult specimens. In many groups of snails, an adult shell can be identified by the thickened and slightly bent back (reflected) lip that develops in the final stage of growth. However, in other groups, more subtle characteristics are needed to determine the age of a shell. In the case of slugs (and to a lesser extent semi-slugs), animal characteristics are key features for identification.

John Stanisic

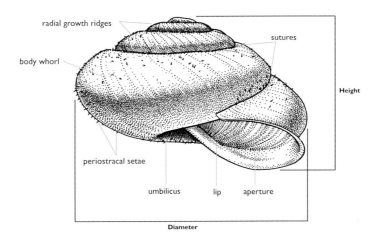

QM

Pleuropoma gouldiana

Identification: Shell diameter 6 mm. Top-shaped, profile sharply angled; lip thickened; no umbilicus; operculum present. Yellow to brownish-pink with irregular, diffuse brown markings or single brown spiral band. Deep spiral grooves. Animal light brown.

Habitat and Range: Arboreal, on leaves of rainforest trees. Torres Strait to south of Mossman, Qld.

Similar Species: *P. macleayi,* south of Mossman to Innisfail, Qld.

QM

Pupina thomsoni

Identification: Shell height 7 mm. Shiny, smooth, bullet-shaped; strongly thickened lip; no umbilicus; operculum present. Yellow to pinkish-white. Animal brown.

Habitat and Range: Rotten logs in rainforest. Mossman to Innisfail, Qld.

Notes: One of several related species in Wet Tropics.

QM

Pupina meridionalis

Identification: Shell height 12 mm. Shiny, smooth, bullet-shaped; strongly thickened lip; no umbilicus; operculum present. Yellow. Animal white.

Habitat and Range: Rotten logs and under rocks in rainforest. Shute Harbour to Rockhampton, Qld.

Notes: One of several related species in Proserpine–Mackay region.

Subulina octona

Identification: Shell height to 20 mm. Shiny, smooth, elongated; no umbilicus. White to dirty yellow. Animal small, yellow.

Habitat and Range: Leaf litter in disturbed areas. Torres Strait to Mission Beach, Qld.

Notes: Introduced.

QM

Coelocion australis

Identification: Shell height to 40 mm. Long, thin; drab with fine, radial ribs; umbilicus tiny; tip of shell usually missing. Dirty grey. Animal yellow.

Habitat and Range: Among rocky gravel in rainforest. Bowen to Sarina, Qld.

QM

Strangesta sheridani

Identification: Shell diameter 30–40 mm. Almost flat spire, thin lip; umbilicus widely open; prominent radial ribs; base smooth. Yellow to brown. Animal brown with central creamy stripe on long neck.

Habitat and Range: Under logs and rocks in rainforest. Helenvale to Ingham, Qld.

Notes: Carnivorous, preys on invertebrates, including other land snails.

QM

Strangesta franklandiensis

Identification: Shell diameter to 35 mm. Almost flat spire; thin lip; umbilicus widely open; fine radial ribs crossed by several spiral grooves; base smooth. Yellow with a few, darker brown radial markings. Animal dark grey with white central stripe on neck.

Habitat and Range: Under logs and rocks in rainforest. Cape York to Cardwell, Qld.

Notes: Carnivorous.

QM

Strangesta ptychomphala

Identification: Shell diameter to 30 mm. Large, with strong radial growth lines and open umbilicus. Yellow. Animal brown.

Habitat and Range: Under logs and rocks in rainforest. Townsville to Bowen, Qld.

Notes: Similar species, *S. confusa*, in rainforest, Proserpine to Sarina, Qld.

QM

QM

Pandofella whitei

Identification: Shell diameter 30 mm. Ear-shaped; drab, smooth; no umbilicus. Yellow with broken, spiral brown bands. Animal greyish-brown.

Habitat and Range: Rotting palm litter in wet rainforest. Clarke Ra. (Dalrymple Heights–Mt Macartney), Qld.

Notes: Shell shape similar to true semi-slugs (see p. 13).

QM

Pedinogyra effossa

Identification: Shell diameter to 75 mm. Very large, flattened; smooth with wide, excavate umbilicus. Brown to white with brown bands above, brown below. Animal grey.

Habitat and Range: Buried under leaves or soil in rainforest. Proserpine to Mackay, Qld.

QM

Danielleilona marycolliverae

Identification: Shell diameter 5–6 mm. Flat spire, strong radial ribs; lip thin; umbilicus small. Light yellow-brown with prominent, irregular, darker brown markings. Animal grey.

Habitat and Range: Under logs in high altitude rainforest. Known only from North Bell Peak in Malbon Thompson Ra., Qld.

Notes: One of many charopid species in TNQ; many restricted to tops of high mountains.

QM

Red-triangle Slug
Triboniophorus graeffei

Identification: Length to 90 mm when crawling. Single pair of tentacles; upper surface with pronounced creases; breathing pore (pneumostome) visible on back behind head region. Usually white with red triangle surrounding pneumostome; bright orange form on Mt Bellenden Ker (pictured p. 13).

Habitat and Range: Buries in ground under logs during day; crawls on trees at night and in wet weather; rainforest and moist eucalypt woodland. Cooktown, Qld to Illawarra, NSW.

Notes: Feeding tracks (lines of small circular markings) often visible on smooth-barked eucalypts.

QM

Thularion semoni

Identification: Semi-slug. Shell diameter 20–25 mm; animal length to 60 mm. Shell shiny, yellowish, ear-shaped, fragile; fine radial lines and sparse spiral grooves. Animal black to brown, sometimes with irregular red markings; fine pustules on body and tissue surrounding shell; thick mucus.

Habitat and Range: Under logs and discarded palm fronds, mainly in upland rainforest. Helenvale to Cape Tribulation, Qld.

QM

Fastosarion brazieri

Identification: Semi-slug. Shell diameter to 20 mm; animal length to 60 mm. Shell shiny, yellow, ear-shaped, fragile; weak radial lines. Animal reddish-brown to dark grey; smooth skin; short raised thickenings on tissue surrounding shell.

Habitat and Range: Under logs and in discarded palm fronds in rainforest. Mossman to Ingham, Qld.

QM

Fastosarion superba

Identification: Semi-slug. Shell large, diameter 25–30 mm; animal length to 50 mm. Shell shiny, ear-shaped, yellow, fragile. Animal brown to dark grey.

Habitat and Range: Under logs and in rolled-up palm fronds in rainforest. Conway Ra.–Eungella, Qld.

Notes: Largest of several semi-slug species in Proserpine–Mackay region.

QM

QM

Malandena suturalis

Identification: Shell diameter to 20 mm; height 12 mm. Thin, glassy, weakly angled; almost smooth; umbilicus closed; lip not reflected. Light brown to golden, often with red band where whorls join. Animal light brown.

Habitat and Range: Under logs and rocks in rainforest. Atherton to Cardwell, Qld.

Notes: Undescribed, related species live in rainforest from Helenvale to Mossman, Qld.

QM

Parmacochlea fischeri

Identification: Semi-slug. Shell diameter 8–10 mm; animal length to 35 mm. Shell flat, plate-like, almost enveloped in animal tissue. Animal grey to brown.

Habitat and Range: Under logs and rocks in drier rainforest, also in adjacent eucalypt forests. Cape York to Cardwell, Qld.

QM

Expocystis rustica

Identification: Shell diameter 10–12 mm. Thin, glassy, smooth; umbilicus minute; lip not reflected. Grey to light brown, lighter on base. Animal brown.

Habitat and Range: Under logs and rocks in drier rainforest. Cape Flattery to Atherton, Qld.

QM

Gloreugenia blackalli

Identification: Shell height and diameter to 15 mm. Globular. Light brown with dense coverage of short hairs. Animal brown.

Habitat and Range: Under logs and rocks in rainforest. Proserpine area to Whitsunday islands, Qld.

Notes: Related species with 'hairy shells' live in Eungella rainforests.

Meliobba shafferyi

Identification: Shell diameter to 45 mm, height to 25 mm. Top-shaped with strongly angled body whorl; lip strongly reflected, no umbilicus. White to straw yellow with porcelain-white lip and pinkish-brown apex. Animal colour not recorded.

Habitat and Range: Rare. Possibly arboreal in rainforest. Mt Alexandra, north of Daintree R. to Mt Lewis, west of Mossman, Qld.

Notes: Closely related species in New Guinea.

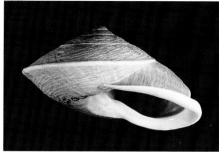

QM

Rhynchotrochus macgillivrayi

Identification: Shell height to 25 mm. Top-shaped with strongly angled body whorl; smooth; lip irregularly twisted and weakly reflected; no umbilicus. Mustard with irregular, tiny black speckles; dark brown to black behind lip and around umbilical area; lip white; tip dark. Animal black.

Habitat and Range: Common. Arboreal in rainforest. Cooktown to Cardwell, Qld.

Notes: Many related species in New Guinea.

QM

Noctepuna cerea

Identification: Shell height to 12 mm. Top-shaped with weakly angled body whorl, smooth; lip not reflected, no umbilicus. White. Animal white.

Habitat and Range: Arboreal in rainforest. Cooktown to Mossman, Qld.

QM

Noctepuna mayana

Identification: Shell height to 25 mm. Top-shaped with weakly angled body whorl; smooth; lip weakly reflected; no umbilicus. Yellow with wide brown spiral band; yellow base, white lip and dark grey tip. Animal dark grey to brown with white to yellow speckling; tentacles orange.

Habitat and Range: Arboreal in rainforest. Cooktown to Cape Tribulation, Qld.

QM

QM

Spurlingia portus

Identification: Shell diameter to 40 mm. Globular with weakly reflected lip; umbilicus small; strong radial growth lines and spirally arranged scales. Dirty yellow, lip white. Animal dark grey.

Habitat and Range: Under logs, rocks, bark of trees in dry rainforest. Helenvale to Cairns, Qld.

Notes: Largest land snail in drier rainforests of Wet Tropics. Related species on Atherton Tableland, and Gordonvale to Ingham, Qld.

QM

Hadra webbi

Identification: Shell diameter 40–60 mm; height to 50 mm. Solid with strongly reflected and thickened lip; angular body whorl; weak radial growth lines, almost smooth; umbilicus open, but small. Light brown to yellow on spire, dark brown on base, lip white. Animal dark grey.

Habitat and Range: Under logs, rocks in rainforest. Mossman to Tully, Qld.

Notes: Largest land snail in Wet Tropics. Related species, *H. bipartita,* from Cooktown to north of Daintree R., Qld.

QM

Gnarosophia bellendenkerensis

Identification: Shell diameter 35–55 mm, height to 50 mm. Solid with rounded body whorl; lip strongly reflected; weak radial growth lines, almost smooth; umbilicus small, barely open. Dark brown with two yellow spiral bands, lip dark brown. Animal dark grey.

Habitat and Range: Under logs and rocks in high altitude rainforest. Cooktown to Tully, Qld.

Notes: Distinguished from *Hadra* spp. (see above) by fine zig-zag sculpture on shell.

QM

Prisma prismatica

Identification: Length to 50 mm. Leathery, minutely pimpled surface; ridged back; sole of foot divided into three distinct longitudinal zones. Animal brown to dark grey with small, darker dots.

Habitat and Range: Under logs in rainforest. Cape York to north of Townsville, Qld.

Notes: Carnivorous.

Vaginula plebeius

Identification: Length to 60 mm. Flattened with leathery upper surface; light to dark brown, sole of foot yellowish.

Habitat and Range: Suburban gardens, paddocks and cultivated areas. Widespread in eastern Qld.

Notes: Introduced to Pacific region from tropical America.

QM

Garden Snail
Helix aspersa

Identification: Shell diameter to 40 mm. Thin with reflected lip; no umbilicus; sculpture of prominent growth ridges and irregular spiral wrinkles. Yellow to brown with darker brown, interrupted spiral bands. Animal grey.

Habitat and Range: Common. Suburban gardens. Australia-wide.

Notes: Introduced from Europe in early 1800s; established garden pest. Edible.

QM

Giant African Snail
Achatina fulica

Identification: Shell length to 200 mm, common at 50–100 mm. Long, conical, almost smooth; lip not reflected; no umbilicus. Colour variable, but mostly light brown with alternating bands of brown and cream (or white). Animal large, to 300 mm long; brown to grey.

Habitat and Range: Wide ranging from disturbed areas to rainforest.

Notes: Native of East Africa; widespread Indo-Pacific region. Diet of more than 500 plants makes it a serious pest in every country to which it has been introduced. Poses significant threat to Australian agriculture. Discovered in Cairns region in 1970s, but successfully eradicated. Frequently found on cargo by Customs and Quarantine officers. Vigilance necessary to avoid another outbreak.

QM

Sphaerospira

The land snails of TNQ include a diverse array of large-shelled species, many still undescribed. A small selection of these species is shown here. Pending a re-evaluation of their relationships, most species are included in a single genus, *Sphaerospira*. They comprise a number of similar looking species, so accurate locality data is essential for their correct identification. Locality of the illustrated specimen, general range of the species and shell height are given in brackets.

Monteithosites helicostracum (Bakers Blue Mtn; Hanns Tableland-Bakers Blue Mtn, 30 mm)   QM

Sphaerospira bellaria (Hinchinbrook I.; Hinchinbrook I., 40 mm)   QM

Sphaerospira mourilyani (Mission Beach; Tully-Innisfail, 35 mm)   QM

Sphaerospira mazee (Edmund Kennedy National Park; Ingham-Cardwell, 35 mm)   QM

Sphaerospira mulgravensis (Orpheus I., Palm Is., 37 mm)   QM

Sphaerospira rawnsleyi (Mt Elliot; Mt Elliot, 37 mm)   QM

Sphaerospira zebina (Giru; Townsville-Giru and hinterland, 35 mm)   QM

Sphaerospira sardalabiata (Bowen, Bowen area, 25 mm)   QM

Sphaerospira coxi (Banks of Andromache R.; Proserpine–Calen, 40 mm) QM

Sphaerospira etheridgei (Banks of Andromache R.; Proserpine–Mackay, 30 mm) QM

Sphaerospira gavisa (Conway Range; West of Proserpine–Conway Ra., 30 mm) QM

Sphaerospira thorogoodi (Banks of Andromache R.; Andromache R. environs, 25 mm) QM

Sphaerospira macleayi (Hook I.; northern Whitsunday islands, 30 mm) QM

Sphaerospira fortasse (Haslewood I.; southern Whitsunday islands, 32 mm) QM

Sphaerospira informis (Mt Charlton; Mt Dryander, Clarke and Connors Ra., 60 mm) QM

Sphaerospira oconnellensis (Sarina; Clarke-Connors Ra., 20 mm) QM

White Flower Spider, QM, Jeff Wright

SPIDERS, OTHER ARACHNIDS AND MYRIAPODS

Tropical North Queensland has a wealth of arachnids. These include not just the spiders, but some quite bizarre beasts. Many of these animals live unseen in the dense rainforest, but others live with us in the suburbs and even come into our homes.

The richest diversity of spiders known in Australia, and possibly the world, is to be found in Tropical North Queensland, which is home to thousands of species. Many find their niches in the moist rainforests of the Wet Tropics World Heritage Area. Others occur throughout the drier lowland areas to the east and west of the Great Dividing Range. These much neglected open forests and vine thickets show fewer species in any one patch than in the rainforest, but each dry forest area has a different suite of species to that nearby. Both the rainforest and open forests are critical centres of Australia's spider biodiversity.

Two large spiders, found in north Queensland, capture the attention of most people. The most common and obvious is the Giant Golden Orb-weaver, which spins its magnificent, golden circular webs in forests, among trees and in spacious gardens. These beautiful denizens of the north accept a number of hangers-on, tiny spiders (in the same family as Redbacks) that steal small food items from the orb-weaver webs. They are often mistaken for males of the giant female, but these 'kleptoparasites' are far more brave than males, sometimes drinking the liquefied food from the very mouth of their tolerant hostess.

The second noticeable group are the Whistling Spiders, Australia's own tarantulas. They are found throughout the forest and outback, but also occur in suburban Townsville and are highly sought by pet keepers.

Just as interesting, but smaller in size, are the Domed-web Tent Spiders. Colonies of 10–50 spiders form a mass of webs as big as a small room and also accept many small hangers-on. Perhaps the most remarkable from a scientific viewpoint is *Portia fimbriata*, a jumping spider that has telephoto vision second only to an eagle. In a tortuously slow and painstaking play, *Portia* stalks other spiders on their webs.

The accurate identification of spiders often requires a microscope and a considerable knowledge of the animals and their anatomy. The Identification Chart and species accounts that follow are not intended to be comprehensive, but an introduction to spiders. Species selection has been based on the most common public inquiries to the Queensland Museum.

In the Identification Chart, spiders are grouped according to where they are found, their web types, and the shape of their egg sacs. Within each category, spiders appear in descending order of size with a scale comparison to actual size. (Size refers to a spider's body including legs.) The species accounts are arranged alphabetically by common name. Entries marked with an asterisk (*) are not listed in the Identification Chart. The species accounts also contain a brief summary of bites and known reactions.

Robert J Raven

SPIDER IDENTIFICATION CHART

LOCATION	**On wall (no web)**	0.2 × Life Brown Huntsman Spider	0.2 × Life Grey Huntsman spider	0.2 × Life Net-casting Spider	0.5 × Life Garden Orb-weaver
	Above ground	0.3 × Life Whistling Spider	0.3 × Life Wolf Spider	0.8 × Life Spotted Ground Spider	Life size White-tailed Spider
	On vegetation	0.2 × Life Slender Sac Spider	0.2 × Life Net-casting Spider	Life size Slender Sac Spider	1.5 × Life Black House Spider
WEB TYPE	**Circular web**	0.2 × Life Golden Orb-weaver	2 × Life Northern Jewelled Spider	0.5 × Life Garden Orb -weaver	0.5 × Life St Andrew's Cross
	Tangled web	0.2 × Life Net-casting Spider	0.1 × Life Tent Spider and web	0.4 × Life	0.5 × Life Daddy -long- legs
	Funnel-shaped web	0.1 × Life Tent spider and web	0.4 × Life	0.5 × Life Black House Spider	0.5 × Life Funnel-web Spider
EGGS		0.2 × Life Tent Spider	0.3 × Life Magnificent Spider	0.3 × Life Wolf Spider	0.5 × Life Brown Widow & Redback

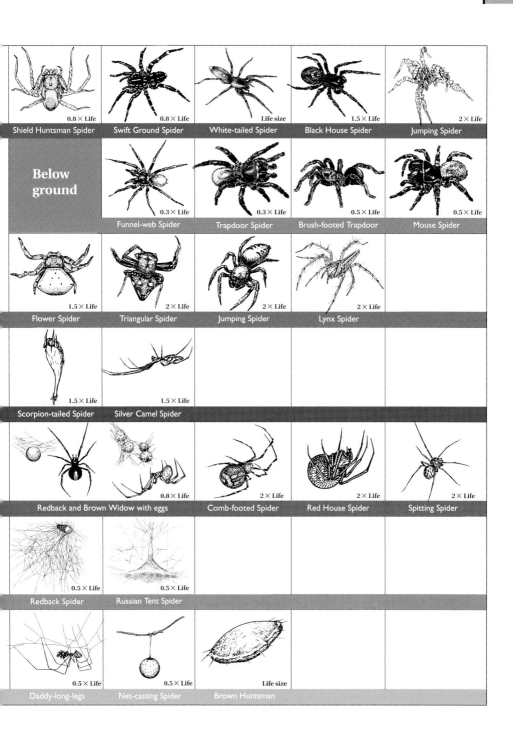

0.8 × Life	0.8 × Life	Life size	1.5 × Life	2 × Life
Shield Huntsman Spider	Swift Ground Spider	White-tailed Spider	Black House Spider	Jumping Spider

Below ground

0.3 × Life	0.3 × Life	0.5 × Life	0.5 × Life
Funnel-web Spider	Trapdoor Spider	Brush-footed Trapdoor	Mouse Spider

1.5 × Life	2 × Life	2 × Life	2 × Life
Flower Spider	Triangular Spider	Jumping Spider	Lynx Spider

1.5 × Life	1.5 × Life
Scorpion-tailed Spider	Silver Camel Spider

	0.8 × Life	2 × Life	2 × Life	2 × Life
Redback and Brown Widow with eggs	Comb-footed Spider	Red House Spider	Spitting Spider

0.5 × Life	0.5 × Life
Redback Spider	Russian Tent Spider

0.5 × Life	0.5 × Life	Life size
Daddy-long-legs	Net-casting Spider	Brown Huntsman

QM, Garth May

QM

Black House Spider
Badumna longinqua

Identification: Full size — 50c piece; leg diameter — pin. Black to brown.

Habitat and Range: Gardens, trees, corners in houses, spread via toys, cars, tables. More common in summer. Australia-wide.

Web: Sail-like panels or lacey web leading to funnel. Young of related species live with adult in colonial nest in bushes.

Bite: Spiders knocked down when cleaning web can bite arms, body, lower legs. Mild to severe reaction; considerable disagreement about severity. Local pain, redness, with systemic involvement, local tissue damage and ulcers (necrosis). Infection a known problem, needs careful medical management.

Notes: Reclusive; usually seen only at night or when males are wandering.

Heteropoda jugulans, QM, Jeff Wright

Brown Huntsman Spiders
Heteropoda spp.

Identification: Full size — hand span; leg diameter — pin to letter 'O'. Mottled brown abdomen and legs, carapace with black 'X'. Crab-like legs, front legs much longer than back.

Habitat and Range: Houses, forested areas, gardens, rainforest. Most common in summer. Eastern Australia.

Web: None, free-roving.

Bite: Ready biter; mild local pain.

Notes: Fast, hunts easily upside down on ceilings or walls. Many species, most common *H. jugulans*.

Brown Widow Spider
Latrodectus geometricus

Identification: Full size — 50c piece; leg diameter — pin. Pale to dark legs; pea-shaped abdomen, no red stripe above, but yellow to red hourglass mark under abdomen.

Habitat and Range: Sedge-like vegetation, seats, buildings. Most common in summer. North-eastern and south-eastern Qld. Introduced; almost worldwide.

Web: Strong, fine, tangled and untidy, conical retreat. Egg sacs spherical, spiky.

Bite: Mild to severe local and generalised pain. Redback antivenom effective.

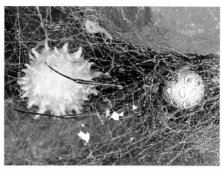

QM, Bruce Cowell

Brush-footed Trapdoor Spiders
Ozicrypta, Mandjelia, Moruga, Sason, Trittame, Zophorame spp.

Identification: Full Size — 50c piece; leg diameter — letter 'O'. Short stumpy spinnerets.

Habitat and Range: Cool moist areas of rainforests, also suburban gardens, bark, litter. Northern Australia.

Web: Open burrows or trapdoors in ground and on trees.

Bite: Minor local pain from larger species.

Notes: Can climb vertical glass faces easily. Adult males active in spring.

Trittame loki, QM, Bruce Cowell

Mandjelia banksi, QM, RJ Raven

Sason colemani, QM, Bruce Cowell

QM, RJ Raven

Comb-footed Spiders
Achaearanea spp.

Identification: Full size — 20c piece; leg diameter — pin. Mottled, pea-shaped abdomen.

Habitat and Range: Corners of houses, under leaves. Most common in summer. Australia-wide.

Web: Tangled, fine, exposed 'retreat'.

Bite: Mild local pain.

Thomisus spectabilis, QM, Jeff Wright

Sidymella sp., QM, Jeff Wright

Stephanopis sp., QM, Garth May

Crab and Flower Spiders
Thomisus spectabilis, Sidymella spp., *Stephanopis* spp.

Identification: Full size —- 20c piece; leg diameter — pin to match. Stout legs held like a crab.

White Flower Spider (*T. spectabilis*) white or yellow. Other species dark brown; rough body surface.

Habitat and Range: Flowers, shrubs, clotheslines, clothes. Darker species in leaves and on bark. Most common in summer. Australia-wide.

Web: Free-roving; 'sit and wait predator'.

Bite: White Flower Spider is ready biter; mild local pain.

Daddy-long-legs
Pholcus phalangoides, Artema atlanta

Identification: Full size — hand span; leg diameter — pin. Long springy legs.

Habitat and Range: Dark corners. Most common in summer. Australia-wide.

Web: Tangled, fine, exposed 'retreat'.

Bite: Venom harmless to humans.

Notes: Preys on Redback and Huntsman spiders. Several similar large species.

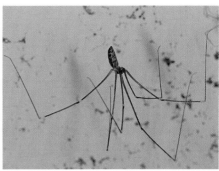

QM, Bruce Cowell

Funnel-web Spiders
Hadronyche spp.

Identification: Full size — 50c piece; leg diameter — pin to matchstick. Jet black shiny head; black legs; black to grey (when gravid) abdomen. Abdomen as large as last joint of adult thumb.

Habitat and Range: Rainforest. Rare in TNQ; one locality in mountains west of Mossman. Other species in mountain rainforest or moist forests along east coast, west of Gladstone, Qld, to Tas. and SA.

Web: Strong silk lines radiate from dirty 'sock' of silk under rocks and logs; burrows not obviously funnel-shaped. In trees, web appears like an 'X' or 'T' with 3 or 4 entrances.

Bite: Easily aggravated. Long, strong fangs strike vertically like snakes. Male venom more toxic, severe effects, sometimes death (without antivenom). Muscular trembling a symptom of bite. **Seek medical aid immediately.** Apply crepe bandage.

Notes: Slow-moving; do not jump but lunge when aggravated. During light rain, males often wander in search of females. Males capable of climbing vertical, slightly roughened surfaces (not glass).

QM, Jeff Wright

QM, Jeff Wright

QM, Bruce Cowell

QM

Garden Orb-weaver
Eriophora transmarina

Identification: Full size — 50c piece or more; leg diameter — matchstick. Body large, fat. Deep red head; hairy legs. Abdominal pattern variable, paired white dots to central brown, yellow or rusty red stripe.

Habitat and Range: Trees, shrubs, eaves of houses, clotheslines, clothes. Eastern Australia.

Web: Large, sticky circle across open pathways, in trees. Silk silver. Web spun at night, spider removes and consumes it each morning. Moves web if current site is not rich in insects. Eggs sacs dark green, laid in nest set on tree, house or upper corner of web.

Bite: Hard, strong bite, readily delivered. Typically, mild local pain for 30 minutes; atypically, 3–4 hours of strong pain. Most bites in summer.

QM

Giant Green Huntsman Spider *
Typostola barbata

Identification: Full size — hand span or larger; leg diameter — pin to letter 'O'. Fawn to grey head and abdomen; green 'blood' visible through leg joints. Legs crab-like, front legs much longer than back

Habitat and Range: Houses, gardens, open forest. Most common in summer. Eastern Australia.

Web: None, free-roving.

Bite: Timid biter; probably mild local pain.

Notes: Fast, hunts easily upside down on ceilings or walls.

Giant Water Spider *
Megadolomedes australianus

Identification: Full size — more than hand span; leg diameter — pin to matchstick. Mottled dark abdomen or with pale, broad stripes down length; head with pale edges. Legs extremely flexible.

Habitat and Range: Creek banks and streams. Most common in summer. Australia-wide.

Web: None, free-roving, but builds nursery retreat for egg sac.

Bite: Timid biter; probably mild local pain.

Notes: Hunts on water, eats fish and insects.

QM, Jeff Wright

Golden Orb-weavers
Nephila spp.

Identification: Full size — hand span or more; leg diameter — letter 'O'. *N. pilipes*, large, black legs; *N. edulis*, *N. plumipes* smaller, legs yellow and black. Males tiny, black.

Habitat and Range: Prefers warm moist areas — gardens, trees, across paths. Most common and largest in summer. Eastern Australia.

Web: Large (1 m) orb of strong golden silk strung between trees, around sunny parts of buildings; web sometimes traps small animals, including birds. Tiny, Silver Dew Drop Spiders (see p. 36) also live in web.

Bite: Only if forced; adult humans bitten most often. Reactions none to severe.

Notes: *N. pilipes* buries eggs in ground.

N. pilipes, QM

Green Water Spider *
Hygropoda lineata

Identification: Full size — 50c piece; leg diameter — letter 'O'. Light green body; long, thin green legs.

Habitat and Range: Rainforest, north of Townsville, Qld.

Web: Fine, on big leaves.

Bite: Not recorded.

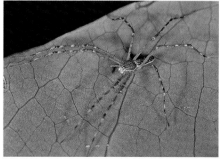

QM

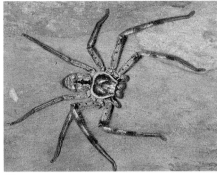

QM

Grey Huntsman Spider
Holconia immanis

Identification: Full size — hand span; leg diameter — pin to letter 'O'. Grey head with brown edge; abdomen grey with brown 'dagger'. Crab-like legs, front very long.

Habitat and Range: Houses, open forested areas, gardens. Most common in summer. Eastern Australia.

Web: None, free-roving.

Bite: Timid biter; probably mild local pain.

Notes: Fast, hunts easily on ceilings or walls.

Mopsus mormon, QM, Jeff Wright

Jumping Spiders
Salticidae

Identification: Full size — up to 20c piece; leg diameter — pin. Many species, colourful and drab; all jump and turn head separate from abdomen. Large pair of eyes on front of head.

Habitat and Range: Rainforest, open forest, common in houses and gardens. Most common in summer. Australia-wide.

Web: Free-roving, hangs from web lines at night.

Bite: Rarely bites; mild local pain.

Notes: More than 400 species. *Portia* stalks other spiders on their web and has second best vision of any known animal.

Portia fimbriata, QM, Bruce Cowell

Cosmophasis bitaeniatus, QM, Garth May

Diolenius phrynoides, QM, Bruce Cowell

Leaf-curling Spider *
Phonognatha sp.

Identification: Full size — 50c piece; leg diameter — pin. Brown body; long sac-like abdomen with pale paired markings.

Habitat and Range: Open forest, open gardens. Most common in summer. Australia-wide.

Web: Circular with curled leaf retreat in upper corner.

Bite: Mild local pain.

QM, RJ Raven

Lynx Spiders
Oxyopes spp.

Identification: Full size — 20c piece; leg diameter — pin. Many different species. Colourful abdomen with spiky legs. Springs and leaps.

Habitat and Range: Vegetation. Most common in summer. Australia-wide.

Web: None, free-roving.

Bite: None recorded.

QM

Magnificent Spider
Ordgarius magnificus

Identification: Full size — 50c piece; leg diameter — pin to matchstick. Mottled abdomen; spiked head.

Habitat and Range: Open forest, gardens. Most common in summer. Eastern Australia.

Web: Single line at night; spins bolas of sticky silk and captures moths in flight. Spindle-shaped egg sacs.

Bite: None recorded.

QM

Egg sacs, QM

QM, Gary Cranitch

Mottled Ground Spider *
Uliodon tarantulina

Identification: Full size — 50c piece; leg diameter — pin to letter 'O'. Dark brown, radiating dark bands on head.

Habitat and Range: Open grassland, rainforest and woodland. Coastal Australia.

Web: Free roving.

Bite: Pain, dizziness and weakness.

Female, *Missulena* sp., QM

Mouse Spiders
Missulena spp.

Identification: Full size — 50c piece; leg diameter — letter 'O'. Black, shiny head with distinct 'step'. Tiny eyes spread widely across head. Short stocky legs. Two common species: Red-headed Mouse Spider (*M. occatoria*), male with deep red front of head and satin blue abdomen; Eastern Mouse Spider (*M. bradleyi*), male all black except large pale area at front of abdomen. Females similar.

Habitat and Range: Gardens, forests. Males wander from March–September. Australia-wide.

Web: Short burrows in ground with floppy door projecting just above ground.

Bite: 'Bull-terrier', does not let go. Aggressive. Fangs strike towards each other diagonally, not vertically. Bite hard and deep, but most envenomations minor; severe reaction rare, with systemic symptoms potentially requiring funnel-web antivenom. Gardeners and babies most often bitten.

Male, *M. occatoria*, QM

Male *M. bradleyi*, QM, Bruce Cowell

Net-casting Spider
Deinopis subrufa

Identification: Full size — palm of hand; leg diameter — pin. Long, slender brown abdomen sometimes with V-shaped markings; long brown legs (first and second often held as one). Large pair of front eyes.

Habitat and Range: Cool dark areas in gardens, shrubs, low trees, among dead twigs and tangles of branches. Most common in summer. Australia-wide.

Web: Messy tangle. Holds large rectangular web in front legs, swung with great speed over moths and other passing insects. Young hang in groups near large brown, marble-like eggs.

Bite: None recorded.

QM

Northern Jewelled Spiders
Gasteracantha spp.

Identification: Full size — 20c piece; leg diameter — pin. Abdomen bright yellow and white on black with 6 strong spikes.

Habitat and Range: Gardens, mangroves, forests. Most common in summer. Northern Qld.

Web: Fine, circular.

Bite: Mild local pain.

G. quadrispinosa, QM

Racing-stripe Spiders *
Miturga spp.

Identification: Full size — 50c piece to palm of hand; leg diameter — pin to letter 'O'. Dark stripes down body.

Habitat and Range: Open grassland and woodland. Dry parts of Australia.

Web: Massive temporary nest of silk built overnight.

Bite: Pain; some cases with circumstantial indication of tissue damage and ulceration (necrosis).

Notes: Fast runner.

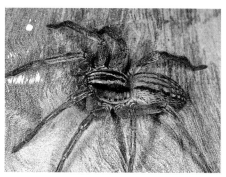

M. lineata, QM, Bruce Cowell

QM

Redback Spider
Latrodectus hasseltii

Identification: Full size — 50c piece; leg diameter — pin. Dark brown to black legs; pea-shaped abdomen with distinct red (rarely orange-yellow) stripe down back.

Habitat and Range: Prefers hot, dry areas in gardens, bark, walls, rubbish. Spread via vehicles. Most common in dry south and west, rare in urban areas north of Rockhampton; Australia-wide.

Web: Strong, untidy, tangled with concealed 'retreat', in area with sun exposure.

Bite: Effects variable, mild to severe (death without antivenom). Typically intense local pain. Early medical attention required (but no tourniquet). Most bites August–May.

Notes: Aggressive predator of other spiders, insects, small mammals, lizards and snakes. Minute male presents himself as food during mating.

QM, Jeff Wright

Red House Spider
Nesticodes rufipes

Identification: Full size — 20c piece; leg diameter — pin. Mottled, pea-shaped, rust-red abdomen and legs.

Habitat and Range: Dark corners in houses. Most common in summer. Australia-wide.

Web: Tangled, fine, exposed 'retreat'.

Bite: Mild to severe local pain.

St Andrew's Cross Spider
Argiope keyserlingi

Identification: Full size — 50c piece; leg diameter — pin. Flat, ornately coloured abdomen with transverse bands; silver head; banded legs. Several similar species.

Habitat and Range: Open forest, gardens. Most common in summer. Australia-wide.

Web: Fine orb with 1–4 bars of thicker web forming cross.

Bite: Mild local pain.

Notes: Common food of Friarbirds.

QM

Scorpion-tailed Spider
Arachnura higginsi

Identification: Full Size — 10c piece; leg diameter — pin. Long, thin, tapering flexible abdomen ending with four spikes on a knob. Abdomen changes colour with age, from fawn or grey to bright mauve and orange.

Habitat and Range: Gardens, trees, shrubs. Eastern Australia.

Web: Circular.

Bite: None recorded.

QM, Garth May

Shield Huntsman Spiders
Neosparassus spp.

Identification: Full size — up to hand span; leg diameter — pin to letter 'O'. Pale or fawn legs and body; no markings above; below with black and yellow or orange 'badge'. Carapace arched. Crab-like legs, front legs much longer than back.

Habitat and Range: Houses, gardens, forested areas, rainforest. Most common in summer. Eastern Australia.

Web: None, free-roving.

Bite: Ready biter, large fangs. Mild to severe local pain, often with temporary cardiac complications.

Notes: Fast, hunts easily upside down on ceilings or walls.

QM, Jeff Wright

Silver Camel Spider
Leucauge dromedaria

Identification: Full size — 20c piece; leg diameter — pin. Long, bright silver abdomen, light green legs, dark green head.

Habitat and Range: Open vegetation, gardens. Most common in summer. Australia-wide.

Web: Weak, circular; usually horizontal or almost.

Bite: None recorded.

QM

QM, Jeff Wright

Silverback Trapdoor Spiders *
Idiommata spp.

Identification: Full size — hand span; leg diameter — letter 'O'. Male brown, very hairy with shiny silver 'hair' on head region. Females like Whistling Spider (see p. 40), but with tiny spinnerets.

Habitat and Range: Open grassland, rainforest. Many species Australia-wide.

Web: Open burrow in ground with side pocket trapdoor.

Bite: Pain, headache, nausea.

A. antipodiana, QM, Garth May

Silver Dew Drop Spiders *
Argyrodes spp.

Identification: Full size — 5c piece; leg diameter — hair. Short arched silver body; other species can be long and orange.

Habitat and Range: On webs of Golden and Garden Orb-weavers. Most common in summer. Coastal Australia.

Web: None; usually many live on web of host spider; often mistaken for male of host spider.

Bite: Rare, mild local pain.

Notes: Steals food from larger host spider, usually from web, but sometimes from its mouth.

QM, Bruce Cowell

Slender Sac Spiders
Cheiracanthium spp.

Identification: Full size — 20–50c piece, leg diameter — pin. Pale slender body; long pale legs.

Habitat and Range: On vegetation. Most common in summer. Several species Australia-wide.

Web: None, night rover.

Bite: Mild to severe local pain.

Spitting Spiders
Scytodes spp.

Identification: Full size — 10c piece; leg diameter — hair. Dark brown body; long fine legs.

Habitat and Range: Upper corners of houses, inside and out. In north Qld, Cape York to Townsville.

Web: Fine, tangled web leading to small tunnel in corner.

Bite: Not known; venom is a toxic glue spat at prey.

Notes: Slow moving. Related to introduced Fiddleback Spider (*Loxosceles* spp.), known only from WA, NSW, SA.

Scytodes thoracica, QM, Gary Cranitch

Spotted Ground Spiders
Storena spp., *Habronestes* spp.

Identification: Full size — 20c piece; leg diameter — pin. Shiny black head; shiny colourful body; legs black.

Habitat and Range: Gardens, open ground. Most common in summer. Many species, Australia-wide.

Web: None, free-roving, fast runner.

Bite: Mild local pain.

QM, Jeff Wright

Swift Ground Spiders
Supunna spp.

Identification: Full size — 20c piece; leg diameter — pin. Spotted black head and body. *S. picta*, legs orange and black; *S. funerea*, legs black.

Habitat and Range: Gardens, open ground. Most common in summer. Many species Australia-wide.

Web: Free-roving, fast runner.

Bite: Mild local pain.

Supunna picta, QM, RJ Raven

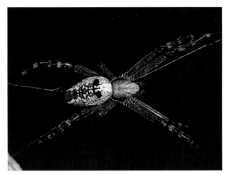

C. *moluccensis*, QM

C. *moluccensis*, (web), QM

Tent Spiders
Cyrtophora spp.

Identification: Full size — 50c piece; leg diameter — pin. *C. moluccensis* often has broad, rusty-red stripe down back of abdomen; *C. hirta* smaller, white.

Habitat and Range: Shaded warm areas of gardens, leaf litter, trees, walls, paths. Most prevalent in summer. Northern Australia to Coffs Harbour, NSW.

Web: Easily recognised by form of webs. *C. moluccensis* builds large web about 60–90 cm diameter; consists of low, inverted saucer-like dome amongst large tangle, webs join together to form massive colonies. *C. hirta* builds smaller (30 cm diameter) peaked web like a Russian tent; spider hides in cap, rarely seen.

Notes: Eggs of *C. moluccensis* suspended in web above spider, parasitised by sarcophagid flies.

Aname sp., QM. Jeff Wright

Misgolas sp., QM

Trapdoor Spiders
Idiopidae, Nemesiidae

Identification: Full size — 50c piece; leg diameter — letter 'O'. Accurate identification possible only by specialists.

Range and Habitat: Cool moist areas of closed forests, suburban gardens, bark, leaf litter.

Web: Open burrows with tube webs or trapdoors in ground.

Bite: Minor local pain.

Notes: Cannot climb vertical glass faces. Adult males active in spring.

Triangular Spiders
Arkys spp.

Identification: Full size — 20c piece; leg diameter — pin. Abdomen small and flat, triangular to heart-shaped. Front legs with strong spines. Spikes going sideways from front of head.

Habitat and Range: Gardens on trees, shrubs, clotheslines, clothes. More common in summer. Australia-wide.

Web: None, free-roving.

Bite: Mild local pain for about 30 minutes, heat and red welt forms.

A. cornutus, QM, Garth May

Two-spined Spider *
Poecilopachys australasiae

Identification: Full size — 20c piece; leg diameter — pin. Yellow, brown and white body with two spines on abdomen that form 'eyes'.

Habitat and Range: Gardens. Most common in summer. Australia-wide.

Web: Circular, built at night.

Bite: Mild local pain.

QM, Jeff Wright

Water Spiders *
Dolomedes spp.

Identification: Full size — 50c piece; leg diameter — pin to matchstick. Mottled dark abdomen; head with silver or dark gold border.

Habitat and Range: Creek banks and streams, hunts on water. Most common in summer. Many species Australia-wide.

Web: Free-roving, but builds nursery retreat for egg sac.

Bite: Mild local pain.

Notes: Feeds on fish and frogs.

QM, Garth May

Selenocosmia stirlingi, QM

Selenocosmia crassipes, QM

Phlogiellus sp., QM, Bruce Cowell

Whistling Spiders
Selenocosmia, Selenotypus, Phlogiellus spp.

Other name: Australian Tarantulas

Identification: Full size — more than hand span; leg diameter — pipe cleaner. Grey or brown, hairy.

Habitat and Range: Open grassland; *Selenocosmia*, north of Rockhampton; *Selenotypus*, north-western Qld. *Phlogiellus*, rainforest, north of Innisfail.

Web: Open burrow in ground.

Bite: Severe pain, headache, nausea, vomiting for up to 6 hours. Fatal to dogs and cats within one hour.

Notes: When aggravated produce whistling or hissing sounds. Targeted for sale in southern states as pets.

QM, Jeff Wright

Whip Spider *
Ariamnes sp.

Identification: Full size — 50c piece; leg diameter — hair. Long, worm-like body; short legs.

Habitat and Range: On vegetation. Most common in summer. Australia-wide.

Web: Single thread at night, hunts freely.

Bite: None recorded.

White-tailed Spider
Lampona murina

Identification: Full size — 50c piece; leg diameter — pin. Grey, cigar-shaped abdomen with white spot on end; sometimes banded legs and light bands on abdomen.

Habitat and Range: Cool dark areas — gardens, under bark, in leaf litter, walls, beds. Many similar species Australia-wide; introduced to New Zealand.

Web: None, free-roving.

Bite: Bites repeatedly. Most bites, spring to autumn. Usually mild local pain, redness and, rarely, small local ulcers that clear up in a few days. No serious reactions proven in Qld, venom has no necrotic components. Media reports of bites are typically 'spider-less' incidents.

Notes: Preys on large Curtain-web, Black House Spiders and presumably other spiders.

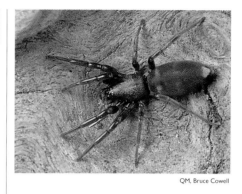

QM, Bruce Cowell

Wolf Spiders
Lycosa spp.

Identification: Full size — 50c piece to palm of hand; leg diameter — pin to letter 'O'. Most have black X on head, underside all black. Large front eyes, strongly reflect torch-light at night.

Habitat and Range: Prefers hot dry areas in gardens, under bark, leaf litter. Common in open country and deserts. Each species often restricted to particular micro-habitats. More common in summer. Many species Australia-wide.

Web: Free-roving. Some build open burrows, trapdoors, retreats in shrubs. Female carries egg-sac at end of abdomen, young are carried on top of abdomen.

Bite: Mild local effects. Fatal to cats and dogs.

Notes: Two species are predators of cane toads. *L. lapidosa* in south-eastern Qld eats small toads and frogs; *L. obscuroides* in north noted biting a large toad on head; toad died in 1 hour.

QM, Bruce Cowell

OTHER ARACHNIDS AND MYRIAPODS   Phil Lawless

Scorpions

Scorpions, with their large pincers (chelate pedipalps) and long tails tipped with hooked stings, are familiar to most people. Scorpions can be distinguished by the shape of the sternum, the number of lateral eyes, the presence or absence of tibial spurs and a secondary bump on the sting. The sternum is the central plate under the body between the bases of legs 3 and 4. The lateral eyes are found on the front corners of the head plate (carapace); median eyes are in the middle. The tibia is the third segment from the outermost end of the leg. Some species have a spine, the tibial spur, on the lower outermost edge of the tibia.

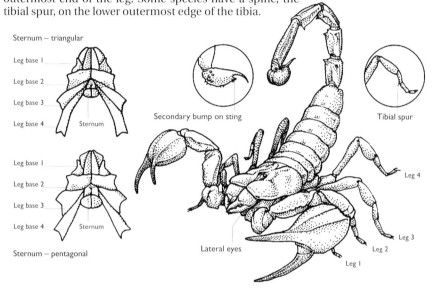

Sternum – triangular

Leg base 1
Leg base 2
Leg base 3
Leg base 4   Sternum

Secondary bump on sting

Tibial spur

Leg base 1
Leg base 2
Leg base 3
Leg base 4   Sternum

Sternum – pentagonal

Lateral eyes

Leg 4
Leg 3
Leg 2
Leg 1

QM, Jeff Wright

Large Brown Scorpions
Liocheles spp.

Identification: Length to 7 cm. Dark brown; body tapers to thin, short tail (does not reach head when bent over body). Robust claws; pentagonal sternum; three pairs of lateral eyes; two ridges along under surface of tail; sting lacks bump.

Habitat and Range: Under logs and rocks, in shallow burrows in earth banks. Common in gardens and forests in northern Australia. Three species TNQ.

Notes: Nocturnal. Sting delivered by tail; not known to be dangerous.

Small Mottled Scorpions
Lychas variatus, Isometrus maculatus, I. melanodactylus

Identification: Length to 5 cm. Mottled brown; body tapers gradually to long, stout tail (can reach head). Fine claws; sternum triangular; three pairs of lateral eyes; sting with bump. *Lychas*, tibial spurs on legs 3 and 4; *Isometrus*, no tibial spurs.

Habitat and Range: Moist forest areas. *L. variatus*, northern Australia; New Guinea, Bougainville. *I. maculatus*, Torres Strait to Townsville, Qld; New Guinea, tropical areas worldwide. *I. melanodactylus*, Bamaga to Finch Hatton, Qld; New Guinea.

Notes: Sting not known to be dangerous.

QM, Bruce Cowell

Mites and Ticks

Mites and ticks include several orders of parasites and predators. The mites are a diverse group feeding on juices from a wide variety of animals and plants, living and dead. Ticks (suborder Ixodides) are much bigger than mites and are all parasites on vertebrate animals.

Scrub Itch Mites
Trombiculidae

Identification: Identification only possible by experts. Adults free-living, rarely encountered; 8 legs. Larvae minute, length about 0.3 mm; external parasites of birds, lizards; body reddish, oval; 6 hairy legs. Cause 'scrub itch' in humans; dematitis consisting of intensely itchy, pink, pointed lumps capped by blisters.

Habitat and Range: In TNQ, mostly rainforest. Several species Australia-wide.

Notes: Larvae have usually dropped off once dermatitis has developed. Bites heaviest in areas under pressure, such as around waist, and lower parts of body that brush vegetation. Larval Scrub Ticks can cause similar dermatitis. Larvae of related mite, *Leptotrombidium deliense*, parasitise rats and bandicoots, but will feed on humans; can transmit rickettsia (*Orientia tsutsugamushi*) that causes Scrub Typhus.

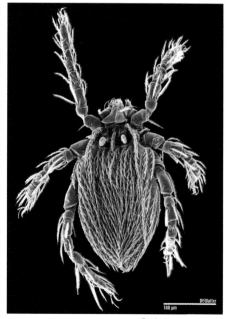

100 µm   DEWalter

Guntheria sp., David Walter

QM, Jeff Wright

Paralysis Tick
Ixodes holocyclus

Other name: Scrub Tick

Identification: Length, larva 0.5 mm; male 3 mm; unfed female 5 mm, after feeding to 1 cm. Larva, 6 legs; nymph and adult, 8 legs. Body greyish-brown, flattened, mouthparts at tip of head. Unfed female with shield-like plate covering front half of body; engorged female has bloated body.

Habitat and Range: Moist forest, sometimes leafy gardens. Eastern Australia.

Notes: Parasite of native mammals and birds, especially bandicoots. Also bites humans and domestic pets. Toxic saliva may cause paralysis and allergic reactions. Removal without squeezing body of tick is important. Fine forceps can be used to catch head and ease it out; or tick can be killed with pyrethroid insect repellent, will shrivel and drop off.

Centipedes, Millipedes and Velvet Worms

Centipedes and millipedes (Myriapoda) share many characteristics, but are seldom confused. A centipede's first pair of legs form large poison fangs (forcipules). The last pair trail behind the flattened body and are both sensory and hooked for grip. The remaining walking legs are arranged one pair per segment. Millipedes have a cylindrical body and the body segments are fused in pairs, so millipede 'segments' seem to have two pairs of legs each.

Velvet Worms (Onycophora) are an ancient group of soft-bodied animals that look much like multi-legged slugs. They are mostly found in moist tropical regions of the world.

QM, Jeff Wright

Giant Centipede
Ethmostigmus rubripes

Identification: Head and body length 7.5–13.5 cm. Body long, flattened, flexible; dark brown or green-brown to orange-yellow or yellow; legs and antennae yellow.

Habitat and Range: Dry and moist habitats, under logs, rocks, bark. Australia-wide, except Tas.; Solomon Is., New Guinea, Java, China.

Notes: Nocturnal predator. Bite causes severe pain, may last for several days. No deaths recorded.

Polydesmid Millipedes
Polydesmida

Identification: Length usually 2–4 cm, but up to 12 cm. Elongated with 19–20 body segments that may have side flanges; most segments with 2 pairs of leg. Eyes absent. Colour variable, sometimes bright stripes or bands.

Habitat and Range: Most common in forested areas, in leaf litter, under rocks and bark. Many species, Australia-wide. Worldwide.

Notes: Feed on vegetable matter. Repugnatorial glands produce defensive secretions, may stain skin if handled.

Bruce Cowell

Pill Millipedes
Sphaerotheriida

Identification: Length to 4 cm. Body stout, able to roll into tight ball; 11–13 body segments, 21 pairs of legs. Large compound eyes, small antennae; mostly glossy black or dark brown.

Habitat and Range: Moist forests, in leaf litter, under logs and rocks. Australia-wide. Widespread in tropics, Asia, Africa, New Zealand.

Notes: Feed on decomposing vegetable matter.

QM, Bruce Cowell

Velvet Worms
Onychophora

Identification: Length 3–4 cm. Slow moving, elongated, soft-bodied. Skin with minute bumps, giving velvety appearance. One pair of antennae, 14–16 pairs of fleshy, non-jointed, conical legs.

Habitat and Range: Rainforest, other moist habitats. Under logs, leaf litter, rocks. Patchy distribution eastern Australia, Cape York, Qld, to Adelaide, SA, south-western WA. Nine species in TNQ; six Wet Tropics, one Mt Elliot, two Mackay area.

Notes: Food caught in slime ejected from ducts near mouth; slime serves as defence against predators.

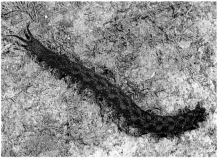

QM, Jeff Wright

Yellow Striped Hermit Crab, Bruce Cowell

CRUSTACEANS

Crustaceans belong to the group Arthropoda, which is characterised by the presence of an external shell and jointed limbs. On land, this group is primarily represented by insects and spiders, but in the sea crustaceans dominate.

Crustaceans are found in all habitats, from the deep sea to shallow reefs, intertidal mangrove and seagrass communities, freshwater streams and even in the most arid Australian deserts. They are important ecologically as a food resource for fish and other predators (including humans), as well as being major consumers and predators themselves. Crustacean larvae are a significant component of the plankton and are essential to the food chain maintaining our fishing industry.

The best known group of Crustaceans is the Decapoda (meaning 10 legs), which contains all the large familiar species, such as crabs, shrimps, prawns and lobsters. With around 1000 species, it is estimated that Queensland has the greatest number of decapods of all Australian states, and it is in Tropical North Queensland that this diversity is at its highest. Of the tropical marine environments, reefs have the greatest number of species, followed by seagrass, mangrove and then soft-sediment, subtidal communities.

Tropical North Queensland also has an abundance of permanent freshwater habitats, ranging from torrential mountain streams to meandering flood plain rivers and stagnant lowland swamps. This abundance of habitats is reflected in the richest freshwater crustacean fauna in Australia. Some of the species occurring in TNQ have restricted distributions and specialised habitat requirements. These species are of high conservation value and some are known to be sensitive to habitat disturbance. Species of Spiny Crayfish are limited to cool rainforest streams at altitudes above 800 m, often on a single mountain range. One freshwater yabby, and several freshwater shrimps and prawns, show a similar preference for high altitude rainforest streams.

Most of the freshwater species in TNQ are well protected in nature reserves and national parks. It is also fortunate that the local fauna has not yet been greatly exposed to the impact of introduced species and diseases. The crayfish plague fungus, *Aphanomyces astaci*, which was accidentally introduced to Europe with American crayfish, has all but destroyed the native crayfishery there. Local crayfish have no resistance to the disease and would be severely affected by its introduction here.

The colonisation of land habitats has proven much more difficult for crustaceans and there are only a few specialised terrestrial groups. Unlike, insects and spiders, land crustaceans are vulnerable to desiccation and are generally limited to moist habitats, such as rainforest leaf litter.

Peter JF Davie and John W Short

CRUSTACEANS OF THE SHORE   Peter JF Davie

The shoreline of Tropical North Queensland is home to a wonderful array of crustaceans. These are easily seen while beach walking, or fishing off rocky points, or along the banks of mangrove-lined creeks. The north Queensland coast is protected by the Great Barrier Reef and, with the high annual rainfall of the Wet Tropics, this has allowed the development of extensive mangrove forests. Mangrove crabs are abundant and play an important role in tropical mangrove ecology by burying and consuming up to 80 per cent of the annual leaf fall. This helps to retain nutrients within the mangrove system. Mangroves and seagrass meadows are vital nursery areas for a variety of crustacean species, particularly some commercially important prawns and Mud and Sand Crabs.

Shrimps

Many species of shrimps and prawns occur in TNQ, but almost all are found below low tide mark in the creeks, inshore coastal waters and on the reefs. A shrimp has small claws on only the first two pairs of legs, whereas a prawn has claws on the first three pairs.

QM, Jeff Wright

Edward's Snapping Shrimp
Alpheus edwardsii

Identification: Length to 40 mm. Lime-green head; cream marks on sides of tail.

Habitat and Range: Under rocks on sandy-mud, also in crevices in dead coral. Australia-wide; Indo-West Pacific.

Notes: Numerous species, distinguished by colour patterns. Large claw of all species has peg-and-socket mechanism, when closed rapidly, causes characteristic 'clicking' noise often heard in mangroves.

Yabbies, Mud Lobsters and Allies

These burrow-dwelling animals resemble both shrimps and lobsters. Yabbies are the most familiar, but many other types occur in various habitats from mud banks to living inside sponges and corals.

QM, Isobel Bennett

Mud Lobster
Thalassina squamifera

Identification: Length to more than 100 mm. Grey to orange, lobster-like. Strong, heavy claws; long, thin abdomen.

Habitat and Range: Common in mangroves. Northern Australia; south-east Asia.

Notes: Seldom seen, but builds tall mounds of dry mud. Moults in burrow; moulted shells sometimes found as fossils.

Yabby
Callianassa australiensis

Other Names: Ghost Nipper, Australian Ghost Shrimp.

Identification: Length to 40–50 mm. Soft, translucent, cream-pink body. Male has large, white, flattened claw.

Habitat and Range: Large numbers burrow on sheltered intertidal, shallow subtidal muddy-sand flats. Eastern Australia.

Notes: Used for bait; sucked from burrows using 'yabby pump'.

QM, Bruce Cowell

Hermit Crabs

Many species of hermit crabs live in TNQ. Most larger species can be identified by their distinctive colours. As they grow, they find larger shells to protect their fleshy abdomens.

Yellow-striped Hermit
Clibanarius taeniatus

Identification: Body length 35–40 mm (removed from shell). Green and yellow striping on legs, claws and upper body.

Habitat and Range: Common, intertidal and shallow subtidal zones, from exposed rocky headlands to reefs and mangroves. Northern Australia, Shark Bay, WA, to Port Hacking, NSW; eastern Indo-west Pacific.

Bruce Cowell

Porcelain Crabs

The tail is flattened and tucked under the body, but unlike true crabs it has a tail fan like a shrimp. A few species are found on the shore, but most occur on the Great Barrier Reef.

Rounded Porcelain Crab
Petrolisthes haplodactylus

Identification: Length to 8 mm. Body smooth, lacks spines. Arm of claw has single tooth at inner end; simple sharp claw on last segment of walking legs.

Habitat and Range: Underside of rocks, on muddy sand flats; estuaries, sheltered inlets. Endemic to Northern Australia.

Similar Species: *P. teres*, similar habitats; 3 small spines on inside of last segment of walking legs.

QM, Jeff Wright

True Crabs

True crabs come in an enormous variety of shapes and sizes. The abdomen is reduced and narrow, but lacks a tail fan and is kept tucked under the body.

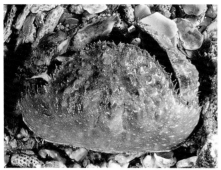

Peter Davie

Common Box Crab
Calappa hepatica

Identification: Body to 50 mm across. Pale olive to olive-grey or olive-yellow, with flecking; lacks strong markings. Back of shell forms wide flange hiding legs.

Habitat and Range: Rocky and coral reefs, on sand or muddy-sand bottoms; shallow subtidal zone to 50 m depth. Northern Australia; Indo-Pacific from Red Sea to Clipperton I. (eastern Pacific).

Notes: Extra tooth at base of one claw common to all *Calappa* species; used to open snail shells like a can opener.

QM

Red-banded Sand Crab
Ashtoret granulosa

Identification: Body to 60 mm across. Dark red speckling, round body; strong spine either side with broad band at base. Flattened paddles on walking legs for swimming and digging.

Habitat and Range: In shallow water below low-tide mark. Northern Australia; Indonesia east to Tahiti.

Notes: Several species, most easily distinguished by colour. Swimmers sometimes stand on crabs, which then move off quickly and bury into sand.

Peter Davie

Giant Shore Crab
Cardisoma carnifex

Identification: Largest Australian shore crab. Body to 65 mm across. Swollen, rounded body; one claw bigger and stronger than other.

Habitat and Range: Burrows in firm mud to sandy soil around edge of mangroves or creeks. Main Australian population is on Lizard I., but also known from Cape Tribulation, Qld and Port Essington, NT; Indo-West Pacific.

Broad-fronted Mangrove Crab
Metopograpsus frontalis

Identification: Body to more than 30 mm across, but mostly smaller. Smooth; sides of shell narrow towards back; row of spines on outer hind edge of major segment of walking legs. Mottled purplish to greenish, brownish, or blue with orange borders.

Habitat and Range: Common in sheltered mud or muddy-sand environments from mangroves to sheltered rocky shores; intertidal zone. Northern Australia; Sri Lanka through Indonesia east to New Caledonia.

Notes: Active predator and scavenger; does not burrow.

QM, Jeff Wright

Tropical Rock Crab
Grapsus tenuicrustatus

Identification: Body to 65 mm across. Dark maroon with light, blue-green mottling on shell; yellow bands on walking legs; red claws with white fingertips.

Habitat and Range: On and under rocks; upper intertidal zone. Northern Australia; Indo-West Pacific to Hawaii.

John Short

Purple and Cream Mud Crab
Helice leachii

Identification: Body 25 mm across. Thick-body; stout sharp claws; purple body and legs.

Habitat and Range: Around inlets and bays, though rarely far up estuaries. Burrows high on beach, near or above high water mark; on firm ground from dirty sand to mud or hard-packed earth. Northern Australia to northern NSW; East Africa to Japan and New Caledonia.

Notes: Mostly nocturnal.

QM, Jeff Wright

A Elliott

Scarlet Three-spined Mangrove Crab *Neosarmatium trispinosum*

Identification: Body to 40 mm across. Thick body; scarlet claws; male claw with three short, sharp spines on top of movable finger near base.

Habitat and Range: Burrows in mud, often with mounds at entrance; mid to upper intertidal zones. Eastern Qld, Cape York to Moreton Bay; New Guinea, New Caledonia, Vanuatu and Fiji.

Notes: Eats leaves; vegetable matter comprises more than 90 per cent of diet. Fresh leaves taken into burrow to decompose before eating. Mostly nocturnal, but sometimes seen around dusk or on rainy, overcast days.

QM. Jeff Wright

Red-fingered Marsh Crab *Parasesarma erythodactyla*

Identification: Body to 25 mm across. Claw with red fingertips; large males bright green. Square shell lacks tooth on edge behind eyes; fine meshwork of short hairs either side of mouth.

Habitat and Range: Under stones and logs, and in crevices of logs; burrows in banks; mangroves and saltmarshes. Endemic. Eastern Australia, north Qld to Vic.

Notes: Leaf-eater; occasionally climbs trees to feed on fresh mangrove leaves.

Peter Davie

Maroon Mangrove Crab *Perisesarma messa*

Identification: Body to 25 mm across. Claws dark maroon, sometimes almost black. Square shell with tooth on edge behind eyes. Fine meshwork of short hairs either side of mouth.

Habitat and Range: Coastal mangrove swamps and estuaries. Endemic. Eastern Qld.

Banded Mangrove Crab
Bresedium brevipes

Identification: Body to 25 mm across. Square-shaped; colour varies from dirty green to dark brown. Legs have broad dark bands.

Habitat and Range: Arboreal species living under bark or in fallen logs; coastal mangrove swamps and estuaries penetrating into coastal freshwater. Northern Australia; tropical Indo-West Pacific.

Notes: Nocturnal.

John Short

Soldier Crab
Mictyris longicarpus

Identification: Body to 25 mm across. Globular; adults sky blue and cream with red 'knees'.

Habitat and Range: Muddy-sand flats, intertidal zone. On falling tide, crabs emerge from burrows in thousands to form 'armies'. Able to walk forwards. When disturbed, crabs burrow corkscrew-like into sand. Endemic. Eastern Australia.

QM, Jeff Wright

Ward's Hairy-legged Crab
Paracleistostoma wardi

Identification: Shell to 11 mm across. Wider than long; smooth, hairless shell except for patches of short hair near bases of broad, flattened, furry legs.

Habitat and Range: Burrows in mud, around mangroves; mid to higher intertidal zone. Endemic. Eastern Qld

Similar Species: *P. mcneilli*, has two teeth either side of shell behind eyes.

A Elliott

QM, Jeff Wright

Sand Bubbler
Scopimera inflata

Identification: Body to 12 mm across. Globular, sandy-coloured. Broad oval patch (tympanum) on largest segment of each leg.

Habitat and Range: Wave-exposed and estuarine sandy beaches, intertidal zone. Endemic. Eastern Australia.

Notes: 'Tympanum' originally believed to act as ear drum for hearing, but found to absorb oxygen from air (adaptation for spending long periods out of water). Distinctive patterns of small sand balls radiating away from burrows, are result of feeding and burrow maintenance.

Furry-clawed Crab
Australoplax tridentata

Other name: Tuxedo Crab

Identification: Body to 15 mm across. Adult male, blue claws with large, round patch of fur at base of fingers; female, small claws. Broad, vertical black and white bands across front of mouthparts.

Habitat and Range: Common in mangroves and on muddy creek banks. Endemic. Darwin, NT to Sydney, NSW.

QM, Jeff Wright

QM, Jeff Wright

Australian Sentinel Crab
Macrophthalmus setosus

Identification: Body to 40 mm across. Muddy-grey; flattened; long, thin eyestalks; long, flat, hairy legs.

Habitat and Range: Lives in burrows, mostly on open, soft mud-flats and low on river and creek banks. Endemic. Eastern Australia, Cape York, Qld, to Sydney, NSW.

Similar Species: *M. crassipes*, narrower, has orange spine on inside of claw.

Horn-eyed Ghost Crab
Ocypode ceratophthalma

Identification: Body to 40 mm across. Horny stalks on top of eyes develop and lengthen with age. Dark maroon on lower surfaces of body and legs; 'H' marking on lower back.

Habitat and Range: Common on coastal sand beaches, intertidal zone; only found on open beach below frontal dunes. Northern Australia; Indo-West Pacific.

Similar Species: *O. cordimanus* lacks maroon colouring and horns on eyes; lives on dunes above high tide mark.

Notes: Mainly active at night; fast-moving scavenger and predator.

A Elliott

Fiddler Crabs (*Uca* spp.)

Male Fiddler Crabs have one claw greatly enlarged. Colour patterns are used for identification.

Orange-clawed Fiddler
Uca coarctata

Identification: Body to 40 mm across. Large male claw with upper half of palm roughened; palm orange gradually fading along fingers to white at tips. Male, conspicuous white spot on upper surface of last walking leg.

Habitat and Range: Common on muddy upper shoulders of creek and river banks; estuarine. Endemic. Eastern Australia Cape York to Moreton Bay, Qld.

Peter Davie

Lemon Fiddler
Uca triangularis

Identification: Body to 16 mm across. Large male claw dull lemon-yellow with brown-orange spots on upper surface; eyestalks dull orange to orange-brown.

Habitat and Range: On shaded shoulders of protected creeks, also on open muddy-sand banks at about mid-tidal level. Northern Australia; western Pacific from New Caledonia north to Japan.

Peter Davie

Peter Davie

Yellow-clawed Fiddler
Uca perplexa

Identification: Shell to 16 mm across. Large male claw yellow; front of shell between eyes broad compared to other *Uca* species.

Habitat and Range: Sand to sandy-mud on landward and seaward edge of mangroves in sheltered bays, creeks and river mouths. Endemic. Eastern Australia, Torres Strait to Trial Bay, NSW.

QM, Jeff Wright

Two-toned Fiddler
Uca vomeris

Identification: Body to 30 mm across. Large male claw with bottom finger and lower half of hand orange; upper part grey to pink, top finger bluish-white.

Habitat and Range: Common in unshaded sandy-mud along lower tide levels of open bays and creeks and isolated sand or mud banks. Endemic. Northern Australia, Darwin, NT, to Trial Bay, NSW.

QM

Sand Crab
Portunus pelagicus

Other name: Blue Swimming Crab

Identification: Body to 190 mm across. Mottled blue and olive-green; long strong spine each side of shell; last legs have flattened paddles for swimming.

Habitat and Range: Common in shallow, sandy-muddy inshore waters and seagrass beds. Australia-wide; Indo-West Pacific.

Notes: Commercially important trawled species. Good swimmer; can quickly burrow into sand.

Mud Crab
Scylla serrata

Identification: Body to more than 200 mm across. Olive-green with evenly serrated edges; last legs have flattened paddles for swimming.

Habitat and Range: Estuarine and mangrove areas; intertidal and subtidal zones. Makes large, oval burrows in banks. Common sub-fossil (1000–5000 years old). Northern Australia to Sydney, NSW. Indo-west Pacific.

Notes: Commercially important species; caught in baited pots.

QM, Bruce Cowell

Four-lobed Swimming Crab
Thalamita sima

Identification: Body to 85 mm across. Front edge of shell between eyes formed by pair of broad, flat lobes and much narrower arched lobe just before eye; last legs with flattened paddles for swimming.

Habitat and Range: Common on exposed and sheltered rocky shores, under stones, mussel clumps on sandy mud flats and on reefs; often in trawl catches. Intertidal zone to 35 m depth. Australia-wide; Indo-West Pacific south to New Zealand.

Notes: Several species with different colour patterns occur in intertidal zone.

John Short

Long-fingered Shore Crab
Epixanthus dentatus

Identification: Body to 55 mm across. Broad smooth, dark shell with lighter spotting. Long, pointed fingers of claws unique among shore crabs.

Habitat and Range: Common; inside rotting logs or stumps or in holes; muddy and mangrove environments; intertidal zone. Northern Australia; tropical Indo-West Pacific.

Notes: Appears slow-moving, but is active predator.

A Elliott

QM

Slow-moving Shore Crab
Myomenippe fornasinii

Identification: Body to 75 mm across. Steely blue-grey; massive claws with black fingers; smooth, oval shell has four teeth on edge behind eyes, last 2 sharply pointed.

Habitat and Range: Common in crevices and holes in rotting logs or stumps, especially in mangroves. Northern Australia; Indo-West Pacific.

FRESHWATER AND TERRESTRIAL CRUSTACEANS
John W Short

This section focuses on the common freshwater decapod crustaceans and also briefly deals with terrestrial isopods and amphipods. The tropical isopod fauna, in particular, appears to be very rich, but has not been studied in detail. Tropical North Queensland also has a diverse fauna of water fleas (Cladocera), copepods, seed shrimps (Ostracoda), clam shrimps (Conchostraca) and fairy shrimps (Anostraca). However, as these are generally very small or are too difficult to identify without the aid of a microscope, they have not been included here. In the following accounts, all body lengths are measured from the tip of the rostrum (the beak-like projection between the eyes) or head, to the tip of the tail. Egg size, an important identification feature for shrimps, is measured as the maximum diameter of the egg.

Amphipods

Amphipods are mostly small with high, narrow, elongated bodies. They are diverse and abundant in the sea. A few families have freshwater representatives. The Talitridae is well established on land. The freshwater and terrestrial amphipods of TNQ are poorly known.

QM, Bruce Cowell

Garden Land Hopper
Talitroides topitotum

Identification: Average length 7 mm. Pale, grey or bluish-grey; orange when dead.

Habitat and Range: Common, moist leaf litter in suburban gardens. Introduced from Indian Ocean islands.

Notes: Enters houses or becomes trapped in swimming pools, quickly dies. Now spreading into native bushland. Native *Arcitalitrus* and *Brevitalitrus* spp., known from rainforest and eucalypt forest in Qld.

Isopods

Isopods sometimes resemble amphipods, but their bodies tend to be low and flattened, rather than high and narrow. There are many more marine than freshwater and terrestrial species. Almost 40 terrestrial isopods are known from Queensland, but the real number of species is probably much higher. One freshwater species, *Tachaea caridophaga*, is a common external parasite on freshwater shrimps in Queensland.

Garden Slater
Porcellionides pruinosus

Identification: Length to 10 mm. Bluish-grey.

Habitat and Range: Damp areas, under bricks, timber, bark, rocks, compost heaps. Common in suburban gardens. Worldwide.

Notes: Appears to have been introduced from Europe.

QM, Bruce Cowell

Atyid Shrimps

These are generally small, semi-transparent, fast moving animals, sometimes sold in aquarium shops as food for native fish. With the aid of a microscope or good hand lens they are easily recognised by the stiff tufts of hairs on the fingers of the pincers (used for gathering food). Females carry eggs underneath the tail (attached to the swimmerets), until they hatch as larvae. Species with a freshwater life cycle have relatively few, large eggs and few larval stages. Those that develop in brackish water tend to have numerous small eggs and many larval stages.

Australian Paratya
Paratya australiensis

Identification: Length to 35 mm. Differs from other Australian atyids by spine above eye cavity (hard to see without micro-scope). Translucent with dark brown specks and light yellow markings. Eggs size variable, large in Qld (around 0.8 mm).

Habitat and Range: In TNQ, restricted to open forest streams on Atherton Tableland. Widespread subtropical and temperate eastern Australia.

John Short

John Short

Indistinct Caridina
Caridina indistincta

Identification: Length to 30 mm. Rostrum long, straight or slightly upturned, teeth more or less evenly spread on upper edge. Translucent with indistinct markings and specks. Eggs large (about 1 mm), few in number.

Habitat and Range: Lowland to mid-catchment areas among leaf litter or aquatic plants. Widespread eastern Qld, northern Australia.

Similar Species: *Caridinides wilkinsi*, similar rostrum; differs from *Caridina* spp. by well-developed exopod gill (short filament) on base of first pair of legs (with pincers). Widespread, northern Australia to Innisfail, Qld.

John Short

Long-beaked Caridina
Caridina longirostris

Identification: Length to 37 mm. Rostrum long, curved upwards or straight, with distinctive area lacking teeth on upper edge. Translucent with thin, dark stripes on side of body, upper rostrum white. Eggs small (0.4 mm), numerous.

Habitat and Range: Most abundant atyid in coastal lowland streams. Widespread north-eastern Australia; Indo-West Pacific.

Similar Species: Several similar forms in Indo-West Pacific with distinctive area lacking teeth on upper rostrum; grouped together as *C. nilotica*. Northern Australian form of *C. nilotica* slightly smaller (to 30 mm) than Long-beaked Caridina; translucent with indistinct markings; has larger eggs (0.7 mm).

Spiny-beaked Caridina
Caridina serratirostris

Identification: Length to 25 mm. Rostrum short, fairly straight, numerous teeth (to about 20) on upper edge, 3–6 teeth on lower edge. Two main colour forms: brown bands and cream specks, or more evenly brown with white stripe along back. Eggs small (0.4 mm), numerous.

Habitat and Range: Lowland streams, usually in rainforest, amongst roots of bank vegetation or leaf litter. Widespread northern Australia; Indo-West Pacific.

QM, Bruce Cowell

Slender-beaked Caridina
Caridina gracilirostris

Identification: Length to 35 mm. Rostrum extremely long, curved upwards, lower edge with many (to about 30) teeth, upper edge with less than 15 teeth, 1 or 2 on front third. Body translucent, a few faint dark stripes on tail, rostrum translucent orange. Eggs numerous, small (about 0.5 mm).

Habitat and Range: Lower freshwater reaches and brackish zone of major rivers. Widespread northern Australia; Indo-West Pacific.

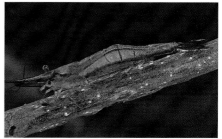

QM, Bruce Cowell

Typical Caridina
Caridina typus

Identification: Length to 30 mm. Rostrum very short, no teeth on upper edge, 1–6 teeth on lower edge. Body translucent brown to dark brown, often with light stripe along back. Eggs numerous, small (about 0.4 mm).

Habitat and Range: Adults in coastal freshwater streams; larvae in brackish waters. North-eastern Qld, common Proserpine–Whitsundays area; widespread Indo-West Pacific.

Similar Species: Zebra Shrimp (see p. 62); False Zebra Shrimp (*C. confusa*), Atherton Tableland; McIlwraith Ra. Caridina (*C. spinula*). All upper catchment freshwater species; rostrum usually lacking teeth on upper and lower edges; relatively few, large eggs (around 1 mm).

John Short

John Short

Zebra Shrimp
Caridina zebra

Identification: Length to 20 mm. Rostrum very short, usually no teeth on upper and lower edges. Two colour forms: one with black and white bands on body, restricted to Cardwell Ra. (upper Tully and Herbert Rs); other is translucent with brown specks, restricted to Atherton Tableland–Lamb Ra. (upper Barron and Johnstone Rs). Eggs large (about 1 mm), few in number.

Habitat and Range: Well-shaded streams with fringing, undisturbed rainforest. Restricted to upland freshwater streams above 150 m. Endemic to TNQ.

Similar Species: False Zebra Shrimp (*C. confusa*), similar to Atherton Tableland–Lamb Ra. form; rostrum longer and body more elongated; restricted to more open streams on Atherton Tableland with disturbed or cleared rainforest on banks.

John Short

Riffle Shrimp
Australatya striolata

Identification: Length to 60 mm. Robust, with thicker, more opaque shell than other Australian atyids. Pincers with elongated fingers, no palm region, rostrum short. Dark green or brown; light stripe down middle of back, 5 stripes along each side of head-thorax. Eggs numerous, small (0.6 mm).

Habitat and Range: Riffles and rapids where it filter feeds; shelters under rocks. Eastern Australia, Cooktown, Qld, to Shoalhaven R., NSW.

Notes: Protandrous, males change to females within 30–36 mm size range. Mating occurs between old transformed females and young untransformed males.

Palaemonid prawns

These are larger and more robust than atyid shrimps. The pincers lack the tufts of hairs characteristic of atyids. Two groups occur in the freshwaters of TNQ: *Palaemon* and *Macrobrachium*. *Palaemon* species mostly inhabit tidal rock pools. Thirteen species of *Macrobrachium* are found in Australia, of which only one does not occur in TNQ. As a group they are difficult to identify due to the high degree of sexual and male developmental variation. Egg size is a useful identification feature.

Common Australian River Prawn
Macrobrachium australiense

John Short

Identification: Length to 90 mm. Dominant males have mat of hairs on fingers of claws; rostrum short to medium length. Colour varies with age — old males dark brown or grey; younger males and females have irregular grey blotches on head-thorax and dark stripes on palm and wrist of claws. Eggs large (1.4 mm), few in number.

Habitat and Range: Lowland to upper catchment areas; prefers still pools rather than running water. Most widespread river prawn in Australia, occurs over eastern, northern and central parts of continent.

Similar Species: Ida's River Prawn, (see p. 64).

East Australian River Prawn
Macrobrachium tolmerum

John Short

Identification: Length to 100 mm. Pincers of claws lack mat of hairs in dominant males. Rostrum of medium length. Adults usually reddish-brown, fingertips lighter; old males darker, more evenly coloured; dominant males with orange patch on base of claws. Juveniles mottled on abdomen with irregular blotches on head-thorax. Eggs small (0.6 mm), numerous.

Habitat and Range: Most common river prawn in north-eastern Qld. Prefers running water, but found in variety of habitats in permanent streams, lakes and lagoons. Tolerates acidic water in coastal sand dunes. Eastern Australia, tip of Cape York, Qld, to Sydney, NSW.

John Short

Ida's River Prawn
Macrobrachium idae

Identification: Length to 100 mm. Pincers of claws with mat of hairs covering movable finger and cutting edge of fixed finger in dominant males; rostrum of medium length, straight with irregularly spaced teeth, slender at tip. Large, irregular brown blotches on head; abdomen ornate, lightly blotched; dark stripes or irregular blotches on claws, feelers banded. Eggs small (0.6 mm), numerous.

Habitat and Range: Brackish water and lowland freshwater, generally in areas of low flow near upstream limit of tidal influence in coastal creeks and large rivers. North-eastern Qld to Herbert R.; widespread Indo-West Pacific.

(Left claw missing), QM, Bruce Cowell

Giant Jungle Prawn
Macrobrachium lar

Identification: Length to 195 mm. Dominant males have long claws with gaping pincers bearing large incisor teeth. Body olive-brown to olive-grey, swirled with orange-brown, blue-grey and light olive-grey; claws dark brown with maroon fingers, walking legs blue-grey. Old dominant males darker and more evenly coloured. Eggs small (0.6 mm), numerous.

Habitat and Range: Rainforest pools near running water with good cover such as fallen trees, large tree roots, boulders. High rainfall, tropical streams with permanent flow. Coastal lowland areas to around 100 m. Widespread Indo-West Pacific

Similar Species: Giant River Prawn (*M. rosenbergii*), larger (length to 320 mm); has mat of hairs on two-thirds of movable finger on adult claws; long, slow-flowing river systems. Monsoonal northern Australia, Kimberley region, WA, to McIvor R., (Cape York) Qld.

Koombooloomba Prawn
Macrobrachium sp.

Identification: Length to 65 mm. Rostrum short, upper edge convex; claws of dominant males broad, left and right claw same shape, but of unequal length. Mottled olive-brown to olive-grey, palm of claws usually has reticulated pattern. Eggs large (1.9 mm), few in number.

Habitat and Range: Upland freshwater; flowing rainforest streams. Restricted to Tully R. catchment above Tully Falls, Qld.

Similar Species: Handschin's River Prawn (*M. handschini*), widespread freshwaters, northern Australia to Normanby R., Qld. Broad-fingered River Prawn (*M. latidactylus*), widespread Central Indo-West Pacific, lower reaches of major rivers and coastal streams in north-eastern Qld. Dominant males of both species have left and right claws markedly different in shape and size.

John Short

Freshwater Crayfish

Freshwater crayfish have broad, well-developed claws and robust bodies. They are poor swimmers and are largely bottom-dwellers. Two groups are represented in TNQ — spiny crayfish (*Euastacus* spp.) and yabbies (*Cherax* spp.). The spiny crayfish are confined to mountain top areas. Yabbies are mostly found at lower elevations. Many can survive droughts by burrowing down to the water table.

Redclaw
Cherax quadricarinatus

Identification: Length to 200 mm; weight to 600 g (usually below 300 g). Rostrum long, slender with 2–3 pairs of spines; two pairs of well-defined ridges behind eyes. Colour varies with habitat, bluish-green to almost black, purple flecks on abdomen; mature males with soft red patch on outer fixed finger of claws.

Habitat and Range: Permanent and semi-permanent creeks, rivers, swamps. Constructs short burrows or shelters under rocks, submerged timber. Northern Australia, Daly R., NT, to Normanby R., Qld; introduced to upper Barron R. catchment, (including Lake Tinaroo) and Burdekin Dam. Used as aquaculture species in Qld.

John Short

John Short

Orange-fingered Yabby
Cherax depressus complex

Identification: Length to 100 mm. Rostrum short, triangular, without well-developed spines; single pair of poorly developed ridges behind eyes. Fingertips orange or red, rest of body olive-brown to bluish-green. More than one species.

Habitat and Range: Semi-aquatic, burrow along water line of creeks and gullies or down to water table in swamps, commonly in farm dams. Widespread eastern Qld.

Notes: Five species recognised, but further study of this group needed. Two species from TNQ — *C. wasselli*, Cape York Peninsula and Kuranda; *C. cairnsensis*, Cairns.

John Short

Rainforest Yabby
Cherax parvus

Identification: Length to 65 mm. Rostrum short, triangular, without well-developed spines, body slender. Mottled light orange-brown to dark brown, fingertips of claws orange.

Habitat and Range: Under rocks in shallow rainforest streams. Restricted to Tully R. catchment above Tully Falls, Qld.

John Short

Balan Spiny Crayfish
Euastacus balanensis

Identification: Length to 80 mm. Wrist of claws with well-defined groove, teeth along edge of rostrum restricted to front half. Body brown to olive.

Habitat and Range: Rainforest streams above 800 m; under rocks and timber or in burrows near water line. Lamb Ra., Mt Bartle Frere, Mt Bellenden Ker, Qld.

Similar Species: Yigara (*E. yigara*), above 750 m, Tully R. catchment on Cardwell Ra., Qld; Mt Elliot Spiny Crayfish (*E. bindal*), above 1000 m on Mt Elliot, Qld; and Eungella Spiny Crayfish (*E. eungella*), above 740 m, Clarke Ra., Qld.

Flecker's Spiny Crayfish
Euastacus fleckeri

Identification: Length to 250 mm. Rostrum of large specimens U-shaped, wrist of claws without well-defined groove. Body dark green to blue or brown with red spines.

Habitat and Range: Under rocks and timber or in burrows near water line. Rainforest streams above 1000 m. Mt Carbine Tableland, Qld.

Similar Species: Robert's Spiny Crayfish (*E. robertsi*), Mt Finnigan, Qld, above 1000 m.

John Short

Crabs

Two groups of freshwater crabs are commonly seen in TNQ. The true freshwater crabs, represented by *Holthuisana* spp., spend their whole life cycle in freshwater. Grapsids or shore crabs are inhabitants of brackish and marine shores, but the River Swimming Crab and the Banded Mangrove Crab (see p. 53) extend into lowland freshwaters.

Agassiz's Freshwater Crab
Holthuisana agassizi

Identification: Width to 40 mm. Rounded, body and legs tan to maroon or orange, dark band down back in large specimens.

Habitat and Range: Semi-aquatic, edges of watercourses, swamps, seepage areas. McIlwraith Ra. to Ravenshoe, Qld.

Similar Species: Inland Crab (*H. transversa*), central and north-western Australia, in dry coastal areas, Townsville to Gladstone, Qld. Wassell's Freshwater Crab (*H. wasselli*), similar range, smaller, back of body has large specks, no dark bands or blotches.

John Short

River Swimming Crab
Varuna litterata

Identification: Width to 55 mm. Square-shaped. Legs hairy, paddle-like; body flat on top. Mottled brown to almost black.

Habitat and Range: Lowland coastal freshwater near limit of tidal influence. Under rocks and timber in shallow water. Widespread Indo-West Pacific.

Notes: Breeds in estuaries.

John Short

Cairns Birdwing, QM, Bruce Cowell

INSECTS

I nsects are the most diverse and numerous of all terrestrial animals. They have many special features that contribute to this success. Their hard external skeleton shields them from the environment and from predator attack. They have a waxy outer skin that stops them dehydrating in the hot sun. They have an efficient way of walking with six legs. Most have wings and enjoy the advantages of flight. Many have larval stages (grubs, maggots, caterpillars), which act as feeding machines to ensure rapid growth to the adult stage.

These remarkable animals have populated the tropical environments of Queensland in vast numbers of species. Most are dependent on plants, so the rainforests are exceptionally rich in insects. A different range of species occurs in the eucalypt forests, paperbark swamps and mangroves. Many mountain insects have lost the power of flight. Since the rainforest-covered mountains of Tropical North Queensland are separated from each other by low, dry valleys, their insects have evolved as separate species over millions of years of isolation. Today, we find quite different insects on the different mountain ranges, such as Carbine Tableland, Bellenden Ker, Kirrama, Paluma, Mt Elliot and Eungella.

We can only guess at how many species of insects there are in the whole of Tropical North Queensland. A few fragments of information are available. A Queensland Museum survey of Mt Bellenden Ker in 1981 yielded about 5100 species, of which there were 1514 different beetles and 1345 different moths. A considerable proportion of all these insects have still not been scientifically named. However, the butterflies of TNQ are well known. More than 240 species occur in the area, more than half the number known from all of Australia. Similarly, almost half of Australia's known 300 species of dragonflies and damselflies occur in the coastal region from Cooktown to Mackay. In the past 10 years, intensive surveys of native dung beetles have yielded 190 different kinds from Cooktown to Townsville alone, almost half the number known from Australia. An easy way to see a selection of this great diversity of insects is to look at the swarms that come to an outside light at night in mid-summer.

This handbook can mention only a few of these many insects and treatment is limited to some of the more common and conspicuous species or those of special significance. The giant dragonfly, *Petalura ingentissima*, is one of the world's largest. The massive Giant Burrowing Cockroach, is the world's heaviest cockroach, and the Giant Wood Moth, is the heaviest moth known. Females of the Hercules Moth have the largest wings of any moth. The burnished beauty of Mueller's Stag Beetle makes it one of the world's most magnificent beetles. Females of the Cairns Birdwing are Australia's largest butterfly.

Insects are classified into about 25 Orders, which correspond to familiar groups such as beetles (Coleoptera), flies (Diptera), bees, wasps and ants (Hymenoptera) and moths and butterflies (Lepidoptera).

Chris J Burwell and Geoff B Monteith

DRAGONFLIES AND DAMSELFLIES

Dragonflies and damselflies have two pairs of stiff, net-like wings that cannot be folded flat against their long, thin abdomens. They are common around rivers, streams, lakes, ponds, swamps and even temporary pools, but strong-flying and migratory species may be found far from water. All are predators, catching insects on the wing or gathering them and spiders from vegetation. Their immature stages or larvae live in freshwater, but one species of dragonfly has larvae that live in damp leaf litter in the rainforests of TNQ. The larvae are also predators, feeding on aquatic invertebrates and sometimes tadpoles and small fish.

A small selection of TNQ's 150 or so species of dragonflies and damselflies are treated here. *The Australian Dragonflies*, by J.A.L. Watson, G. Theischinger and H.M. Abbey (CSIRO), is an invaluable guide to damselflies and dragonflies.

Damselflies

These are generally smaller and more delicate than dragonflies and have widely separated eyes. Both pairs of wings are similar in shape. When perched, most damselflies hold their wings pressed together above their bodies, but some species sit with their wings outspread. Their larvae have three leaf-like, sac-like or spine-like gills at the tip of the abdomen.

QM, Jeff Wright

Ischnura aurora

Identification: Wingspan 25–30 mm. Male (pictured), head dark with two pale spots behind eyes; top of thorax dark with green stripes, sides pale; abdomen reddish, tip black with blue spot. Female similar, but abdomen dark above, without blue spot.

Habitat and Range: Still and slow flowing waters. Australia-wide.

Notes: Weak flier, perches frequently on grass and reed stems.

Steve Wilson

Ischnura heterosticta

Identification: Wingspan 35–45 mm. Male (pictured), head black, blue band on face and two blue spots behind eyes; top of thorax black with two blue stripes, sides blue; abdomen black, blue at base and tip with thin blue bands in between. Female dull olive-brown, sides of thorax pale green.

Habitat and Range: Still and flowing waters, including temporary ponds. Australia-wide.

Notes: Weak flier, perches frequently on vegetation at water's edge.

Agriocnemis argentea

Identification: Wingspan 20–25 mm. Mature male has top of head and thorax black, rest of body covered in white dusting.

Habitat and Range: Still and flowing waters, including temporary ponds. Northern Australia and north-eastern Qld.

Notes: Weak flier, perches frequently on vegetation at water's edge.

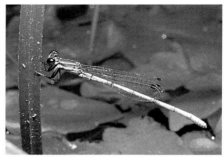

Steve Wilson

Nososticta solida

Identification: Wingspan 40–45 mm. Black with orange markings on thorax and base of abdomen. Base of wings often yellowish.

Habitat and Range: Still and flowing permanent waters, including stagnant pools. Widespread, eastern Australia.

Notes: Agile flier.

QM, Jeff Wright

Lestoidea conjuncta

Identification: Wingspan 45–50 mm. Male (pictured) black, sides of thorax mostly pale orange, green or blue. Female, more dark markings on sides of thorax.

Habitat and Range: Rainforest streams. North-eastern Qld.

Notes: Only two Australian species, both in TNQ; *L. barbarae* differs slightly in wing venation and male abdominal appendages.

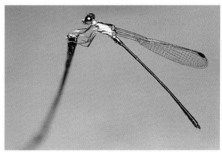

QM, Steve Wilson

Episynlestes cristatus

Identification: Wingspan 50–60 mm. Head and top of thorax greenish-black; side of thorax pale yellow with thick, greenish-black, diagonal stripe. Abdomen brownish-black with thin, pale yellow bands at bases of segments. Male (pictured), pair of pale appendages at tip of abdomen.

Habitat and Range: Rainforest streams. North-eastern Qld.

QM, Jeff Wright

Anthony O'Toole

Austroargiolestes aureus

Identification: Wingspan 55–65 mm. Face and sides of thorax bright yellow or orange, abdomen black.

Habitat and Range: Streams, mostly in rainforest. North-eastern Qld.

Notes: Perches on streamside vegetation in sunlight.

QM, Jeff Wright

Diphlebia euphaeoides

Identification: Wingspan 60–70 mm. Male (pictured), head black, thorax bright blue and black. Two segments at base and two segments at tip of abdomen bright blue; rest of abdomen black, sometimes with small blue spots. Wings dark brown with clear bases and tips. Female, dull olive-green with clear wings.

Habitat and Range: Streams and rivers in Cape York and north-eastern Qld.

Similar Species: *D. hybridoides* has more blue on abdomen of male.

Notes: Perches on rocks and streamside plants with wings outspread.

Dragonflies

Dragonflies range in size from small to large and are more thickset than damselflies. The front and back pairs of wings are slightly different in shape, especially at the base. Dragonflies hold their wings outspread when perched. In most species, the eyes either meet in the middle of head or are close together, but in some are widely separated. The gills of dragonfly larvae are concealed within the body and they have a triangle of stout plates at the tip of the abdomen.

QM, Jeff Wright

Hemianax papuensis

Identification: Wingspan 100–110 mm. Olive-green with black, T-shaped marking on top of head and black markings on abdomen.

Habitat and Range: Breeds in permanent and temporary waters. Australia-wide.

Notes: Fast, strong flying, often found far from water.

Ictinogomphus australis
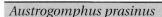

Identification: Wingspan 80–90 mm. Black and yellow; abdomen wider at base and tip. Eyes separated on top of head.

Habitat and Range: Rivers, lagoons, ponds. Northern Australia and eastern Qld.

Notes: Strong flying, often returning to regular perch on streamside plants or sticks.

QM, Jeff Wright

Austrogomphus prasinus
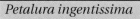

Identification: Wingspan 60–70 mm. Black, marked with yellow or greenish-yellow; top of thorax has two black stripes; abdomen has yellow bands, black towards end; male, two yellow, forked appendages at tip.

Habitat and Range: Streams and rivers. Cape York and north-eastern Qld.

Similar species: Several other species in TNQ. *A. amphilictus*, most similar, male appendages not forked; female, central blunt tooth on back of head.

Anthony O'Toole

Petalura ingentissima

Identification: Wingspan 150–165 mm. Enormous; black with pale stripes on thorax and narrow pale bands on abdomen. Male, leaf-like appendages at tip of abdomen.

Habitat and Range: Rainforest streams. TNQ.

Similar Species: *P. pulcherrima* has wider pale bands on abdomen.

Notes: Australia's largest dragonfly. Rests high on tree trunks. Larvae live in burrows that reach down to water table, but come to surface to feed.

QM, Jeff Wright

Hemicordulia australiae

Identification: Wingspan 60–70 mm. Head between eyes yellowish, dark metallic green on top; thorax and abdomen dark, metallic blue-green with pale yellowish markings; abdomen slender. Tips of wings often brownish.

Habitat and Range: Still and flowing permanent waters, but often found far from water. Most of Australia.

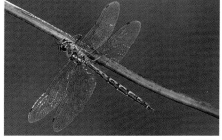

QM, Jeff Wright

Anthony O'Toole

Choristhemis flavoterminata

Identification: Wingspan 60–75 mm. Black, yellow patch on front of head, yellow stripes on top and sides of thorax, abdomen with yellow spots and tip.

Range and Habitat: Streams and rivers. Eastern Australia, Cape York, Qld, to south-eastern NSW.

Notes: Slow, undulating flight; yellow tail-tip very noticeable.

QM, Jeff Wright

Diplacodes bipunctata

Identification: Wingspan 45–55 mm. Male (pictured), reddish with black, heart-shaped markings on top of abdomen. Female sandy-yellow. Wings clear except for small brownish-yellow spot at base of hindwing.

Habitat and Range: Still and slow flowing waters, temporary ponds. Australia-wide.

Notes: Adults fly close to ground, often land on ground or perch on low plants.

QM, Jeff Wright

Diplacodes haematodes

Identification: Wingspan 50–60 mm. Male (pictured), bright red; brownish spot at base of hindwing. Female abdomen yellowish with central row of black markings; tips of wings brownish.

Habitat and Range: Still and flowing waters, but favours streams and rivers. Australia-wide, except Tas.

Similar Species: *D. bipunctata* (see above).

QM, Jeff Wright

Neurothemis stigmatizans

Identification: Wingspan 50–60 mm. Male, reddish-yellow thorax; abdomen yellowish with three dark stripes. Wings with large reddish-brown patch at base, tips clear. Female similar, more yellowish; brown patches at base of wings lighter and narrower than male; wing tips brownish.

Habitat and Range: Widespread, eastern Qld, northern Australia.

Notes: Large numbers of adults often found together in grassy areas near still waters.

Orthetrum caledonicum

Identification: Wingspan 70–80 mm. Newly emerged male yellowish with black markings; abdomen with ladder-like pattern of dark markings. Thorax and abdomen of older males turn light powder blue; tip of abdomen black. Wings usually with brownish tips. Female, similar to young male, thorax and abdomen becomes powdery blue-grey with age.

Habitat and Range: Breeds in still and flowing waters, including temporary ponds. Australia-wide, except Tas.

Notes: Adults fly close to ground, often patrol edge of water, perch on waterside plants and sticks.

QM, Jeff Wright

Orthetrum villosovittatum

Identification: Wingspan 65–75 mm. Male (pictured), face and abdomen bright red; thorax reddish-brown. Female mostly orange-red. Both sexes have clear wings with brown bases, abdomen constricted near base.

Habitat and Range: Streams, lakes, ponds, swamps. Northern and eastern Australia, NT to Vic.; Moluccas, New Guinea and nearby islands.

Notes: Strong, fast flying, but perches frequently.

Steve Wilson

Trapezostigma loewii

Identification: Wingspan 80–90 mm. Abdomen reddish-brown with black tip; wings clear; hindwing with saddle-shaped, reddish-brown spot at base.

Habitat and Range: Mostly still waters. Australia-wide, except parts of WA and Tas.

Notes: Strong flying; often seen patrolling back and forth high above ground.

QM, Jeff Wright

ORTHOPTEROID INSECTS

The 'orthopteroids' is a name given to a group of closely related orders of insects that include grasshoppers, stick insects, cockroaches, termites, mantids, earwigs and others. These insects do not have a larval and pupal stage in their life cycle. The juvenile stages are all nymphs that resemble the adults in body form and life-style.

Most orthopteroids are plant-eaters and a few have become pests. In tropical areas, such as North Queensland, many orthopteroids are large insects. Since they spend much of their time resting on their food plant, they are potential food for sharp-eyed predators, such as birds. To guard against this, many orthopteroids have developed camouflage to a great degree in appearance and behaviour. Others have become nocturnal and spend the day in concealed situations. For these reasons, the casual observer does not often notice many orthopteroids, yet they include many of the most attractive and bizarre members of the insect world.

Grasshopper Country — the Abundant Orthopteroid Insects of Australia, by D.C.F. Rentz (University of NSW Press), is a good reference book to learn more about tropical orthopteroid insects.

Cockroaches

Most cockroaches are active, nocturnal insects with long legs. The head of a cockroach is covered by an overhanging, shield-like thorax. Quite a few are wingless and one group of these has developed powerful legs and a burrowing lifestyle.

All the household pest cockroaches have been introduced into Australia and have given cockroaches a 'bad name'. There are hundreds of harmless, often attractive, native cockroaches that live in the bush.

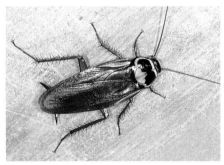

P. australasiae, QM, Bruce Cowell

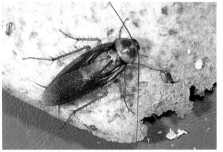

P. americana, QM, Jeff Wright

Australian Cockroach
Periplaneta australasiae

Identification: Length 40 mm. Reddish-brown; yellow and brown on thorax; yellow edges to front of wing covers.

Habitat and Range: Towns and cities in houses; widespread in warmer latitudes worldwide.

Similar Species: American Cockroach (*P. americana*), pattern on thorax indistinct, wing covers reddish-brown.

Notes: Common, nocturnal pest; feeds on food scraps, book bindings, etc. Lays hard egg capsules in concealed situations, such as crevices and among folds of fabric. Many young cockroaches hatch from each capsule. Despite name, not native to Australia, probably from Asia.

Bush Cockroaches
Methana spp.

Identification: Length 23 mm. Reddish-brown; white edges to wings and white edge around thorax.

Habitat and Range: Several similar species in northern Qld rainforests.

Notes: Live in small colonies under loose bark of recently dead trees; emerge at night and forage on trunk.

QM, Jeff Wright

Banded Cockroach
Cosmozosteria bicolor

Identification: Length 23 mm. Oval, reddish-brown with bright yellow edge that is sometimes partly divided into segments.

Habitat and Range: Open forest, prefers sandy soils, where it shelters under rock slabs and wood debris on ground. Cape York, Qld, to northern NSW.

Notes: Unlike most cockroaches, active in daytime, may be seen basking in sunny spots in early morning. Produces copious aromatic fluid from glands at tail end when handled.

QM, Jeff Wright

Wood Cockroach
Panesthia sloanei

Identification: Length 45 mm. Heavily built, reddish-brown with elongated body; strong spiny legs and indented thorax. End of abdomen has saw-like edge.

Habitat and Range: Common in mountain rainforest. Cooktown to Bluewater Ra., Qld.

Similar Species: P. tryoni, related species in mountains of Mackay region.

Notes: Lives in colonies inside rotten logs. Feeds on soft wood; important in speeding breakdown of logs. Females give birth to live young.

QM, Jeff Wright

QM. Jeff Wright

Giant Burrowing Cockroach
Macropanesthia rhinoceros

Identification: Length 70–80 mm; weight to 30 g. Enormous, smooth, reddish-brown; powerful spiny legs. Upturned spine on each side of second last segment of abdomen.

Habitat and Range: Deep burrows in sandy soils in open forest. Coen (Cape York) to Rockhampton; Whitsunday islands, Qld.

Notes: Heaviest cockroach in world. Feeds on dead leaves that it drags down into burrow. Females give birth to live young (pictured), about October each year. Young are nurtured in burrow for a year before starting independent life. Adult cockroaches sometimes mass on surface after rain. Lives and breeds well in captivity.

Praying Mantids

Praying Mantids are predatory insects with spiny front legs modified for seizing other insects, which they kill and eat. Large, widely-spaced eyes give them good vision and they rely on camouflage to escape detection by prey animals that venture within their reach. Mantids deposit their eggs in a mass surrounded by a foamy secretion that dries to a papery texture.

QM. Jeff Wright

Giant Mantids
Hierodula spp.

Identification: Length 85 mm. Green; wings leaf-like. Inner surfaces of front legs pink. Thorax with extended edges.

Habitat and Range: Rainforest. North Qld.

Notes: Several similar species. Can inflict painful wound with front legs if handled. Lurk among rainforest foliage waiting for prey (usually other insects, but occasionally small frogs). Sometimes attracted to houselights.

Garden Mantid
Orthodera ministralis

Identification: Length 40 mm. Green; wide, straight-sided thorax; full-length wings.

Habitat and Range: Common in open forest and rainforest. Throughout TNQ; worldwide.

Notes: Often seen in gardens where it hunts among foliage. Deposits small egg cases in crevices and under bark.

QM. Jeff Wright

Stick Mantid
Archimantis latistyla

Identification: Length 110 mm. Elongated; pale brown; resembles dried stick. Female with short wings (foreground); male smaller, with full length wings (rear).

Habitat and Range: On shrubs and among long grass in open forest; often in gardens. Cape York, Qld, to Vic.

Notes: Khaki-coloured egg masses, as big as pullet eggs, have thick outer, papery layer; often deposited on topmost twigs of shrubs. Eggs often parasitised by small wasps.

QM. Jeff Wright

Leaf Mantid
Neomantis australis

Identification: Length 25 mm. Delicate, pale green; wings broad, with net-like pattern formed by darker green veins.

Habitat and Range: Rainforest and open forest. Coastal north Qld.

Notes: Resembles leaves; rarely noticed except when it flies to houselights.

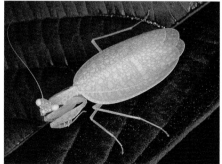

Paul Zborowski

Stick Insects (Phasmids)

These large, leaf-eating insects are masters of camouflage. Some resemble sticks and twigs, while others are more leaf-like. They spend much of their time hanging motionless or swaying slightly to resemble wind movement. Some may be confused with praying mantids, but differ in not having the front legs spined for seizing prey. Phasmids drop their eggs to the ground, from where the hatchling nymphs walk up tree trunks to the leaves.

Stick insects are long-lived for insects and make interesting pets. Take note of the plant on which a stick insect is found and continue to supply it with fresh foliage from that plant. A daily spray of water keeps the foliage fresh and provides the stick insect with drinking water. Eggs from an adult female will collect at the bottom of the cage. Some eggs will hatch within weeks, others take years. During that time it is necessary to store them on moist soil or moss.

QM, Jeff Wright

Spiny Leaf Insect
Extatosoma tiaratum

Identification: Length 160 mm. Female (pictured) fat, spiny, wingless with greatly flattened legs; hangs upside-down with tail curved, scorpion-like, over back. Male, more slender, with long wings.

Habitat and Range: Most habitats along coast and nearby ranges. Daintree, Qld, to southern NSW.

Notes: Feeds on foliage of many plants, including wattles, eucalypts, roses and grapevines. Females move very little; males fly in search of females, which they detect with ultraviolet vision. Established in overseas pet trade.

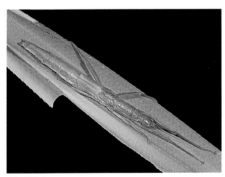

QM, Jeff Wright

Peppermint Stick
Megacrania batesi

Identification: Length 100 mm. Pale green, rather flattened; legs and body without strong spines. Female (pictured), has shortened wings.

Habitat and Range: In Australia, known only from coastal areas near Cape Tribulation and Innisfail, Qld; Indonesia.

Notes: During day hides in bases of prickly leaves of Pandanus (*Pandanus monticola*), feeds on leaves at night. When disturbed, squirts milky fluid with strong peppermint smell from glands at front corners of thorax.

Earwigs

Earwigs are easily recognised by the stout pair of pincers at the tip of the abdomen. These are used for prey capture, defence and also to help fold up the semicircular hindwings to fit under the short, hard wing cases. Some are predatory, others herbivorous. They live in concealed places during the day.

Gum Tree Earwig
Pygidicrania sp.

Identification: Length 20 mm. Elongated; pale head, legs and thorax; abdomen dark. Tip of abdomen swollen before pincers.

Habitat and Range: Widespread in open forest, especially at higher altitudes. North Qld.

Notes: Lives under loose bark of gum trees. Protrudes tip of abdomen at night to catch small insects as food.

Paul Zborowski

Grasshoppers, Crickets and Katydids

Almost all these insects have the front wings thickened into leathery covers, which protect the delicate hind wings that fold up underneath. The hind legs are enlarged so the animal can jump to begin flight or to escape its enemies. Most are herbivorous.

Hedge Grasshopper
Valanga irregularis

Identification: Length 85 mm. Large, usually plain khaki, but spotted and banded (pictured) variations occur. Nymphs green or have black and orange patterns.

Habitat and Range: Open forest close to coast. Qld and northern NSW.

Notes: Thrives in well-watered suburban gardens. Feeds mostly on broad-leaved shrubs such as acalypha and hibiscus, but also damages palms. Passes the dry season in adult, winged stage. Mates early summer and lays eggs in pods in ground; hatch when first rains come and nymphs feed and grow rapidly during wet season.

QM. Jeff Wright

Bruce Cowell

Dead Leaf Grasshoppers
Goniaea spp.

Identification: Length 45 mm. Greyish-brown; low crest along middle of thorax. Inner side of hind legs yellow and black.

Habitat and Range: Dry, open eucalypt forest. Australia-wide.

Notes: Several similar species. Rest among dried leaves on ground, strongly camouflaged. Unusual, feed on dead leaves.

QM, Jeff Wright

Spotted Grasshopper
Greyacris profundesulcata

Identification: Length 35 mm. Black with yellow bands and spots; very short wing covers conceal tiny, bright red hind wings.

Habitat and Range: Rocky hillsides in open forest on western slopes of coastal ranges. Cape York to Fraser I., Qld.

Notes: Feeds on paper daisies (*Helichrysum*) and other plants. Lifts wing covers to display red warning colours and regurgitates smelly fluid when handled.

QM, Jeff Wright

Litter Grasshopper
Desmoptera truncatipennis

Identification: Length 35 mm. Mottled brown; pointed head; tips of wings cut off at right angles.

Habitat and Range: Rainforest. Cooktown to Townsville, Qld.

Notes: Rests among leaf litter on ground during day, highly camouflaged. At night feeds on leaves of low shrubs. Many related species in New Guinea.

QM, Bruce Cowell

Matchstick Grasshoppers
Morabinae

Identification: Length 45 mm. Small, elongated, wingless; antennae beaded; tail long and drawn out in male (pictured).

Habitat and Range: Open forest. Australia-wide.

Notes: Many similar species, native to Australia. Feed on grasses and shrubs.

Monkey Grasshopper
Biroella sp.

Identification: Length 32 mm. Small, green, wingless; bulging eyes; hind legs splayed outwards when resting (bowlegged).

Habitat and Range: Rainforest. Cooktown to Innisfail, Qld.

Notes: Feeds and basks in sunlight on broad-leaved shrubs. Rarely seen except in wet season; probably more common in upper canopy. Related species in Cape York and New Guinea.

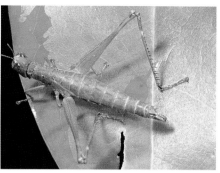

QM, Jeff Wright

Mole Crickets
Gryllotalpa spp.

Identification: Length 33 mm. Elongated; cylindrical; wing covers short. Hind legs not enlarged for jumping; forelegs modified for digging.

Habitat and Range: Variety of habitats, particularly near water. Australia-wide.

Notes: Several species widespread in northern Qld. Burrow in soil, feed on plant roots. Burrow entrance is formed as sounding chamber to amplify their calls, mostly produced at dusk. Sometimes fly to lights.

QM, Jeff Wright

White-kneed King Cricket
Penalva flavocalceata

Identification: Length 80 mm. Shiny, reddish-brown; wingless; hind legs large with prominent white 'knees'.

Habitat and Range: Rainforests of lowlands and mountains. Cooktown to Townsville, Qld.

Notes: Related species without white knees in Proserpine–Mackay region. Lives in smooth-walled, vertical burrows in ground. Emerges on wet nights to scavenge for food. Female deposits eggs into soil with long, sharp ovipositor. Related to New Zealand wetas.

QM, Jeff Wright

QM, Jeff Wright

Northern Field Cricket
Teleogryllus oceanicus

Identification: Length 30 mm. Black; wings drawn out to long point behind. Female (pictured) with long, straight, needle-like ovipositor at rear.

Habitat and Range: Widespread, open forest, pasture and agricultural land. Northern Australia to Brisbane, Qld; Pacific islands.

Notes: Lives under debris and in shallow burrows. Feeds on live and dead plant matter. Males chirp repeatedly at dusk. Sometimes an agricultural pest.

QM, Jeff Wright

Burrowing Crickets
Cephalogryllus spp.

Identification: Length 28 mm. Stout body, powerful hind legs; males with short, square wing covers; females wingless.

Habitat and Range: Mostly rainforest. Several similar species in northern Qld.

Notes: Dig burrows in soil which lead to a chamber that they stock with leaf pieces from ground surface. Females lay eggs in burrow and nymphs are raised on leaf material.

QM, Jeff Wright

Tree Trunk Crickets
Tathra spp.

Identification: Length 12 mm. Mottled colour pattern. Males (pictured), with large, square, reddish wing covers with raised veins; females wingless.

Habitat and Range: Tree trunks in rainforest. Many similar species in northern Qld.

Notes: Male sings with shrill, rapid note while holding wing covers vertically above back. Contributes much of background insect noise inside rainforest at night.

Daytime Katydid
Veria colorata

Identification: Length 27 mm. Glossy black; short broad wings each with two white bars. Female with broad, curved, blade-like ovipositor.

Habitat and Range: Dry, open forest. Northern Australia.

Notes: Calls in heat of day from foliage of low trees. Mimics a wasp; has jerky wasp-like movements, reinforced by bold colour pattern.

QM, Jeff Wright

Predatory Katydid
Hexacentrus sp.

Identification: Length 42 mm. Front and mid-legs with two rows of spines. Male (pictured), has broad, green wings, with flattened brown area used to produce sound. Female with narrow wings and long ovipositor.

Habitat and Range: Among long grass in lowland, coastal areas. Northern Australia, Kimberley region, WA, to Bundaberg, Qld.

Notes: Predatory. Calls loudly on summer nights, especially after rain, with repeated, drawn-out harsh note. Often heard by motorists from long grass beside roads.

QM, Jeff Wright

Prickly Katydids
Phricta spp.

Identification: Length 95 mm. Mottled green and grey; spines along all legs and around edge of thorax. Inside surface of hind legs with bright orange and black marks.

Habitat and Range: Rainforest. Coastal Qld and northern NSW.

Notes: Spend daytime flattened in camouflage pose against mossy trunk of rainforest tree. Lift hind legs in threat when disturbed, showing coloured patches. At night, forage over low shrubs. Despite fearsome appearance will not bite and are leaf-feeders.

QM, Jeff Wright

QM. Jeff Wright

Leafy Katydid
Paracaedicia serrata

Identification: Length 65 mm. Green. Wing covers leaf-like with yellow streak along front edge. Hind legs have fine teeth.

Habitat and Range: Lowland rainforest. Cooktown to Townsville, Qld.

Notes: Lives among rainforest foliage and feeds on leaves. When disturbed, adopts rigid pose to enhance camouflaged

Termites

Termites are social insects distantly related to cockroaches. They are not related to true ants and for this reason the name 'white ants', which is often used for termites, is not really appropriate. They live in nests made of soil that may be completely subterranean, project above the ground surface, or be inside or attached to the outside of trees and stumps. The termites inside a nest are mostly workers, who gather food and build the nest, and soldiers, who are armed to defend the nest. There is also a male and female, called the king and queen, whose role is breeding.

Some termites eat dead wood and can be serious pests of wooden buildings and fence posts. But most of the large mounds that rise directly from the ground in TNQ contain termites whose sole food is dead grass, which they harvest at the end of the wet growing season. These are beneficial to the environment.

QM, Bruce Cowell

Giant Termite
Mastotermes darwiniensis

Identification: Length 15 mm. Very large, with 5 segments to 'feet' (tarsi). Soldiers with rounded heads and stout jaws with single tooth on inner edges.

Habitat and Range: Open forest. Northern Australia south to Mackay, Qld.

Notes: Most primitive termite in world and one of largest. Lays eggs in pods, somewhat like cockroaches. Does not build distinct mound; forms galleries underground and inside tree bases and logs. Destructive pest of timber buildings.

Rainforest Termites
Termes spp.

Identification: Build small, rounded or tapering mounds that rise directly from ground. Soldiers have enlarged, asymmetrical jaws that cross in front of head.

Habitat and Range: Lowland rainforest. Northern Qld.

Notes: When attacked, jaws of soldiers are squeezed shut under tension and then released with loud click. Mounds are hollowed out as nesting site by Buff-breasted Paradise Kingfisher (see p. 278).

G Thompson

Spinifex Termite
Nasutitermes triodiae

Identification: Length 3–5 mm. Soldiers have dark, pear-shaped heads drawn out into a point. Build large mounds with thick walls formed into prominent bulges.

Habitat and Range: Open, grassy eucalypt forest. Most of northern Australia, conspicuous around Mareeba, Qld.

Notes: At night, workers come to surface and cut dried grass stems into short lengths for food. These are carried back to mound and stored in special chambers. After rain, mound is enlarged by building new 'bulges' from moist soil bound together with saliva and faeces. Soldiers (pictured) do not have jaws, but defend colony by squirting sticky fluid at attackers from nozzle on front of head.

Mound, Paul Zborowski

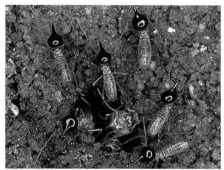

Soldiers, Paul Zborowski

SUCKING BUGS

Sucking bugs (Order Hemiptera) all feed on liquid food through a pointed, hollow tube (rostrum) beneath the head. The great majority of species feed on plant juices, which they obtain by inserting the tip of their rostrum into living plants. A few sucking bugs are predatory (e.g. assassin bugs) and suck juices from other small insects, while some, such as bed bugs, even suck blood from vertebrates. The young stages of bugs are nymphs, which resemble adults, but lack wings. Most bugs have a triangular structure in the middle of the back called the scutellum. This is often shield-shaped or may be enlarged.

Paul Zborowski

Thin Water Scorpion
Ranatra sp.

Identification: Length 45 mm. Pale brown, Long slender body with thin legs. Long, straight tail at tip of abdomen. Curved beak beneath head.

Habitat and Range: Aquatic in still, weedy water. Australia-wide.

Notes: Ambush predator, lurks among water weeds with hollow tail reaching surface to get air supply. Seizes small creatures with hooked front legs and sucks juices from them through piercing beak. Can fly at night to reach new habitats.

QM, Jeff Wright

Ixora Shield Bug
Catacanthus punctus

Identification: Length 24 mm. Reddish-brown; head, legs and antennae black. Wings white with large, metallic green blotch and black tip.

Habitat and Range: Drier rainforest. Coastal areas, Cape York to Bundaberg, Qld.

Notes: Feeds on hard green berries of rainforest shrub, *Ixora queenslandica*. If disturbed, squirts acrid fluid.

Bruce Cowell

Eucalypt Shield Bug
Poecilometis gravis

Identification: Length 17 mm. Pale brown; cream spots at each corner of triangular scutellum in middle of back.

Habitat and Range: Eucalypt forest. Cooktown, Qld, to Sydney, NSW.

Notes: Several similar related species on trunks of eucalypt trees; suck sap from bark. Nymphs patterned black and white; have jerky, wasp-like movements.

Hibiscus Harlequin Bug
Tectocoris diophthalmus

Identification: Length 15 mm. Rounded, convex. Colour variable from pale orange to heavily patterned in metallic green, blue and red. Back covered with enlarged, shield-like scutellum.

Habitat and Range: Northern and eastern Australia; New Guinea, some Pacific islands.

Notes: Sucks sap from hibiscus plants and related species; Beach Hibiscus (*Hibiscus tiliaceus*) main native food plant; also attacks cultivated cotton. Female lays clusters of eggs around twigs and guards them until hatching.

Bruce Cowell

Wingless Bark Bug
Granulaptera alticola

Identification: Length 12 mm. Flattened, brown, wingless; prominent, forward-pointing spines on head.

Habitat and Range: Upland rainforest. Mossman to Innisfail, Qld.

Notes: Found in colonies on underside of logs and sticks lying on rainforest floor. Feeds on juices of wood-rotting fungi. Remains motionless and camouflaged when exposed. Many related species.

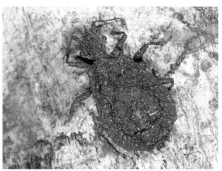

QM, Jeff Wright

Tip-wilting Bug
Pomponatius luridus

Identification: Length 19 mm. Elongated; yellowish-brown, speckled; body tapers at ends. Antennae long; white bands on last two segments.

Habitat and Range: Along watercourses. NT, Cairns, Qld, south to Sydney, NSW.

Notes: Feeds on soft, new shoots of bottlebrush trees (*Callistemon* spp.) causing shoots to wither and die. Prefers Creek Bottlebrush (*C. viminalis*) in wild, but also found on cultivated species. Related species, *P. typicus*, feeds on paperbarks (*Melaleuca* spp.).

QM, Jeff Wright

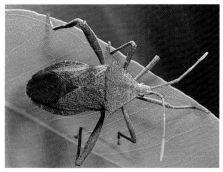

QM, Jeff Wright

Mictis Bug
Mictis caja

Identification: Length 26 mm. Dark brown; white tips to antennae. Prominent angles on corners of thorax. Hind legs: female (pictured), slender; male, thickened with broad angular tooth.

Habitat and Range: Widespread in open forest. Northern and eastern Australia.

Notes: Powerful, smelly defence secretion. Feeds on variety of plants including tomatoes and beans. Related Crusader Bug (*M. profana*) has white cross on back.

QM, Jeff Wright

Ground Coreid Bug
Sciophyrus australicus

Identification: Length 12 mm. Dark, mottled, thickset; banded legs and long rostrum.

Habitat and Range: Rainforest. Cape York to Cairns, Qld.

Notes: Swarms to leafy heads of newly fallen trees; sucks sap from wilting leaves.

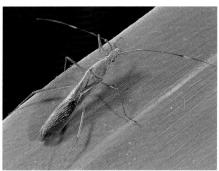

QM, Jeff Wright

Paddy Bug
Leptocorisa acuta

Identification: Length 16 mm. Elongated, pale green; long, slender legs and long antennae.

Habitat and Range: Coastal open forest and rainforest edges. NT, Cape York to Rockhampton, Qld; New Guinea.

Notes: Feeds on grasses including cultivated species, such as rice and sugar cane; can be serious pest. During dry season, hibernates in large numbers in sheltered places; swarms when disturbed.

Red Assassin Bug
Gminatus wallengreni

Identification: Length 17 mm. Bright red; black legs; black patch on wing. Narrow head with strong, curved rostrum.

Habitat and Range: Rainforest and open forest. Eastern Australia.

Notes: Slow-moving. Rests on foliage and pounces on small insects. Injects salivary enzymes into prey through rostrum, then sucks up pre-digested innards like soup. Can stab attackers painfully with rostrum.

QM. Jeff Wright

Bee Killer Assassin Bug
Pristhesancus plagipennis

Identification: Length 25 mm. Yellowish-brown, sometimes darker; wings transparent. Head elongated; strong, curved rostrum beneath.

Habitat and Range: Widespread in open forest. Eastern Australia.

Notes: Lurks in concealed situations among foliage and blossoms, ambushes passing insects, honey bees a favourite. Lays clusters of elongated, red eggs; hatch to bright red nymphs with black legs, sometimes confused with Redback Spider (see p. 34).

Bruce Cowell

Seed Bug
Physopelta gutta

Identification: Length 13 mm. Red with black scutellum; each wing with black patch and tips.

Habitat and Range: On ground and among foliage in rainforest. Eastern Australia, Cape York, Qld, to northern NSW.

Notes: Sucks sap from seeds. Comes to lights in large numbers in summer; may form big clusters that remain until morning.

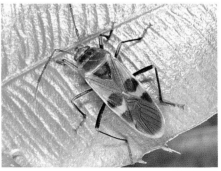

QM. Jeff Wright

Bruce Cowell

Giant Water Bug
Lethocerus insulanus

Identification: Length 70 mm. Dark khaki - brown; stout claw-like front legs, flattened hind legs; large eyes, short tail siphon.

Habitat and Range: Aquatic, in lakes, dams and pools; hides among bottom debris. Australia-wide.

Notes: Breathes through tail siphon at surface. Seizes prey, including tadpoles and small fish, with needle-tipped front legs and impales with stout rostrum. Largest sucking bug in Australia.

Bruce Cowell

Northern Greengrocer Cicada
Cyclochila virens

Identification: Length 75 mm. Green; transparent wings with broad green leading edge.

Habitat and Range: Mountain rainforest. Mossman to Townsville, Qld.

Notes: Lives high in canopy. Song a loud, harsh, continuous note; all cicadas at a locality sing together for about 15 minutes just at dusk. This is the well-known 'possum alarm' of mountain rainforests.

Anthony O'Toole

Northern Double Drummer
Cicada *Thopha sessiliba*

Identification: Length 70 mm. Head tan with dark brown markings; rest of body dark brown, tan 'm'-shaped marking and two white stripes on top of thorax; white band at tip of abdomen. Male has bulbous expansions either side of abdomen.

Habitat and Range: Open forest and woodland with eucalypts. Northern and eastern Australia to northern NSW.

Similar Species: Double Drummer Cicada (*T. saccata*), jet black markings on head and thorax, no white on abdomen.

Notes: Sits on upper limbs of eucalypt trees. Males have loud, high pitched, droning song.

Green Whizzer Cicada
Macrotristria intersecta

Identification: Length 45–50 mm. Two colour forms — head and thorax greenish with dark band across body at base of wings (pictured); or back half of thorax brown with 5 black patches. Abdomen black with tan bands, white near tip.

Habitat and Range: Open forest, sometimes rainforest edges. Northern and eastern Australia to about Gladstone, Qld.

Notes: Sits in small trees, especially eucalypts and cocky apples (*Planchonia careya*). Male song a fluctuating hiss-like buzz.

Anthony O'Toole

BEETLES

Beetles (Order Coleoptera) are one of the most abundant and easily recognised insect groups. They have a compact body with their forewings forming tough covers for their fragile hind wings, which fold up underneath. The wing covers meet in a line down the middle of their back. Their appearance is usually hard and shiny, often in bright, glossy colours that give them an attractive appearance. They also have biting jaws with which they chew solid food. Beetles have a larval and pupal stage in their life cycle before transforming into winged adults. The larvae usually live inside concealed situations, such as soil, litter or rotten wood.

Bombardier Beetle
Pheropsophus verticalis

Identification: Length 25 mm. Dark brown; yellow blotches on wing covers; yellow legs.

Habitat and Range: Eucalypt forest. Shelters under debris around damp edges of streams and waterholes. Australia-wide.

Notes: Nocturnal predator of other small insects. When disturbed, produces audible chemical explosion from rear end, accompanied by puff of smoke and acrid smell.

Owen Kelly

QM, Jeff Wright

Snail-eating Carabid
Pamborus opacus

Identification: Length 32 mm. Metallic green; marked waist; short curved jaws.

Habitat and Range: Under logs in mountain rainforest. Cooktown to Mossman, Qld.

Similar Species: *P. tropicus* on mountains between Cairns and Townsville; *P. transitus* on mountains north and west of Mackay, including Eungella, Qld.

Notes: Runs actively on forest floor at night. Feeds on snails and earthworms, which it grips with specialised jaws. When handled, sprays pungent fluid from rear, which can burn skin and eyes.

QM, Jeff Wright

Mountain Carabid
Trichosternus montorum

Identification: Length 20 mm. Emerald-green; prominent jaws and raised ridges on wing covers.

Habitat and Range: Under logs at high altitudes. Only from summit areas of Mt Bellenden Ker and Mt Bartle Frere, Qld.

Notes: Nocturnal predator. One of many species of wingless carabid beetles with restricted distributions on high mountains between Cooktown and Townsville, Qld. Different species at Mt Elliot and Eungella.

Owen Kelly

Banded Water Beetle
Hydaticus bihamatus

Identification: Length 12 mm. Streamlined; dark with irregular pale bands across wing covers.

Habitat and Range: Aquatic in temporary pools and ponds. Northern Australia, coastal Qld to Brisbane; New Guinea.

Notes: Hides among debris at bottom of pools. Feeds on other aquatic invertebrates. Occasionally bobs rapidly to surface to renew air bubbles (pictured) that it stores under wing covers. Larvae also aquatic predators.

Whirligig Beetles
Macrogyrus spp.

Identification: Length 12 mm. Metallic grey; flattened, torpedo-shaped; long front legs and short, paddle-shaped hind and middle legs.

Habitat and Range: Swim in gregarious groups on surface of still pools and back-waters. Several species, widespread eastern Australia.

Notes: Divided eyes enable beetles to see above and below water surface simul-taneously. Feed on live and dead insects floating on surface. When disturbed, swim in rapid wild circles, hence common name.

QM, Bruce Cowell

Mueller's Stag Beetle
Phalacrognathus muelleri

Identification: Length 40–50 mm. Large, iridescent, metallic, with reflections of green, gold and purple. Male (pictured), long jaws that may fork at tip. Female, less iridescent and lacks long jaws.

Habitat and Range: Rainforest. Cooktown to Townsville, Qld; more common in up-land rainforest.

Notes: One of world's most beautiful beetles. Larvae are smooth white grubs (pictured) that feed on rotten wood inside logs. Adults may fly to lights at night or are sometimes seen at fermenting sap flows.

Adult male, Owen Kelly

Larva, Gary Cranitch

Scaly Stag Beetle
Cacostomus squamosus

Identification: Length to 30 mm. Pale reddish-brown; surface covered with tiny, pale scales; legs long, slender. Male (pictured) has elongated, toothed jaws.

Habitat and Range: Rainforest and open forest. Widespread eastern Australia.

Notes: Larvae are white grubs that feed in and under dead logs. Adults fly to lights or may be found on foliage in daytime.

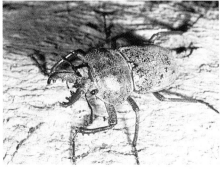

Owen Kelly

QM, Jeff Wright

Nebulosus Stag Beetle
Rhyssonotus nebulosus

Identification: Length 35 mm. Brown with matt texture; irregular pattern of dark marks on wing covers. Jaws of male have angular tooth on outer edge.

Habitat and Range: Mostly rainforest. Widespread coastal Qld.

Notes: Adult male and pupa shown with soft, rotten wood in which they breed.

QM, Jeff Wright

Rhinoceros Beetle
Xylotrupes gideon

Identification: Length 40 mm. Large, black. Male (pictured), forked horns on head and thorax; female, matt texture and lacks horns.

Habitat and Range: Rainforest and open forest, especially at lower elevations. Eastern Australia south to Sydney, NSW; south-east Asia across Indo-Pacific Archipelago.

Notes: Larvae are large, grey, curled grubs that breed in humus and are common in suburban compost heaps. In summer, grubs hatch to adults that aggregate for mating in poinciana trees, where they feed on soft bark of young shoots; also come to lights. Harmless, but adults squeak loudly when disturbed.

Owen Kelly

African Dung Beetle
Onthophagus gazella

Identification: Length 9 mm. Yellowish-brown with dark greenish reflections; dark patches on underside where legs join body. Male has two vertical horns on head.

Habitat and Range: Widespread in open cattle pastures.

Notes: Introduced from Africa to bury cattle dung that was not being utilised by native dung beetles. Flies to fresh dung at night and buries it in burrows as food for larvae.

Native Dung Beetle
Onthophagus tricavicollis

Identification: Length 10 mm. Wing covers black; thorax brilliant metallic green with deep indentations, especially in male (pictured). Antennae yellow.

Habitat and Range: Open forest. Cape York to Townsville, Qld.

Notes: One of more than 180 native species of dung beetles in TNQ. Flies to fresh dung in daytime. Digs tunnels in soil and buries dung at source; other species form dung into balls and roll it away.

Owen Kelly

Grayanus Christmas Beetle
Calloodes grayanus

Identification: Length 25 mm. Enamelled green with yellow border around body.

Habitat and Range: Open forest. Cape York to Bundaberg, Qld.

Notes: White 'curl grub' larvae live in soil and feed on roots of living plants. Grubs have been found in sandy river beds during dry season. Adults hatch in summer and feed on foliage. Often flies to house lights.

Owen Kelly

Passalid Wood Beetles
Mastachilus spp.

Identification: Length 45 mm. Black with parallel-sides and strongly grooved wing covers. Antennae have spaced side branches and roll up when withdrawn.

Habitat and Range: Common in rainforest. Eastern Australia.

Notes: Slow-moving. Several species. Passalid beetles play an important role in breaking down dead logs. Family groups live inside logs where adults chew wood to feed larvae. Large black eggs hatch to elongated white grubs (pictured) that communicate with adults by squeaking.

QM, Jeff Wright

QM, Jeff Wright

Carrion Beetle
Diamesus osculans

Identification: Length 30 mm. Elongated, black; shortened wing covers have red blotches.

Habitat and Range: Widespread in open forest and rainforest.

Notes: Flies strongly, follows odour trails to dead animals. Eggs hatch to flattened larvae that live beneath corpse and feed on carrion.

QM, Jeff Wright

Striped Firefly
Atyphella olivieri

Identification: Length 9 mm. Soft-bodied; dark wing covers with white edges; thorax white with dark, central spot.

Habitat and Range: Widespread in rainforest. Cooktown to Townsville, Qld.

Notes: Fireflies have one (female) or two (male) segments at tip of abdomen forming light organ. Male, light bright white; female weaker. Fireflies blink lights at dusk to bring sexes together. Males fly high and fast, while females remain on ground. When males see a female light they dive down. Different species of fireflies have individual flashing patterns used for recognition. Eggs hatch to flattened larvae that live in leaf litter and feed on minute snails.

QM, Jeff Wright

Red and Black Firefly
Luciola humilis

Identification: Length 7 mm. Smaller and narrower than Striped Firefly (see above); red thorax and black wing covers.

Habitat and Range: Coastal lowlands. North Qld to Brisbane.

Notes: Flies low with meandering direction. Light yellowish and duller than Striped Firefly.

Piedish Beetles
Pterohelaeus spp.

Identification: Black, flattened with oval outline and expanded edges to thorax and wing covers.

Habitat and Range: On dead and dying timber; may be found under loose bark. Many different species, widespread in Australia.

Notes: Nocturnal. Larvae are 'wireworms' that live in soil and feed on organic matter and roots.

Bruce Cowell

Beach Tortoise Beetle
Aspidomorpha deusta

Identification: Length 9 mm. Flattened, yellowish-orange; two black spots on thorax and various spots on wing covers. Edges of thorax and wing covers expanded and semi-transparent, covering head and legs.

Habitat and Range: Along beaches. NT, Cape York to Rockhampton, Qld; New Guinea and Indonesia.

Notes: Feeds on leaves of Beach Convolvulus (*Convolvulus pes-caprae*) that grows prolifically above strandline. Flattened, spiny larvae (pictured) also feed on leaves; carry shed skins and faeces on backs as camouflage.

Adult, QM, Jeff Wright

Larva, QM, Jeff Wright

Wombat Vine Beetle
Aproida balyi

Identification: Length 12 mm. Green with dark edges to body; dark spine at end of each wing cover. Antennae have white tips.

Habitat and Range: Open forest and rainforest edges. Tableland regions at Eungella and Cairns; coastal southern Qld.

Notes: Adults and larvae feed on leaves of Wombat Vine (*Eustrephus latifolius*). Adults mimic small, green grasshoppers. Larvae slug-like and camouflaged. Pupae suspended from dried larval skins and resemble buds of plant.

Owen Kelly

QM, Bruce Cowell

Eucalypt Leaf Beetles
Paropsis sexguttata complex

Identification: Length 12 mm. Rounded, dark brown with three red patches on each wing cover.

Habitat and Range: Widespread in open forest. During dry season, adults often hibernate under loose bark at base of trees.

Notes: Many similar species; feed on leaves of eucalypts. Groups of caterpillar-like larvae also feed on leaves and regurgitate smelly fluid when disturbed

Owen Kelly

Orchid Beetle
Stethopachys formosa

Identification: Length 11 mm. Yellow with two black blotches on each wing cover.

Habitat and Range: Open forest and rainforest. North-eastern Australia.

Notes: Adults and larvae feed on flowers and soft leaves of orchids. Pests in orchid shadehouses. Larvae white and slug-like; feed in groups and cover backs with own faeces. Pupate in mass covered with polystyrene-like foam.

QM, Jeff Wright

Pipturus Weevil
Pantorytes stanleyanus

Identification: Length 11 mm. Shiny, dark brown or black; metallic, blue-green spots on wing covers.

Habitat and Range: Lowland rainforest. Cooktown to Proserpine, Qld.

Notes: Feeds on Native Mulberry tree (*Pipturus argenteus*). Only Australian species of genus. Many species in New Guinea; some are serious pests of cocoa plantations. Larvae bore into roots and stems.

Cryptorhynch Weevil
Poropterus magnus

Identification: Length 23 mm. Hardbodied; dark brown with prominent bumps on wing covers and thorax. Head with long, slightly curved rostrum that folds into groove on underside of thorax.

Habitat and Range: Rainforest. Eastern Qld.

Notes: Clings to outside of dead trees and logs. When disturbed, retracts legs, drops to ground and remains motionless for long period.

QM, Jeff Wright

Long-nosed Weevil
Sipalus gigas

Identification: Size variable. Length 20–35 mm. Brown, mottled with black and pale spots. Head with long, curved rostrum that does not fold into a groove. Strong, curved spines on ends of legs.

Habitat and Range: Rainforest. Northeastern Qld.

Notes: Found in groups on outside of dead logs and trees. When disturbed, grips strongly to wood with hooks on legs. Larvae are white, legless grubs that bore inside wood.

QM, Jeff Wright

Brenthid Weevil
Ithystenus hollandiae

Identification: Length 20–36 mm. Narrow, elongated body; head with extremely long, straight rostrum. Legs slender. Pale stripes along wing covers that end in spines.

Habitat and Range: Rainforest. Cape York to Townsville, Qld.

Notes: Occur in groups on trunks of freshly fallen trees. Males joust with each other over possession of females and use long rostrum to tip opponent off log. Males guard females while they drill holes in log surface for eggs to be inserted.

Owen Kelly

Owen Kelly

Prionid Longicorn
Agrianome spinicollis

Identification: Length 50–60 mm. Khaki wing covers; thorax reddish-brown, edged with pointed teeth. Antennae as long as body.

Habitat and Range: Open forest, rainforest and suburban gardens. Widespread, eastern Australia south to Sydney, NSW.

Notes: Larvae are large, white, legless grubs in rotten wood, often in dead poinciana trees in suburban areas. Adults sometimes blunder into house lights and can bite if handled.

QM, Jeff Wright

Flower Longicorn
Aridaeus thoracicus

Identification: Length 25 mm. Orange; two dark brown bands across wing covers. Legs and antennae long and spindly.

Habitat and Range: Open forest. Eastern Australia.

Notes: Active in daytime; often flies to white flowering garden shrubs to feed on nectar. Movements and bright colours mimic those of a large wasp and protect it from predator attack. Larvae bore into wood.

Owen Kelly

Longicorn
Cyocyphax praonethoides

Identification: Length 30 mm. Pale brown with two oblique, vivid white blotches on each wing cover. Long antennae.

Habitat and Range: Rainforest. Cairns region and Cape York, Qld; New Guinea.

Notes: Uncommon. Rests among dead leaves where its disruptive colour pattern provides camouflage. Like most longicorns, larvae are wood-borers.

TRUE FLIES

True flies differ from most insects in having a single pair of wings, the forewings. Their hindwings are reduced to tiny dumbbell-shaped knobs that are used for balance during flight. True flies include the delicate craneflies, mosquitoes and midges, as well as the more robust horseflies, houseflies and blowflies. Adult flies mostly feed on fluids or solids that they liquefy with saliva and then suck up using a spongy proboscis. The females of some, for example mosquitoes, biting midges and horseflies, feed on blood. Fly larvae have no legs and many are maggot-like. Most feed on decaying organic material either plant or animal, although some feed on living plants, or are predators and parasites of insects. A few are parasites of vertebrates.

Cranefly
Nephrotoma australasiae

Identification: Length 15–20 mm. Elongated; long legs; yellow with three black stripes on thorax and series of black bands on abdomen.

Habitat and Range: Moist forests, leafy gardens. NT, eastern coastal Qld.

Notes: More craneflies (over 700 species) than any other group of flies in Australia. Most active at dusk/dawn or at night. Larvae occur in water, moist soil or rotting vegetable matter.

QM, Bruce Cowell

Dengue Mosquito
Aedes aegypti

Identification: Length 4–6 mm. Long, black proboscis; body dark; top of thorax has white, lyre-shaped marking and two central stripes; abdomen and 'feet' with white bands.

Habitat and Range: Breeds in all kinds of artificial containers that hold water, rainwater tanks, indoor plant pots, old tyres, always close to human habitation. Widespread in Qld except south; once common in NSW, NT, WA, but now absent. Native to Africa, but spread throughout tropical and subtropical regions of world by humans.

Notes: Adult females feed on mammalian blood during day, indoors; males feed on nectar. Transmit Dengue Fever, dog heartworm.

Similar Species: *A. notoscriptus,* thorax has white, lyre-shaped marking, but single central stripe, proboscis has white band; not known to transmit diseases.

Female, QM, Jeff Wright

Female, QM, Jeff Wright

Common Banded Mosquito
Culex annulirostris

Identification: Length 5–7 mm. Long, dark proboscis with central white band; thorax dark brown; abdomen square at tip, dark with pale bands that are pointed in middle.

Habitat and Range: Breeds in freshwater swamps, lagoons, temporary grassy pools. Australia-wide, except Tas.; Moluccas to New Guinea, many south Pacific islands.

Notes: Adult females bite at night. Transmit Ross River Fever, Murray Valley Encephalitis, dog heartworm.

Bruce Cowell

Giant Mosquito
Toxorhynchites speciosus

Identification: Length 12–16 mm. Long black proboscis that is bent downwards; body metallic purple and blue with silver markings; abdomen with tufts of scales along sides.

Habitat and Range: Breeds in water-filled tree hollows and artificial containers in forests. Northern NT, eastern Australia from Cape York, Qld, to Sydney, NSW.

Notes: Adults often rest on tree trunks. Both sexes feed on nectar. Larvae are predators of other mosquito larvae.

QM, Jeff Wright

Plecia amplipennis

Identification: Length 10–13 mm. Head, abdomen and legs black, thorax reddish; wings smoky-black.

Habitat and Range: Moist forests. NT, eastern Qld.

Notes: Adults sluggish, poor fliers, sometimes seen resting on leaves during day, but probably more active at night, attracted to lights. Larvae probably occur in rotting vegetation.

Horsefly
Cydistomyia doddi

Other name: Marchfly

Identification: Length 15–18 mm. Stout; black with row of white triangular spots down centre of abdomen; wings with smoky-brown markings.

Habitat and Range: Forested areas, including rainforest. Northern Qld. Similar species, *C. alternata* in southern Qld.

Notes: Adult females feed on mammalian blood (including humans); males feed on nectar. Females often attracted to dark objects, such as car tyres.

QM, Jeff Wright

American Soldier Fly
Hermetia illucens

Identification: Length 15–18 mm. Elongated, black; long antennae; two pale 'windows' at base of abdomen; black legs with white feet; smoky wings.

Habitat and Range: Close to human habitation. Australia-wide, except cool southern areas. Tropical and subtropical areas worldwide.

Notes: Adults wasp-like in appearance and behaviour. Larvae flattened, brown, leathery with narrow peg-like head; live in decaying organic matter, compost bins, worm farms, carrion.

Steve Wilson

Robberfly
Colepia lanata

Identification: Length 30–35 mm. Elongated; head has large eyes and sharp, beaklike proboscis; stout, dark thorax; abdomen brown with long hairs at base; legs orange.

Habitat and Range: Rainforest. Cape York to Mission Beach, Qld.

Notes: Alights on branches for short time, then flies off. Predator of other insects, often captured on wing. Injects powerful saliva that liquefies body contents, which are sucked out with proboscis. Can deliver painful bite if handled.

QM, Jeff Wright

QM, Jeff Wright

Dolichopodid Fly
Austrosciapus connexus

Identification: Length about 5 mm. Metallic green, dusted with white; abdomen with black bands; wings with two black bands towards tips.

Habitat and Range: Moist forest, leafy gardens. Common eastern Australia, Cairns, Qld, to Sydney, NSW, also southwest WA; Norfolk I., French Polynesia, Hawaii.

Notes: Often lands on upper surfaces of large leaves, quickly flies off again. Preys on small, soft-bodied insects.

Adult QM, Jeff Wright

Larva, QM, Jeff Wright

Hoverfly
Ischiodon scutellaris

Identification: Length 10–12 mm. Bold black or brown and yellow markings; sides of thorax yellow; abdomen with yellow bands and two yellow spots at base.

Habitat and Range: Favours open weedy areas. Australia-wide. Widespread Asia and Western Pacific islands.

Notes: Fast flying; often hovers in one spot. Adults visit flowers and feed on nectar. Larvae (pictured), green with white stripe down middle of body, feed on aphids.

Paul Zborowski

Stalk-eyed Fly
Achias australis

Identification: Length 10–13 mm. Dark; wings with dark front edge. Male (pictured), eyes at ends of long stalks; female, short eye stalks.

Habitat and Range: Rainforest. Northeastern Qld, south of Cooktown to Paluma.

Notes: Adults rest underneath leaves, on tree trunks; sometimes attracted to light and mammal dung.

Fruit Flies
Bactrocera spp. and *Dacus spp.*

Identification: Length about 5–10 mm, varies with species. Stout bodied, black or various shades of brown; thorax often with yellow shoulders, two or three yellow stripes on top, yellow tip and yellow patches on sides. Wings usually have dark front edge and streak near base, often with extra dark markings. Abdomen rounded, narrow at base. Many similar species, can be distinguished only by specialist.

Habitat and Range: About 50 species in TNQ, most confined to moist coastal strip and ranges. Many species northern Australia; tropical and subtropical regions worldwide.

Notes: Larvae develop inside fruit. Most feed on native fruits, but some are pests of commercial varieties. Queensland Fruit Fly (*B. tryoni*) is major pest species in Australia; occurs Cape York, Qld, to eastern Vic. Papaya Fruit Fly (*B. papayae*), native of south-east Asia, accidentally introduced to Cairns area, major threat to Australian fruit industry, but seems to have been eradicated.

Bactrocera bancrofti, QM, Jeff Wright

Bactrocera tryoni, Anthony O'Toole

Bushfly
Musca vetustissima

Identification: Length 4–7 mm. Thorax dusted with grey, top has 2 dark stripes which split into 4 near front. Female, abdomen black and grey; male, abdomen yellow with black base and central stripe.

Habitat and Range: Drier areas including arid interior. Australia-wide, except Tas.; possibly widespread Pacific islands, New Guinea and Asia.

Notes: Maggots live in dung, particularly cattle. Occur in great numbers in summer, cluster on backs, crawl into mouth, eyes, nose.

QM, Bruce Cowell

Bruce Cowell

Housefly
Musca domestica

Identification: Length 5–8 mm. Thorax dusted with grey, top with 4 thin, black stripes; abdomen yellowish with thin black bands and central stripe.

Habitat and Range: Close to human dwellings, stables, chicken sheds, rubbish tips. Australia-wide; almost worldwide.

Notes: Maggots live in range of moist fermenting organic matter, including animal dung mixed with straw and household garbage.

QM, Jeff Wright

Amenia imperialis

Identification: Length 10–15 mm. Head bright yellow, thorax and abdomen metallic green or bronze with silvery-white spots. Wings clear with dark bases.

Habitat and Range: Common in open and closed forest. Eastern Qld and NSW.

Notes: Often rests on rocks and fallen wood. Gives birth to large, well-developed larvae that are probably parasites of land snails.

QM, Jeff Wright

Australian Sheep Blowfly
Lucilia cuprina

Identification: Length about 6–8 mm. Head dark, dusted with silver, eyes reddish; thorax and abdomen metallic green; wings clear.

Habitat and Range: Drier more open habitats, urban areas, gardens. Almost Australia-wide (except Tas.), including arid interior; Asia, Pacific islands.

Notes: Major pest of sheep industry; maggots live in open wounds on live animals and on carrion. Also breeds in household refuse.

Flesh Flies
Sarcophagidae

Identification: Length 5–15 mm. Grey with red eyes, three black stripes on thorax and chessboard pattern of grey and black on abdomen.

Habitat and Range: All habitats, including gardens. Australia-wide.

Notes: Many similar species; can only be distinguished by specialist. Larvae of most species develop in carrion or dung. Flies often emerge inside houses after larvae have developed on dead rodents in ceilings and wall cavities.

QM, Bruce Cowell

Bristle Flies
Rutilia spp.

Identification: Length 7–20 mm. Stout; thorax and abdomen usually have metallic colours, sometimes with silver or white spots. Abdomen often with central black stripe or dark bands; wings clear with black marking at base

Habitat and Range: More common in forested areas. Australia-wide.

Notes: Rest on tree trunks. Males often gather on tops of hills and mountains. Larvae are parasites developing within grubs of scarab beetles.

Bruce Cowell

BUTTERFLIES AND MOTHS

The beautiful colours of moths and butterflies are formed by thousands of tiny scales that cover the wings. Another characteristic feature is the long, tubular proboscis through which they suck up liquid food. The larval stages of moths and butterflies are caterpillars and almost all feed on plants, usually eating the leaves. Caterpillars spin threads of strong silk from glands just behind their mouth. Many use the silk to build a shelter, the cocoon, in which the pupa or chrysalis is concealed during the transformation from caterpillar to adult. Butterfly caterpillars do not make a cocoon.

There is no hard and fast rule for telling the difference between a moth and a butterfly. Butterflies generally fly in the daytime, they have swollen ends to their antennae and their front and rear wings are not hooked together during flight. Moths, on the other hand, are mostly nocturnal, their antennae are varied in shape, but are rarely swollen at the end and they generally have some bristles that lock the wings together in flight.

Butterflies

More than 240 species of butterflies occur in Tropical North Queensland. Nearly, all are treated in detail in *Butterflies of Australia,* by Common and Waterhouse (Angus & Robertson). Just 30 of the more conspicuous and interesting species are featured here.

Skippers

QM, Jeff Wright

Regent Skipper
Euschemon rafflesia

Identification: Wingspan 55 mm. Black with yellow patches above and below on wings. Tip of abdomen bright red.

Habitat and Range: Upland and lowland rainforest. Cooktown to Paluma, Qld. Different subspecies in coastal south-eastern Qld and north-eastern NSW.

Notes: Caterpillars semi-transparent, grey-green, black striped; feed on *Tetrasynandra,* shrub along forest edges.

QM, Jeff Wright

Common Red-eye
Chaetocneme beata

Identification: Wingspan 60 mm. Orange-brown or brown; forewing with band of large, pale spots; hindwing with a few small, pale spots. Eyes red.

Habitat and Range: Wet open forest and rainforest edges, mostly in uplands of tropical north. Coastal eastern Australia, Cairns, Qld, to Wollongong, NSW.

Notes: Adults fly at dusk, rest on undersides of leaves during day. Caterpillars found within joined leaves of Custard Apple, Camphor Laurel and *Acmena* spp.

Yellow Palmdart
Cephrenes trichopepla

Identification: Wingspan 40mm. Pale orange and black; hindwing pale orange-yellow beneath with large black spot.

Habitat and Range: Various habitats near palms, common in gardens. Northern Australia, WA to Cape York, south to Brisbane, Qld.

Similar Species: Orange Palmdart (*C. augiades*), wings darker orange with more black.

Notes: Rests in sun on upper side of leaves, then darts off at great speed. Eggs laid on palms; caterpillars sew adjacent leaves together to form retreats from which they feed. Larvae yellowish or greenish with striking banded heads. Pupate inside same shelter, producing whitish, floury deposit. This species and Orange Palmdart can damage garden palms.

QM. Jeff Wright

Orange Dart
Suniana sunias

Identification: Wingspan 20–25 mm. Forewing bright orange with thick black outside edge and parallel black stripe; hindwing black with thick orange band; paler beneath.

Habitat and Range: Grassy clearings in rainforest and other moist coastal areas; unkept gardens. Coastal northern Australia, WA to Cape York, south to Brisbane, Qld. Other subspecies in NT, south-eastern Qld and northern NSW; Moluccas to New Guinea, Solomon Is.

Similar Species: Several orange and black species of *Suniana*, *Ocybadistes* and *Taractrocera*; difficult to distinguish.

Notes: Adults have quick darting flight, rest in sunshine on grass with hindwings flat and forewings raised. Caterpillars green with black heads, feed on paspalum grass.

QM. Jeff Wright

QM, Jeff Wright

Whites, Yellows and Jezabels

Lemon Migrant
Catopsilia pomona

Identification: Wingspan 70 mm. Cream to yellow; sometimes with black edges above and reddish blotches beneath.

Habitat and Range: Variety of habitats including gardens; uncommon in closed forests. Northern Australia; widespread Asia.

Notes: Adults strong fliers. Massive migrations sometimes occur with butterflies flying from south to north. Green larvae feed on cassias, including Golden Rain Trees (*C. fistula*); lie along midrib of leaves, difficult to see.

QM, Jeff Wright

Common Grass Yellow
Eurema hecabe

Identification: Wingspan 40 mm. Bright yellow; notched black edge to forewing; variable pattern of brown spots and blotches beneath.

Habitat and Range: Open grassy habitats. Coastal northern Australia, Geraldton, WA, to Sydney, NSW. Other subspecies from India to Japan, south-east Asia and some Pacific islands.

Notes: Fluttering flight close to ground. Green caterpillars feed on wattles and cassias.

QM, Jeff Wright

Union Jack
Delias mysis

Identification: Wingspan 65 mm. White with black edges above and below. Underneath (pictured), bases of wings yellow, hindwing has red stripe within black edge.

Habitat and Range: Varied habitats, but most common near rainforest. Coastal Qld, Cooktown to Yeppoon. Other subspecies on tip of Cape York, northern WA and NT; New Guinea, Aru Is.

Notes: Common, especially winter and spring. Eggs laid in clusters on leaves of mistletoe. Green, hairy larvae feed and pupate together on food plant. Often several pupae found on single leaf.

Common Jezabel
Delias nigrina

Identification: Wingspan 60 mm. White or grey above with black edges. Underneath (pictured), with yellow band on forewing, hindwing with red streaks forming square.

Habitat and Range: In TNQ, more common in upland rainforest. Coastal eastern Australia, Cape York, Qld, to Vic.

Notes: Common throughout year. Gregarious, hairy, brownish caterpillars feed on mistletoes. Pupate singly, often away from food plant. Pupa yellow with black spines.

QM, Jeff Wright

Swallowtails

Blue Triangle
Graphium sarpedon

Identification: Wingspan 60 mm. Triangular wings, each with central pale blue area bordered with dark brown.

Habitat and Range: Rainforest and other thick forested habitats, gardens. Coastal, Cape York, Qld, to Sydney, NSW; New Guinea. Other subspecies widespread in Asia.

Notes: Fast flying. Common, breeds on introduced Camphor Laurel trees. Larvae pale green; rest inconspicuously along upper midrib of leaves. Pupa has pointed front end and, like that of other swallowtails, is supported by loop of silk.

QM, Jeff Wright

Green-spotted Triangle
Graphium agamemnon

Identification: Wingspan 65 mm. Triangular black wings with numerous green spots and streaks.

Habitat and Range: Rainforest and nearby habitats. Coastal Qld, Cape York to Yeppoon; New Guinea. Other subspecies widespread in Asia.

Notes: Fast fliers, often feed on Lantana flowers along rainforest edges. Larvae dark brown with white central saddle; feed on introduced Custard Apple and Soursop (*Annona* spp.) and related native species.

QM, Jeff Wright

QM, Jeff Wright

Orchard Swallowtail
Papilio aegeus

Identification: Wingspan 110 mm. Male (pictured), large, black with narrow white band across forewing; large central pale patch on hindwing. Female larger; extensive pale areas on wings, row of red spots around edge of hindwing.

Habitat and Range: Rainforest to dry interior, gardens, where citrus plants occur. Eastern Australia, Cape York, Qld, to Adelaide, SA. Other subspecies in Torres Strait, New Guinea and nearby islands.

Notes: Larva feeds on citrus. Small brown and white larva resembles bird dropping, but changes to 'camouflage' green as it grows.

QM, Jeff Wright

Ulysses Butterfly
Papilio ulysses

Identification: Wingspan 105 mm. Top of wings brilliant metallic blue with broad black border; hindwing has long tail; underneath dark brown, hindwing with row of spots edged with white and blue.

Habitat and Range: Upland and lowland rainforest. Coastal Qld, Cape York to Sarina. Other subspecies from Moluccas to New Guinea, Solomon Is.

Notes: Males attracted by blue colours. Larvae feed on trees of genus *Melicope*.

QM, Jeff Wright

Red-bodied Swallowtail
Atrophaneura polydorus

Identification: Wingspan 80 mm. Forewing black with white streaks; hindwing black with central white patch and row of dull red spots around edge. End of abdomen red.

Habitat and Range: Rainforest and nearby habitats. Coastal Qld, Cape York to Townsville. Other subspecies from Moluccas to New Guinea and Solomon Is.

Notes: Larvae mottled brown with rows of red or yellow tubercles; feed on native pipe vines (*Aristolochia* and *Pararistolochia* spp.).

Cairns Birdwing
Ornithoptera priamus

Identification: Wingspan, male 130 mm; female 150 mm. Male (pictured), black and brilliant green; abdomen golden-yellow. Female much larger; drab brown and white with red patch each side of thorax.

Habitat and Range: Rainforest, eucalypt forest (Magnetic I.). Coastal Qld, Cooktown to Mackay. Other subspecies Cape York; Moluccas to New Guinea, Solomon Is.

Notes: Largest Australian butterfly. Larvae feed on native pipe vines (*Aristolochia* and *Pararistolochia* spp., especially *A. tagala*). Females will lay eggs on introduced Dutchman's Pipe Vine (*A. elegans*), but larvae die. Mature caterpillars velvety black with long pointed spines.

QM, Jeff Wright

Nymphs, Browns and Crows

Blue Tiger
Tirumala hamata

Identification: Wingspan 75 mm. Black with numerous pale blue, transparent spots and streaks on wings.

Habitat and Range: Creeks near coast and mangroves in winter; disperses widely in wet season. Northern WA to eastern Vic.

Notes: In winter, hundreds or thousands of butterflies cluster together. Black, white and grey-banded larvae feed on native vines, *Secamone elliptica* and *Ischnostemma carnosum*.

QM, Jeff Wright

Wanderer
Danaus plexippus

Other Name: Monarch

Identification: Wingspan 100 mm. Dark-orange with black edges enclosing small white spots; veins black.

Habitat and Range: Open grassy habitats, especially near host plants. Eastern Australia, Cape York, Qld, to Adelaide, SA; Alice Springs, NT, Perth, WA; New Guinea, Pacific islands, North America.

Notes: Strong flier. Larvae black, white and yellow; feed on milkweed bushes.

QM, Jeff Wright

QM, Jeff Wright

Larva, QM

Common Crow
Euploea core

Identification: Wingspan 65 mm. Brown-black; scattered white spots on forewing, band of white spots on hindwing. Narrow mark (sex brand) on each forewing of male.

Habitat and Range: More common in drier open habitats and gardens with oleander. Northern WA to eastern Vic., Adelaide, SA, Alice Springs, NT. Other subspecies New Guinea and much of Asia.

Notes: Adults go into quiescent aggregations in protected, shady sites during winter. Caterpillar orange-brown with black and white bands, 4 pairs of tentacles; commonly feeds on oleander in gardens.

QM, Jeff Wright

Cairns Hamadryad
Tellervo zoilus

Identification: Wingspan 45 mm. Black; forewing with several white spots and hindwing with large white, central spot above and below. Eyes yellow.

Habitat and Range: Rainforest. Cooktown to Paluma, Qld. Other subspecies on tip of Cape York; Celebes to New Guinea and Solomon Is.

Notes: Slow-flying. Larva black and white banded, has a pair of long tentacles; feeds on large leaved vine, *Parsonsia velutina*.

QM, Jeff Wright

Orange Bushbrown
Mycalesis terminus

Identification: Wingspan 40 mm. Orange-brown above; forewing with yellow-orange square containing eyespot; patterned brown beneath; row of eyespots along outer edge of wings.

Habitat and Range: Grassy rainforest edges, along creeks, paperbark swamps. Cape York to Bundaberg, Qld. Other subspecies from Moluccas to New Guinea.

Notes: Flies close to ground, settles frequently. Green or brownish larva has pair of short, pointed horns on head; feeds on grasses.

Tailed Emperor
Polyura sempronius

Identification: Wingspan 75 mm. Cream and black above with two sharp tails on rear edge of hindwings; underside of wings has dark, ornamented pattern of bands and spots on white background.

Habitat and Range: Various habitats, but not arid inland. Northern and eastern Australia, north-eastern WA to Adelaide, SA. Other subspecies from Lesser Sunda Is to New Guinea and Solomon Is.

Notes: Strong and high flying. Adults feed on fermenting plant juices, favour injured pods of Golden Rain Tree (*Cassia fistula*), also a food plant for larvae. Larva green with enlarged, four-horned head and two yellow bands. Also found on Poinciana, Chinese Elm, wattles and bottle trees.

QM, Jeff Wright

Larva, QM

Red Lacewing
Cethosia cydippe

Identification: Wingspan 85 mm. Bases of wings orange-red above, rest of wings black with purple sheen. Forewing with large white patch above and below. Mostly brown beneath with pattern of grey and black spots and stripes.

Habitat and Range: Rainforest, most easily seen along tracks, in clearings. Coastal, Cape York to Townsville, Qld.

Notes: Eggs laid in batches on native passion vine, *Adenia heterophylla*. Larvae banded black and yellow, covered with long, thin spines.

QM, Jeff Wright

QM, Jeff Wright

Blue-banded Eggfly
Hypolimnas alimena

Identification: Wingspan 75 mm. Blue-black above, wings with brighter blue band and rows of white spots along edges; brown beneath with white spots. Some females brown above without blue markings.

Habitat and Range: Rainforest and other dense wet forest. Cape York to south-eastern Qld; rarely NSW. Other subspecies northern NT; Moluccas to New Guinea and Solomon Is.

Notes: Food plant of larva is low-growing rainforest herb, *Pseuderanthemum variabile*. Larva black with branched spines.

QM, Jeff Wright

Blue Argus
Junonia orithya

Identification: Wingspan 45 mm. Forewing mostly black with white band; hindwing blue with black base and two eye spots. 'Camouflage' pattern of brown and orange beneath.

Habitat and Range: Drier open woodland and grassland. North-western NT to south-eastern Qld. Other subspecies in New Guinea, Asia and Africa.

Notes: Flies rapidly, but settles frequently, often on bare ground. Males occupy territories.

QM, Jeff Wright

Glasswing
Acraea andromacha

Identification: Wingspan 45 mm. Black, dark brown and creamy white; most of forewing transparent.

Habitat and Range: Drier open woodland, grassland and gardens. North-western WA to southern NSW.

Notes: Female lays clusters of eggs on upper side of leaves of wild passion vines (*Passiflora, Adenia* spp.). Larvae gregarious with numerous branched, black spines; wander away from food plant to pupate. Elongated, black and white pupae.

Blues and Coppers

Moth Butterfly
Liphyra brassolis

Identification: Wingspan 75 mm. Orange and dark brown above; light brown beneath with dark brown patch on forewing.

Habitat and Range: Lowland rainforest and coastal forest with Green Tree Ants (*Oecophylla smaragdina*). NT, Cape York to Yeppoon, Qld; New Guinea. Other subspecies in India, south-east Asia.

Notes: Eggs laid near nests of Green Tree Ants. Caterpillars crawl inside nests where they feed on ant larvae. Larva oval, flattened with tough skin on top. Pupates within skin of last larval stage. Newly emerged adult covered with loose scales that come off when attacked by ants, allowing it to escape nest.

QM, Jeff Wright

Copper Jewel
Hypochrysops apelles

Identification: Wingspan 30 mm. Wings bright orange above, forewing with black edge; grey-brown beneath, hindwing with red spots and bands.

Habitat and Range: Mainly in mangroves. Darwin, NT; Cape York, Qld, to northern NSW, but common north of Yeppoon; New Guinea.

Notes: Caterpillars greenish, flattened; feed on mangroves at night, hide in shelter or curled leaf during day. Attended by small black ants of genus *Crematogaster*.

QM, Jeff Wright

Male, QM, Jeff Wright

Female underside, QM, Jeff Wright

Apollo Jewel
Hypochrysops apollo

Identification: Wingspan 40 mm. Wings orange-red or orange above, forewing with broad black edge; underside with intricate pattern of reddish-brown and white markings edged with blue.

Habitat and Range: Coastal paperbark swamps and mangroves with ant plants. Cooktown to Ingham, Qld. Different subspecies on tip of Cape York.

Notes: Caterpillars live in galleries within bulbous Ant Plants (*Myrmecodia beccarii*). Share galleries with small ants that feed on fluid produced by larvae. Caterpillars feed on flesh of Ant Plant and sometimes leaves. Full grown larva cuts exit hole and pupates in plant. Butterfly threatened by illegal collecting of Ant Plants and clearing of swamp habitats.

QM, Jeff Wright

Common Oakblue
Arhopala micale

Identification: Wingspan 45 mm. Metallic blue above with black edges; dark underside, patterned with brown; tail on rear edge of each hindwing. Inconspicuous when perched, bright blue only visible in flight.

Habitat and Range: Lowland rainforest. Coastal Qld, Cooktown to Yeppoon. Other subspecies on tip of Cape York, northern NT; Moluccas to New Guinea and Aru Is.

Notes: Caterpillars feed on several native trees; attended by Green Tree Ants.

Common Tit
Hypolycaena phorbas

Identification: Wingspan 35 mm. Male (pictured), dull black above, forewing with dull blue central area and black spot. Female dull black, forewing with white patch. Both sexes pale grey below, with pattern of bands. Each hindwing has two narrow tails.

Habitat and Range: Lowland rainforest. Coastal Qld, Cape York to Yeppoon. Other subspecies in northern NT; New Guinea.

Notes: Adults fly rapidly, settle on ends of twigs. Green caterpillars feed on many different plants; always attended by Green Tree Ants.

QM, Jeff Wright

Small Green-banded Blue
Psychonotis caelius

Identification: Wingspan 25 mm. Male (pictured), bright blue above with central white patch on hindwing. Female, both wings with white centre surrounded by black. Both sexes white and black beneath with green metallic markings.

Habitat and Range: Mainly rainforest, can be common in gardens. Eastern Australia, Cape York, Qld, to Sydney, NSW. Other subspecies from Moluccas to New Guinea.

Notes: Flattened, whitish caterpillars feed on underside of leaves of Red Ash or Soap Leaf Tree (*Alphitonia excelsa*); make distinctive marks which are visible on top of leaves.

QM, Jeff Wright

Moths

Moths are more diverse than butterflies and comparatively little is known of their food plants and habits. Tropical North Queensland is home to several thousand different kinds of moths and on hot summer nights they may be attracted to lights in large numbers. Just 15 of the more conspicuous or interesting species are mentioned here. *Moths of Australia*, by I.F.B. Common (Melbourne University Press), is a good reference.

A. *scotti*, Anthony O'Toole

Splendid Ghost Moths
Aenetus scotti, A. mirabilis

Identification: Female wingspan, *A. scotti* 120 mm; *A. mirabilis* 160 mm. Males smaller. *A. scotti*, forewings dark green, hindwings pale orange with pinkish bases. *A. mirabilis*, female forewings light green, hindwings pale orange; male forewings blue, hindwings white.

Habitat and Range: Rainforest. *A. scotti*, Cairns, Qld, to eastern Vic. *A. mirabilis* Cooktown to Paluma, Qld.

Notes: Early larvae probably live on rainforest floor, feed on decaying wood. Older larvae bore holes in stems and branches of living trees; *A. scotti*, in stinging trees (*Dendrocnide* spp.) and several other species; *A. mirabilis*, in Red Ash (*Alphitonia excelsa*).

QM

Giant Wood Moth
Endoxyla cinereus

Identification: Wingspan to 220 mm. Very large, grey with darker hindwings and blotch on middle of thorax.

Habitat and Range: Open forest and suburban areas with smooth-barked eucalypts. Northern Qld to southern NSW.

Notes: Larva lives in tunnels in trunk of living smooth-barked gum trees and feeds on inner side of bark. Large exit hole is cut when larva is ready to pupate inside tunnel. Moth emerges from hole in mid-summer.

Dysphania fenestrata

Identification: Wingspan 85 mm. Body yellow with black bands. Wings purplish-black, sometimes olive-green, with see-through patches; hindwing has band of yellow near edge.

Habitat and Range: Mainly rainforest. Northern WA, NT, coastal Qld from Cape York to Yeppoon; New Guinea.

Notes: Conspicuous, large, yellowish caterpillar with rows of dark eyespots, feeds on rainforest tree (*Carallia*). Pupates between leaves drawn together with silk.

QM, Jeff Wright

Larva, Bruce Cowell

Pingasa chlora

Identification: Wingspan 45 mm. Wings white above with thin, wavy black lines and dots; underside white, each wing with thick black band near outer edge.

Habitat and Range: Wet forests. Coastal eastern Australia, Cape York, Qld, to northern NSW.

Notes: Camouflaged adults rest with wings held flat against surfaces. Looper caterpillars, pale green with cream stripes along sides; feed on Bumpy Ash (*Flindersia schottiana*) and Macaranga (*Macaranga tanarius*).

QM, Jeff Wright

North Queensland Day Moth
Alcides metaurus

Identification: Wingspan 100 mm. Flies during day, resembles butterfly, but rests with wings outspread. Top of wings with broad bands of black and metallic green, sometimes tinged mauve; wings pale metallic green with black bands beneath.

Habitat and Range: Upland and lowland rainforest, but flies long distances into other habitats. TNQ, Cooktown to Mackay, also tip of Cape York; New Guinea.

Notes: Known to migrate. Caterpillars black with white bands and red thorax; feed on rainforest vine, *Omphalea queenslandiae* in Wet Tropics and small tree, *O. celata*, in southern part of range.

QM, Jeff Wright

QM, Jeff Wright

Syntherata janetta

Identification: Wingspan 105 mm. Variable. Wings yellowish, brown or purplish-grey with darker zigzag markings and sometimes with large, dark blotches. Small central eyespot on each wing.

Habitat and Range: Heavily forested areas including rainforest. Coastal eastern Australia, northern NT, Cape York, Qld, to central NSW; New Guinea.

Notes: Large greenish, spiny caterpillar feeds on wide range of trees.

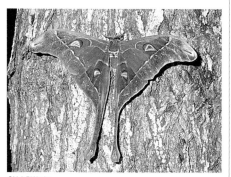

QM, Jeff Wright

Hercules Moth
Coscinocera hercules

Identification: Enormous. Wingspan, male (pictured) 200 mm; female 225 mm. Wings brown with dark, pale-edged stripe and large transparent window. Male with rear corner of hindwing stretched into long tail.

Habitat and Range: Rainforest. Iron Ra. (Cape York) to Ingham, Qld; New Guinea.

Notes: Females have largest wing area of any moth in world. Adults short-lived and do not feed. Large pale-blue caterpillars with rows of yellow spikes feed on several rainforest trees, including Bleeding Heart (*Omalanthus nutans*).

QM, Jeff Wright

Larva, QM

Australian Privet Hawk Moth
Psilogramma menephron

Identification: Wingspan 100 mm. Stout body. Forewing grey above with mottled black and whitish markings; hindwing dark brown above; wings grey-brown beneath.

Habitat and Range: Variety of habitats, including gardens. Eastern Australia, NT and Qld to Sydney, NSW; India and Asia.

Notes: Caterpillars eat wide range of ornamental plants (especially privet and jasmine) and several native species. Larvae greenish with white and pale yellow (and sometimes purple) oblique stripes along side. Thorax, last pair of false legs and short, straight tail covered with tiny warts.

Teleclita dryinopa

Identification: Wingspan 65 mm. Stout body. Top of forewing mottled grey and brown with black streaks, underside brown; hindwings white with dark spot on back edge. Thorax grey with black and white markings, abdomen brown.

Habitat and Range: Coastal Australia, WA, northern NT, Cape York to Townsville, Qld.

Notes: Thick, green larva feeds on coastal Beach Almond Tree (*Terminalia catappa*); has backward-directed horn near front of body; rear segments flattened sideways. At rest, larva curves tip of abdomen forward to touch horn. Underside of abdomen is streaked and resembles young leaf.

QM, Jeff Wright

Larva, Geoff Monteith

Bag Shelter Moth
Ochrogaster lunifer

Identification: Wingspan 55 mm. Stout, woolly; brown with bands of yellow on abdomen. Female has large tuft of white scales at tip of abdomen.

Habitat and Range: Open forest. Coastal eastern Australia, Atherton Tableland, Qld, to Vic., south-eastern SA, Tas.

Notes: Larvae covered with long, dense hairs, that irritate human skin. Live gregariously inside large, pale brown silken bag attached to trunk of wattles. Feed on leaves at night. When larvae leave tree to pupate or to seek new trees they travel in long chain (head to tail) and are known as processionary caterpillars.

QM, Jeff Wright

Ceryx sphenodes

Identification: Wingspan 30 mm. Wings black with see-through windows; hindwings very small. Abdomen with black and orange bands.

Habitat and Range: Rainforest. Mossman, to Innisfail, Qld.

Notes: Belongs to group of similar moths that mimic wasps with colouring. Flies during daytime and visits flowers.

QM, Jeff Wright

QM, Jeff Wright

Agape chloropyga

Identification: Wingspan 65 mm. Wings bright yellow above and below; forewing with scattered reddish-brown spots on top.

Habitat and Range: Forest. Eastern Australia. Malaysia to New Guinea.

Notes: Brownish, hairy larva sluggish and often rests with body tightly bent back on itself; feeds on fig trees (*Ficus* spp.).

QM

Fruit Piercing Moth
Eudocima salaminia

Identification: Wingspan 85 mm. Stout body. Greenish, camouflaged forewings that part when alarmed to expose orange and black hindwings.

Habitat and Range: Wet forest, citrus plantations, gardens. Northern NT, Cape York, Qld, to central NSW; India through Asia to south-western Pacific.

Notes: Uses stout, toothed proboscis to pierce and suck juice from fruit. Larva has black, prominent eyespots on side; rests with loop of body raised. Feeds on heart-shaped leaves of *Stephania* vines.

Bruce Cowell

Granny's Cloak Moth
Speiredonia spectans

Identification: Wingspan 75 mm. Grey, purplish reflections, wavy dark lines and eyespots on forewings.

Habitat and Range: Forests, houses. Coastal eastern Australia, NT, Atherton Tableland, Qld, to central NSW.

Notes: Adults roost in hollow trees and caves in day. In houses, favour darkened rooms, cupboards and under floorboards, also in stormwater drains; sometimes occur in large numbers. Caterpillars and food plant unknown, but may breed on wattles.

Joseph's Coat Moth
Agarista agricola

Identification: Wingspan 65 mm. Dark, blotched with splashes of red, yellow and blue.

Habitat and Range: Forest. Coastal eastern Australia, northern NT, Cairns, Qld, to central NSW; New Guinea.

Notes: Flies in daytime and often mistaken for butterfly. Larva banded white, black and orange; rows of hairs with swollen ends along back. Feeds on native vine, *Cayratia*, occasionally attacks cultivated grape vines.

QM, Jeff Wright

Larva, QM

WASPS, BEES AND ANTS

Wasps and bees have two pairs of gauzy wings, with relatively few veins, that are held together by a row of tiny hooks during flight. Worker ants are wingless, sterile females, but most species of ants have winged males and females (kings and queens) that start new colonies. The most primitive wasps, sawflies, have larvae that feed on plants, either eating leaves or boring in wood. Sawfly adults have no waist and their larvae have 3 pairs of short legs on the thorax. All other adult wasps, bees and ants have a narrow waist at the base of the abdomen and their larvae have no legs. Most species of wasps have larvae that feed on other insects or spiders, either as parasites or inside a nest with prey supplied by the female. Bees feed their larvae on pollen from plants. Many species of wasps have a powerful sting, but most only use it to capture prey. Those wasps that live in colonies, as well as many ants, may also use their stings for defence.

Sawflies

Paperbark Sawfly
Lophyrotoma zonalis

Identification: Length 12 mm. Black with yellow shoulders; abdomen with broad orange band at base and yellow tip; without narrow waist.

Habitat and Range: Coastal areas with paperbarks (*Melaleuca* spp.), gardens; possibly occurs further inland. Northern NT; eastern Qld, south to Rockhampton.

Notes: Larvae feed on leaves of paperbarks, may strip whole trees in summer. Females place eggs in leaf edges with saw-like egg-layer. Larvae caterpillar-like with 3 pairs of short legs and pointed tail; pupate in bark.

QM, Jeff Wright

Wasps

QM, Jeff Wright

Ichneumon Wasp
Xanthocryptus sp.

Identification: Length 20 mm. Body reddish-brown with black and white markings on head and thorax; antennae black with broad white band in middle. Female (pictured), with egg-laying tube (ovipositor) projecting from tip of abdomen.

Notes: Life history unknown, but female probably lays eggs inside moth caterpillars using ovipositor. Wasp larva feeds and develops inside caterpillar killing it. Belongs to one of largest groups of wasps, many hundreds of species.

QM, Jeff Wright

Cuckoo Wasps
Chrysididae

Identification: Length 4–20 mm, varies with species. Stout, heavily armoured; bright metallic blue, green or turquoise.

Habitat and Range: Many similar species in variety of habitats. Australia-wide.

Notes: Lay eggs inside mud nests of other wasps. Cuckoo Wasp larvae either steal other wasps' food supply or feed on host wasp larva itself. Female Cuckoo Wasps often seen flying up and down walls or around posts and fences searching for nests of other wasps; can roll into a ball to protect itself from attacks by owners of nests.

QM, Jeff Wright

Flower Wasps
Campsomeris spp.

Identification: Length 20–30 mm. Hairy, most have bold black and yellow or orange-yellow bands on abdomen. One species all black with two yellow spots on abdomen. Male (pictured), smaller and more slender than female, longer antennae.

Habitat and Range: Rainforest to arid areas. Australia-wide.

Notes: Several species. Visit flowers. Female burrows into ground, lays egg on scarab beetle grub. Larva develops as external parasite of grub, eventually killing it. Some species attack grubs of pest cane beetles.

Potter Wasp
Delta arcuata

Identification: Length: 25–30 mm. Black with pattern of yellow spots and bands; abdomen with long, narrow waist and bulbous tip.

Habitat and Range: Open and closed forest. Northern Australia, Kimberley region, WA, to Bowen, Qld; New Guinea.

Notes: Female builds large, dome-shaped nest of mud (pictured) in sheltered position, often on house walls. Nest contains several chambers or cells filled with caterpillars; egg laid in each cell and wasp larva feeds on caterpillars.

QM, Jeff Wright

Nest, QM, Jeff Wright

Paper Wasps
Polistes spp.

Identification: Length 15–20 mm. Patterned with reddish-brown, black and yellow. Easily identified by type of nest.

Habitat and Range: Prefer open forest and woodland, gardens. Australia-wide.

Notes: Several species. Build disc-like, papery nests suspended from single stalk (pictured). Openings to individual cells visible from beneath. Nests built in sheltered positions, beneath branches in dense foliage, under eaves of houses. Aggressively defend nests, powerful sting.

Bruce Cowell

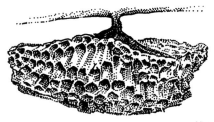

Nest

QM, Bruce Cowell

Nest, QM, Jeff Wright

Paper Wasp
Ropalidia gregaria

Identification: Length 8–12 mm. Mostly brown with yellowish markings on thorax and yellow band on abdomen.

Habitat and Range: Prefers open drier areas, often nest in long grass. Widespread, northern NT, Qld, NSW, Vic; New Guinea, Solomon Is.

Notes: Builds broad nest, several cells wide, and slightly more cells long; attached by single stalk at one end to twigs of low shrubs or stems and blades of long grass. Aggressively defends nests, powerful sting.

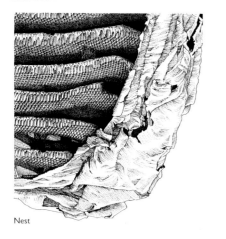

Robert Ashdown

Nest

Paper Wasp
Ropalidia romandi

Identification: Length 6–8 mm. Yellow with black or brown markings on thorax and abdomen.

Habitat and Range: Prefers open forest, nests in trees. Northern NT, Coastal Qld to Sydney, NSW.

Notes: Builds nest of several sheets or combs surrounded by thin, papery envelope; sometimes very large (over 1 m long), attached to trunks or main branches of large trees. In TNQ, smaller nests in foliage of trees are common. Occasionally builds on houses. Large nests are occupied by thousands of wasps. Aggressively defend nests, powerful sting.

Digger Wasp
Sphex cognatus

Identification: Length 20–25 mm. Black, golden hairs on face, golden or silver hairs on thorax; waist thin and tubular; wings clear or pale orange, with darker edges.

Habitat and Range: Prefers open, sandy areas. Widespread, northern, eastern and south-eastern Australia; New Guinea, Asia.

Notes: Females often nest together in sandy soil. Nest is a burrow with several chambers branching from main tunnel. One wasp larva develops in each chamber, feeding on several katydids collected by female wasp. Adults feed on nectar.

QM, Jeff Wright

Bees

Blue-banded Bees
Amegilla spp.

Identification: Length 10–15 mm. Head and thorax with golden hairs; abdomen with black and metallic blue-green bands.

Habitat and Range: Rainforest edges, open forest, woodland, desert, gardens. Australia-wide.

Notes: Females solitary, each building own nest, but many females may nest together in same area. Nest is a burrow in sheltered situation, such as overhanging creek banks or under houses. Clusters of sleeping males cling to twigs or grass stems overnight.

QM, Jeff Wright

Carpenter Bees
Xylocopa spp.

Identification: Length 20–25 mm. Stout. Female black with yellow hair on face and thorax; wings smoky-black. Male with yellow hair on whole body.

Habitat and Range: Rainforest edges, open forest, gardens. Coastal Australia.

Notes: Australia's largest bees. Several similar species; most common and widespread is *X. aruana*. Females buzz loudly as they visit flowers, especially common on flowering trees, such as *Cassia*, *Tipuana* and *Albizia*. Females solitary nesters, excavating tunnels in decaying wood and pithy stems.

QM, Jeff Wright

QM, Bruce Cowell

Native Honey Bees
Trigona and Austroplebia spp.

Identification: Length about 4–6 mm. Small, black, nest in hives. Different species difficult to distinguish, structure of nest often most reliable characteristic.

Habitat and Range: Rainforest to drier inland. Northern WA, NT, Qld, northern NSW.

Notes: Several similar species. Build hives in hollow trees or rock crevices; made from mixture of wax and resin. Pollen and honey stored in pots. Larval cells clustered together or form flat combs. Do not sting, defend nests by swarming and biting. Also called stingless, sweat or sugarbag bees.

Bruce Cowell

Honeybee
Apis mellifera

Identification: Length 12–14 mm. Worker (sterile female) with dark brown and hairy head and thorax, abdomen orange with black bands.

Habitat and Range: All habitats, rainforest to desert. Australia-wide. Native to Africa and Eurasia, now worldwide.

Notes: Introduced for honey production. Workers visit all types of nectar producing flowers. Bees from domesticated hives relatively docile; those from feral hives can be aggressive. Sting left in wound.

Ants

QM, Bruce Cowell

Meat Ants
Iridomyrmex spp.

Identification: Length about 6–8 mm. Reddish head and thorax with metallic purple reflections; abdomen black with green or purple reflections.

Habitat and Range: Drier woodland areas. Two species in tropical Qld — *I. sanguineus*; *I. reburrus*, favours wetter areas, such as creek edges and suburban lawns.

Notes: Nest in soil, several separate entrances to colony. Forage on trees and shrubs for honeydew produced by sap-sucking bugs.

Jumper Ant
Myrmecia nigrocinta

Identification: Length 15 mm. Black head and abdomen; reddish-brown and black thorax. Head with pair of yellowish, long, thin, forward-pointing jaws with many teeth on inner edges.

Habitat and Range: Open and closed forest. Eastern Australia, Qld to Vic.

Notes: Aggressive, has powerful sting; frequently jumps. Nests in soil; raised entrance, often at base of clump of grass or shrub.

QM, Jeff Wright

Trap Jaw Ant
Odontomachus cephalotes

Identification: Length 10–15 mm. Dark brown or black with large, rectangular head and long, thin jaws with strong teeth at tips.

Habitat and Range: Closed forest. Northern Qld and NT; New Guinea, Indonesia.

Notes: Nests in soil. Workers predatory, hold jaws wide apart; when long sensory setae between their bases are triggered, jaws snap shut, impaling prey on teeth at tips. Powerful sting.

QM, Jeff Wright

Green Tree Ant
Oecophylla smaragdina

Identification: Length about 5–10 mm. Yellowish-green thorax, green abdomen; adopts distinctive aggressive stance with raised abdomen.

Habitat and Range: All types of forest, but not in highlands. Northern Australia, Kimberley region, WA, to Gladstone, Qld.

Notes: Workers build nests in trees and shrubs by pulling together leaves and sealing them with silk produced by larvae. Aggressive predators; vigorously defend nests, swarm over attacker and bite with jaws, inject stinging fluid from tip of abdomen into wound.

Bruce Cowell

Striped Scat, QM, Bruce Cowell

FRESHWATER AND UPPER ESTUARINE FISHES

Australia has just over 200 species of freshwater fishes and, of these, about one-quarter occur in the streams of Tropical North Queensland. Of the 87 native species found in the area from Cooktown to Mackay, only 53 are true freshwater fishes. Another 34 species are estuarine or marine, living in freshwater for prolonged periods, but returning to the sea or brackish water to complete their life cycles.

Many Australian freshwater fishes are able to withstand high salinity levels. Estuarine species must be able to withstand seasonal variations in salinity caused by high rainfall and sudden flooding.

The volume and regularity of rainfall affects the suitability of habitat for various fish species. Generally, areas of high and regular rainfall have clearer streams with higher dissolved oxygen and a greater diversity of habitats and species. The Wet Tropics region, between Cooktown and Rollingstone, has the highest rainfall in Australia: 3600 mm annually at Innisfail, with higher falls on the adjacent mountains. It also has the most diverse fish communities in north Queensland and throughout Australia.

The fishes of TNQ are an important commercial and recreational resource. Commercial fishing is generally restricted to waters well downstream, but species such as Barramundi and Mangrove Jack live in freshwater or upper estuaries for most of their lives. Recreational and sports anglers are able to target these and other species, including Jungle Perch, Sooty Grunter and Dewfish.

Keen anglers commonly trek from southern states and overseas specifically to try their luck with the elusive Barramundi. Stocks are protected by size and bag limits, seasonal closures during the breeding season (November to February) and supplemented by a stocking program. Captive propagation, or aqua-culture, involving other estuarine fishes, such as Estuary Cod, Mangrove Jack and Grunter Bream, is being developed.

Tropical North Queensland is also world renowned for the beauty of some of its aquarium fishes, particularly the numerous varieties of Eastern Rainbow-fish. These, as well as archerfishes, a variety of Pacific Blue-eye and many interesting species of gobies and gudgeons, are prized by aquarists elsewhere in Australia, North America, Japan and Europe.

Most Australian freshwater fishes evolved from marine ancestors relatively recently in geological time. Few species have become highly specialised in their habits or behaviour, as has occurred in other tropical regions of the world. Most are tolerant of a wide range of environmental conditions and have broad feeding and habitat requirements.

This lack of specialisation makes the local environment especially vulnerable to the establishment of exotic species that are able to colonise without strong competition from native fishes. At least six exotic freshwater fishes from Africa and Central America are established in TNQ. Government authorities introduced the Mosquitofish in 1942 for mosquito control. However, its aggressive fin-nipping habits have adversely affected native fishes and frogs.

Other species were introduced as deliberate or accidental releases from aquaria. The Tilapia (or Mozambique

Mouthbrooder) and the Niger Cichlid have become established in the Cairns and Townsville areas. Tilapia are valued as food fish in Africa and parts of Asia. However, they are capable of breeding rapidly to enormous concentrations, often to the exclusion of other species. For this reason they are declared noxious under the *Fisheries Act*, making their distribution, sale or possession illegal and subject to a heavy fine.

Several additional exotic cichlid species have also been reported from Townsville, but it is unsure whether they will spread more widely and form viable, self-reproducing populations. Attempts early this century to introduce trout in north Queensland were unsuccessful.

Some native freshwater fishes not previously known from TNQ have been translocated into local waterways. Introductions of Sooty Grunter, Spangled Perch, Barred Grunter and Sleepy Cod have established in some rivers and impoundments. The Barron River system, including the Tinaroo Dam, has been stocked many times and contains some species not occurring in adjacent eastward flowing streams.

The impacts of exotic fish introductions and translocation of native species are unpredictable and largely unknown, but have been highly damaging in at least one instance. A population of Lake Eacham Rainbowfish was eradicated by the introduction of the native Mouth Almighty. This type of action should be discouraged. All unwanted aquarium fishes should be destroyed or returned to the local aquarium store. They should never be released in waterways or public ornamental ponds.

The descriptions that follow include all native fishes currently known from freshwaters of TNQ, with the exception of two unnamed species — a bass found only in a single isolated river and a small carp gudgeon whose relationships are uncertain. Several common, purely estuarine fishes are also included. Eleven species are known only from the Cooktown – Mackay area and another 25 do not occur further south. Maximum sizes are total lengths.

Jeff Johnson

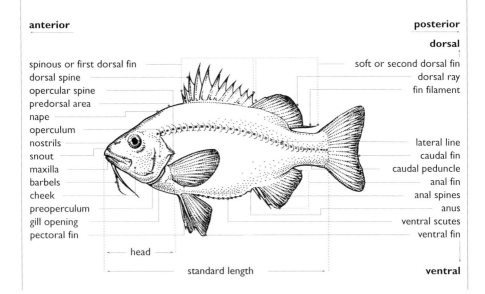

anterior

posterior

dorsal

spinous or first dorsal fin
dorsal spine
opercular spine
predorsal area
nape
operculum
nostrils
snout
maxilla
barbels
cheek
preoperculum
gill opening
pectoral fin

soft or second dorsal fin
dorsal ray
fin filament

lateral line
caudal fin
caudal peduncle
anal fin
anal spines
anus
ventral scutes
ventral fin

head

standard length

ventral

South Pacific Eel
Anguilla obscura

Identification: To about 110 cm. Dark grey to chocolate-brown on head and upper body, creamy-white below; no spotting or mottling. Two gill openings; pectoral fins present.

Habitat and Range: Coastal freshwater streams and swamps; sheltering beneath undercut banks, logs, boulders or aquatic plants. Cape York to Mackay, Qld; tropical south Pacific to New Guinea.

QM, Bruce Cowell

Long-finned Eel
Anguilla reinhardtii

Identification: To about 250 cm, common at 100 cm. Olive-green to grey-brown on upper body, mottled with irregular spots and blotches. Two gill openings; pectoral fins present.

Habitat and Range: Common in brackish coastal streams to uppermost freshwater tributaries and isolated waterholes. Eastern Australia, Cape York, Qld, to Melbourne, Vic.; southern New Guinea, New Caledonia.

Notes: Grows much larger when land-locked in impoundments; harvested for export. Adults migrate to deep channels in Coral Sea off New Caledonia to spawn.

QM, Bruce Cowell

Oxeye Herring
Megalops cyprinoides

Other Name: Tarpon

Identification: To 152 cm, common at 50 cm. Brilliant silvery body. Large eyes, mouth and scales; single dorsal fin with last ray elongated.

Habitat and Range: Bays and estuaries, penetrating far into freshwater. Onslow, WA, to Sydney, NSW; widespread tropical Indo-west Pacific.

Notes: Good sport fish, but poor eating.

QM, Bruce Cowell

QM, Bruce Cowell

Southern Herring
Herklotsichthys castelnaui

Identification: To 20 cm. Greenish-grey above, silvery below; upper scale rows with series of faint dark lines; upper caudal and dorsal fins have dusky to blackish tips. Last dorsal and last 2 anal rays not enlarged.

Habitat and Range: Inshore waters, bays and estuaries to tidal freshwater reaches. Cooktown, Qld, to Pambula, NSW.

Notes: Sought by castnetters as favoured bait for Coral Trout. Large shoals often found well up estuaries.

QM, Bruce Cowell

Bony Bream
Nematalosa erebi

Identification: To 47 cm, common at 25 cm. Greenish-grey on back, silvery below; fin tips clear or opaque. Small mouth; single dorsal fin with last ray filamentous.

Habitat and Range: Inland and coastal freshwater systems, extending well into lower estuary. Widespread northern Australia, coastal drainages from Pilbara, WA, to Brisbane, Qld, also Murray-Darling, Lake Eyre and Barkly Basins.

Notes: Larger fish feed almost exclusively on algae and detritus. Able to tolerate extremes of temperature and salinity.

QM, Bruce Cowell

White Sardine
Sardinella albella

Identification: To 15 cm. Dark green above, silvery-white below; small black spot at base of dorsal fin origin. Eye small; last 2 anal fin rays enlarged.

Habitat and Range: Inshore waters, bays and estuaries. Port Hedland, WA, to Townsville, Qld; tropical Indo-west Pacific.

Notes: Usually in small groups. Often confused with Southern Herring (see above).

Milkfish
Chanos chanos

Identification: To 120 cm. Blue-grey above, brilliant silver on sides. Small head and mouth; single dorsal fin lacks elongated rays of other species; long deeply forked tail.

Habitat and Range: Bays and estuaries, often venturing into lower freshwater reaches. Shark Bay, WA to Jervis Bay, NSW; tropical Indo-west Pacific.

Notes: Widely cultured in south-east Asia, but rarely eaten in Australia.

QM, Bruce Cowell

Forktailed Catfish
Arius graeffei

Identification: To about 70 cm. Dark brown, blue-grey or silvery above, fading to yellowish-cream or white below. Large serrated dorsal and pectoral spines. Snout slightly curved when viewed from above.

Habitat and Range: Bays and estuaries, extending to upper reaches of slow flowing freshwater streams. Coastal streams, from Houtman Abrolhos, WA to Hunter R., NSW; southern New Guinea.

Notes: Males mouthbrood eggs and developing larvae. Usually breeds in estuaries except where landlocked in freshwater lagoons and impoundments.

QM, Bruce Cowell

Freshwater Catfish
Tandanus tandanus

Other Name: Dewfish

Identification: To 90 cm. Slate grey, olive-brown to charcoal-brown, often profusely mottled with darker grey or black. Second dorsal fin long, originating on front half of body near first dorsal fin, joining with anal fin to form rounded eel-like tail.

Habitat and Range: Freshwater rivers, creeks, lakes and impoundments. Daintree R., Qld, to Clarence R., NSW and Murray-Darling basin.

Notes: Male constructs circular nest (to 2 m diameter) of small stones. Mated pair guard eggs and newly hatched brood. Edible fish sought by anglers.

Large juvenile, QM, Bruce Cowell

Adult, QM, Bruce Cowell

Juvenile, QM, Bruce Cowell

Black Tandan
Neosilurus ater

Identification: To 47 cm. Light grey to black, often with darker mottling or flecking on body. Second dorsal fin short, well behind first, joining with anal fin to form rounded eel-like tail. Upper profile of head fairly straight; snout profile pointed.

Habitat and Range: Prefers flowing coastal freshwater rivers and streams. Patchy distribution, Carson R., WA, to Townsville, Qld; southern New Guinea.

Notes: Several colour varieties. Frequently confused with Hyrtl's Tandan (see below).

Hyrtl's Tandan
Neosilurus hyrtlii

Identification: To 45 cm. Olive-brown, light tan to dusky silver-grey on upper body, fins often yellowish. Second dorsal fin short, close to tip of caudal fin, joining with anal fin to form rounded eel-like tail. Upper profile of head slightly curved; snout profile rounded.

Habitat and Range: Clear to turbid freshwater rivers, creeks, lagoons and impoundments. Pilbara region, WA, to Brisbane R., Qld; also Murray-Darling, Lake Eyre and Barkly Basins.

Notes: Common in slow flowing drainages, absent from most Wet Tropics streams, except Barron R. system.

Gunther Schmida

QM, Bruce Cowell

Rendahl's Tandan
Porochilus rendahli

Identification: To about 35 cm. Dark grey-brown to blue-grey, often mottled with lighter blotches. Second dorsal fin short, close to caudal fin tip, joining with anal fin to form pointed eel-like tail. Eight thin barbels around mouth. Upper profile of head slightly concave; snout short.

Habitat and Range: Coastal freshwater rivers, creeks, lagoons and impoundments. Patchy distribution from Fitzroy R., WA, to Brisbane R., Qld.

Notes: Popular with aquarists.

Snubnose Garfish
Arrhamphus sclerolepis sclerolepis

Identification: To 40 cm. Silver stripe along middle of sides. Lower jaw protruding, forming short beak less than half length of head. Single, short-based dorsal fin at rear of body.

Habitat and Range: Bays, estuaries, freshwater rivers and impoundments. Carnarvon, WA, to Rockhampton, Qld; southern New Guinea.

Notes: Feeds mainly on algae. Capable of breeding in freshwater when landlocked by dams. Good edible fish.

QM, Bruce Cowell

Mangrove Garfish
Zenarchopterus dispar

Identification: To 16 cm. Nasal flaps long and slender; upper jaw wider than long. Caudal fin truncated; anal fin with 6th and 7th rays thickened, greatly elongated in males, reaching well beyond caudal fin base.

Habitat and Range: Estuaries and lower tidal reaches of freshwater streams. Darwin, NT, to Townsville, Qld; tropical south Pacific to New Guinea.

Similar Species: Head-stripe Garfish (*Z. buffonis*) has dark brown line along midline of top of head and upper jaw; small black blotch in centre of anal fin, 6th anal ray enlarged, only reaching caudal fin base.

QM, Bruce Cowell

Freshwater Longtom
Strongylura kreffti

Identification: To 80 cm. Body elongated, robust and deep, especially in adults; jaws long with many sharp teeth; caudal fin square cut; dorsal rays 16–18.

Habitat and Range: Estuaries and freshwater rivers, lagoons and impoundments. Coastal drainages, Fitzroy R., WA, to Burnett R., Qld; southern New Guinea.

Notes: Voracious, surface-feeding carnivore. Uncommon in Wet Tropics; common in Burdekin, Pioneer and Ross Rs. May be capable of breeding in freshwater.

Gunther Schmida

QM, Bruce Cowell

Fly-specked Hardyhead
Craterocephalus stercusmuscarum

Identification: To 10 cm. Dark green above, golden-yellow to silver-grey on sides; dark-edged, silver stripe from eye to caudal fin base. Rows of numerous black dots along sides, may be indistinct in specimens from turbid waters.

Habitat and Range: Freshwater creeks, rivers and impoundments. Coastal drainages, Darwin, NT, to Brisbane, Qld.

QM, Bruce Cowell

Cairns Rainbowfish
Cairnsichthys rhombosomoides

Identification: To about 8 cm. Light greenish-grey above, pale dusky yellow below, with narrow, dark stripe along sides; fins clear or yellowish. Males often have dusky edge to anal fin and vague second stripe low on sides. Spines and rays of dorsal and anal fins slender and flexible compared to other rainbowfishes.

Habitat and Range: Clear, strongly flowing rainforest streams, near foot of coastal ranges. Mulgrave R. south to Hull R. (near Tully), Qld.

GR Allen

Lake Eacham Rainbowfish
Melanotaenia eachamensis

Identification: To about 7 cm. Body slender; light bluish-green with vague black stripe; series of faint orange lines on sides; fins clear to yellowish-orange.

Habitat and Range: Originally known only from Lake Eacham, small isolated crater lake on Atherton Tableland. Probably extinct in this lake, but found in nearby Lake Euramoo and some streams of upper North Johnstone and Barron catchments.

Notes: Introduction of Mouth Almighty, Barred Grunter and Archerfish appears to have led to demise of this species in Lake Eacham. Closely related to Eastern Rainbowfish (see p. 143), with which it breeds in captivity. Colour pattern often not enough to distinguish between rainbowfishes from Atherton Tableland.

McCulloch's Rainbowfish
Melanotaenia maccullochi

Identification: To 6 cm. About 9 narrow dark stripes along sides; dorsal and anal fins clear to yellowish with dark bands close to edge and scattered dark spots. Breeding males with crimson red fins and bright stripe on forehead.

Habitat and Range: Coastal freshwater creeks and lagoons. Patchy distribution from near tip of Cape York to Cape Flattery, Daintree R. and several streams between Cairns and Cardwell, Qld; southern New Guinea.

QM, Bruce Cowell

Eastern Rainbowfish
Melanotaenia splendida splendida

Identification: To 20 cm, common at 12 cm. Body deep, especially in large males. Colour varies between, and sometimes within, river systems. Usually with series of thin, horizontal yellow, orange or reddish stripes or rows of spots on sides; lacks dark band on side; dorsal and anal fins usually red, speckled blue-green with black edge.

Habitat and Range: Widespread, eastern coastal freshwater drainages from tip of Cape York to Boyne R., Qld.

Notes: Numerous colour varieties. Among most notable are those from upper Burdekin R., Utchee Ck (near Innisfail), Davies Ck (near Kuranda) and upper Daintree R. Subspecies, *M. splendida inornata*, in Gulf of Carpentaria drainages.

QM, Bruce Cowell

Mulgrave R. variety. Gunther Schmida

Spotted Blue-eye
Pseudomugil gertrudae

Identification: To 3 cm. Small black spots on body, dorsal, anal and caudal fins. Male, longer pectoral, first dorsal and ventral fins and more intense spotting.

Habitat and Range: Clear coastal freshwater creeks and lagoons. Patchy distribution, Darwin, NT, to Murray R. (Cardwell), Qld; southern New Guinea.

Male, Gunther Schmida

Male above, female below, QM, Bruce Cowell

Pacific Blue-eye
Pseudomugil signifer

Identification: To 6 cm, common at 3 cm. Bright blue eye; body olive-yellow, silver-grey or semi-transparent; scales usually with narrow dark edges; often row of scales with pearly-blue spots on sides. Male, leading rays of dorsal, anal and pelvic fins elongated; black blotch on leading rays of second dorsal and anal fins.

Habitat and Range: Coastal freshwater streams to mangrove creeks of estuaries. Tip of Cape York, Qld, to Ulladulla, NSW.

Notes: Several varieties; most distinctive in Wet Tropics. Males intensify colour during courtship and spawning.

QM, Bruce Cowell

Reticulated Estuarine Pipefish
Hippichthys heptagonus

Identification: To 15 cm. No distinctive markings; dorsal fin origin on first tail ring; ridge on side of body angled down at anal ring.

Habitat and Range: Estuaries and tidal freshwater reaches, usually among aquatic plants. Cape York, Qld, to Clarence R., NSW, but rare south of Hinchinbrook I.

Notes: Usually found in groups among seagrass beds or mangrove roots. Like many pipefishes, male cares for eggs in well-developed brood pouch.

QM, Bruce Cowell

Banded Mangrove Pipefish
Hippichthys spicifer

Identification: To 17 cm. Lower half of body has dark brown bands. Dorsal fin origin on or behind second tail ring; ridge on side of body angled down at anal ring.

Habitat and Range: Estuaries and tidal freshwater reaches, sheltering among roots and branches. Cape York to Hinchinbrook I., Qld; tropical Indo-west Pacific.

Notes: Attractive species; difficult to keep in aquaria, feeds on zooplankton.

Bengal Swamp Eel
Ophisternon bengalense

Identification: To about 60 cm. Dark olive to chocolate or reddish-brown above, larger specimens peppered with black dots. Elongated and eel-like; no pectoral or ventral fins; low inconspicuous dorsal and anal fins; single gill opening on throat.

Habitat and Range: Slow flowing, freshwater creeks and lagoons. Darwin, NT, to Ingham, Qld; India to Philippines.

Notes: Rarely seen, although common in some areas. Several similar species may occur. Burrows into soft muddy bottom.

QM, Bruce Cowell

Bullrout
Notesthes robusta

Identification: To 30 cm. Head, body and fins irregularly mottled with dark brown, olive-brown and yellowish-tan. Ridges on head spiny; dorsal fin with 15 strong spines.

Habitat and Range: Estuaries and lower reaches of slow flowing, freshwater streams, among aquatic plants, rocks, logs or roots. Often encountered at foot of dams and weirs. Cape York, Qld, to Clyde R., NSW.

Notes: Venomous fin spines can cause painful wounds. Spends most of lifecycle in freshwater, descends to brackish water to breed.

QM, Bruce Cowell

Barramundi
Lates calcarifer

Identification: To about 180 cm, common at 100 cm. Head pointed, profile of head to dorsal fin slopes steeply giving humped appearance; deep notch between dorsal fins; mouth large, jaws extending beyond vertical through eye; caudal fin rounded. Juveniles with white stripe along top of head from snout tip to dorsal fin.

Habitat and Range: Bays, estuaries, creeks, rivers and lagoons. Pilbara region, WA, to Noosa R., Qld; Persian Gulf to China.

Notes: Renowned for edible and angling qualities. Cultured for stocking impoundments. Smaller specimens all male, change to female with growth. Breeds in estuaries.

QM, Bruce Cowell

QM, Bruce Cowell

Olive Perchlet
Ambassis agassizii

Other Name: Agassiz's Glassfish

Identification: To 8 cm. Pale yellowish-silver to semi-transparent, back and upper sides often darker olive-brown. Profile of head roundish. Specimens in north Qld have tall dorsal fins and high lateral scale counts.

Habitat and Range: Common in fresh-water creeks, rivers, lagoons and impoundments, often associated with beds of aquatic plants. Coastal drainages from Cairns, Qld, to Lake Hiawatha, NSW and Murray–Darling Basin; also reported from Cooktown–Lakefield region, Qld.

Similar Species: Sailfin Glassfish (*A. agrammus*), longer dorsal spine; head and nape profile straight.

QM, Bruce Cowell

Long-spined Glassfish
Ambassis interruptus

Identification: To about 8.5 cm. Body short and deep; opaque silver to semi-transparent; anal and ventral fins with tiny, but distinct white tips. Lower profile of head angular in adults; eye large; longest dorsal spine tall and strong, usually more than one-third standard length.

Habitat and Range: Upper estuary and lower reaches of flowing freshwater creeks and rivers. Common only in Wet Tropics. Patchy distribution, Fitzroy R., WA, to Townsville, Qld; Indonesia to Philippines, New Caledonia.

QM, Bruce Cowell

Reticulated Glassfish
Ambassis macleayi

Identification: To about 10 cm. Body and caudal fin base deep. Scales usually with black edges, forming net-like pattern; pectoral fin base usually blackish.

Habitat and Range: Well-vegetated lagoons and slow flowing streams. Patchy distribution, Carson R., WA, Gulf of Carpentaria drainages, Olive R., Cape York, Qld; southern New Guinea. On east coast known only from Barron R., Qld.

Riverine Glassfish
Ambassis miops

Identification: To about 9 cm. Eye large; dorsal fin membrane blackish between second and third spines; second dorsal fin spine short and weak, shorter than third; lateral line scale row uninterrupted to tail.

Habitat and Range: Upper estuary and lower to middle reaches of strongly flowing freshwater creeks and rivers. Cape Melville to Hinchinbrook I., Qld; south Pacific to Indonesia.

QM, Bruce Cowell

Vachel's Glassfish
Ambassis vachelii

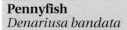

Identification: To 7.5 cm. Upper edge of eye with 3–5 spiny serrations at rear.

Habitat and Range: Bays, coastal islands, estuaries and lower freshwater reaches of rivers. Most widespread and abundant glassfish species in sheltered waters, mangrove creeks and estuaries. Shark Bay, WA, to Yeppoon, Qld; Indonesia.

QM, Bruce Cowell

Pennyfish
Denariusa bandata

Identification: To about 5 cm, common at 3.5 cm. Body robust; semi-transparent; about 6 vertical dark bars, faint in some individuals. Most body scales have dark edges, forming net-like pattern; rear edge of first dorsal fin usually black.

Habitat and Range: Slow flowing, freshwater creeks, lagoons and swamps with dense aquatic vegetation. Patchy distribution, East Alligator R., NT, to Tully, Qld; southern New Guinea.

Gunther Schmida

QM, Bruce Cowell

Flag-tailed Grunter
Amniataba caudavittatus

Identification: To about 30 cm. Head and body silvery with numerous, dark rusty-brown flecks. Fins yellowish; caudal with irregular, dark markings at base and diagonal black blotch near tip of each lobe.

Habitat and Range: Bays and estuaries to lower freshwater reaches. Cape Leeuwin, WA, to Yeppoon, Qld; southern New Guinea.

Notes: Attractive, but pugnacious aquarium fish.

QM, Bruce Cowell

Barred Grunter
Amniataba percoides

Identification: To about 24 cm. Light yellowish-silver to dark silver-grey; 5 or 6 conspicuous vertical black bars, faint in large specimens; scattered black spots on head and body between bars. Caudal fin with a few dots and dashes in centre, lower lobe black edged.

Habitat and Range: Widespread in freshwater creeks, rivers and impoundments. Lake Eacham and Barron R. systems only in Wet Tropics. Ashburton R., WA, to Burnett R., Qld; inland drainages of Lake Eyre and Finke R.

Notes: Hardy, attractive fish but aggressive; unsuitable for community aquaria.

Adult, QM, Bruce Cowell

Juvenile, QM, Bruce Cowell

Sooty Grunter
Hephaestus fuliginosus

Identification: To about 50 cm. Dark silver-grey, grey-brown or bronze; occasionally with large, irregular gold patches and large lips. Mouth large; jaws with conical, immovable teeth. Juveniles with black blotches on rear of dorsal and anal fins.

Habitat and Range: Prefers deep clear pools in flowing creeks and rivers, but inhabits wide range of conditions. Coastal freshwater streams; Daly R., NT, to Pioneer R., Qld; southern New Guinea.

Notes: Widely stocked in impoundments. Popular edible angling fish.

Tully River Grunter
Hephaestus tulliensis

Identification: To about 40 cm. Dark olive-grey, grey-brown to almost black with dark flecks on body. Small head, mouth and teeth; large eye; short snout; long fins.

Habitat and Range: Clear flowing freshwater creeks and rivers. Daintree R. to Murray R. (near Cardwell), Qld. Reportedly translocated to Tinaroo Dam and Barron R.

Similar Species: Sooty Grunter, (see p. 148).

QM, Bruce Cowell

Spangled Perch
Leiopotherapon unicolor

Identification: To 30 cm, common at 18 cm. Silvery; numerous small rusty-brown spots, faint or absent in specimens from turbid water; fins clear or slightly dusky. Juveniles, caudal fin with black lower edge. Teeth conical and immovable.

Habitat and Range: Freshwater coastal and inland drainages. Northern Australia from Murchison R., WA, to Condoblin on Murray–Darling and Hunter R., NSW. In Wet Tropics, known only from Barron R. system, Qld.

Notes: Hardy, aggressive; breeds well in dams, translocated widely.

Gunther Schmida

Silver Grunter
Mesopristes argenteus

Identification: To about 35 cm. Silver to silvery slate-grey. Snout broadly pointed; dorsal spines long, more than half length of head. Juveniles yellowish-silver with several black stripes along body.

Habitat and Range: Upper estuaries and lower reaches of freshwater streams. Cape York to Hinchinbrook I., Qld; south-west Pacific to Philippines and Indonesia.

Notes: Often taken by anglers using freshwater shrimps. Large numbers at Lake Placid Reserve on Barron R.

Adult, QM, Bruce Cowell

Juvenile, QM, Bruce Cowell

Gunther Schmida

Small-Headed Grunter
Scortum parviceps

Identification: To about 40 cm. Grey-brown to bronze; small, dark brown flecks on centres of scales; pearly-white band from snout to below eye; often 1 or 2 irregular black blotches on sides. Head and mouth small; teeth small, numerous, close-set, movable, with tips flattened.

Habitat and Range: Deeper holes, often below rapids. Upper Burdekin R., Qld.

Notes: Locally referred to as Greenhide Jack due to tough flesh.

QM, Bruce Cowell

Crescent Perch
Terapon jarbua

Identification: To 32 cm. Three curved black stripes on sides; black blotch on first dorsal fin; second dorsal and caudal fins with black bars or stripes. Scales very small, 13 to 17 above lateral line; operculum with enlarged spines.

Habitat and Range: Bays, estuaries and tidal freshwater reaches. Carnarvon, WA, to Sydney, NSW; widespread tropical Indo-west Pacific.

Notes: Common on beaches and near river mouths, ventures into freshwater. Attractive, but pugnacious in aquaria.

DPI Walkamin

Spotted Flagtail
Kuhlia marginata

Identification: To about 35 cm. Body silvery with rows of small dark spots on upper sides; dorsal fin with black edge; anal fin with red edge; caudal fin with black edge, but no dark blotches on lobes.

Habitat and Range: Upper estuary to clear rainforest streams. Bloomfield R. to Russell R., Qld; western Pacific, to Japan and New Guinea.

Notes: Found among larger numbers of Jungle Perch (see p. 151). Possibly more widespread in eastern streams of Cape York.

Jungle Perch
Kuhlia rupestris

Identification: To 50 cm, common at 25 cm. Light greenish-silver speckled with numerous diffuse, rusty-brown spots; conspicuous black blotch near tip of each caudal lobe.

Habitat and Range: Upper estuaries and clear flowing freshwater creeks and rivers. Patchy distribution, mainly in coastal rainforest streams. Tip of Cape York to Maroochy R., Qld, rare south of Cape Hillsborough; tropical Indo-west Pacific.

Notes: Popular fish for catch and release. Numbers and range have reportedly diminished significantly due to habitat alteration. Spawns in estuarine conditions.

QM, Bruce Cowell

Mangrove Cardinalfish
Apogon hyalosoma

Other Name: Mangrove Gobbleguts

Identification: To about 17 cm. Robust with large eyes, mouth and belly; caudal fin rounded with conspicuous black spot at centre of base.

Habitat and Range: Estuaries and lower reaches of freshwater rivers and creeks. Cape York to Hinchinbrook I., Qld; tropical Indo-west Pacific.

Notes: Most common among roots and fallen branches in small mangrove creeks; hunts shrimps and small fishes. Capable of swallowing large prey, causing obvious distension of stomach.

QM, Bruce Cowell

Mouth Almighty
Glossamia aprion

Identification: To about 24 cm, common at 8 cm. Body deep; mouth large; greenish-bronze with pale mottling and dark brown irregular blotches, some forming bands.

Habitat and Range: Freshwater creeks, rivers and impoundments, usually among aquatic plants. Fitzroy R., WA, to Clarence River, NSW; southern New Guinea.

Notes: Predatory mouthbrooder. Introduction to Lake Eacham probably led to elimination of Lake Eacham Rainbowfish (see p. 142).

QM, Bruce Cowell

QM, Bruce Cowell

Sand Whiting
Sillago ciliata

Identification: To 47 cm, common to 30 cm. Anal and ventral fins yellow; dusky blotch on pectoral fin base; second dorsal fin rays 17–19. Juveniles have dark blotches, fading with age, on back and sides.

Habitat and Range: Beaches, sandbars, bays and estuaries. Cape York, Qld, to Lakes Entrance, Vic., eastern Tas.

Notes: Edible fish targeted on light gear using worms, yabbies and soldier crabs.

QM, Bruce Cowell

Long-nosed Whiting
Sillago sihama

Identification: To 32 cm, common at 20 cm. Yellowish-silver to bronze, usually with silver stripe along middle of sides; no dark markings on body or pectoral fin base, second dorsal fin rays 21–24.

Habitat and Range: Coastal waters, estuaries and lower tidal freshwater reaches. Broome, WA, to Maroochy R., Qld; tropical Indo-west Pacific.

Notes: Usually found along beaches and sandbanks, often in tidal freshwaters.

QM, Bruce Cowell

Big-eye Trevally
Caranx sexfasciatus

Identification: To 78 cm. Back greenish to bronze, sides silver; small juveniles with 5–6 dark bands across body; soft dorsal and anal fin lobes white tipped; rear of lateral line armed with spiny scutes; chest covered with small scales.

Habitat and Range: Offshore reefs, bays, estuaries and lower freshwater reaches of rivers. Margaret R., WA, to Sydney, NSW; widespread tropical Indo-Pacific.

Notes: Juveniles and small adults commonly enter freshwater. Often takes lures intended for Barramundi.

Barred Ponyfish
Leiognathus equulus

Identification: To 25 cm, common at 10 cm. Silvery; upper sides with numerous, close-set, faint vertical lines; ventral fins and front tip of anal fin orange-yellow. Mouth small, protractible into downward directed tube; scales minute.

Habitat and Range: Bays, estuaries and lower freshwater reaches of rivers. Broome, WA, to Calliope R., Qld; tropical Indo-Pacific.

Notes: Large specimens often found well into freshwater in Daintree and other rivers of Wet Tropics.

QM, Bruce Cowell

Mangrove Jack
Lutjanus argentimaculatus

Identification: To 120 cm. Head and body red to greyish-brown; scales with vague dark centres. Juveniles with narrow, vertical white bars, blue line below eye and darker markings on dorsal, anal and ventral fins. Head and mouth large; outer row of teeth enlarged, forming sharp canines.

Habitat and Range: Rocky and coral reefs, estuaries and all but uppermost reaches of coastal rivers. Shark Bay, WA, to Lake Illawarra, NSW; tropical Indo-west Pacific.

Notes: Edible angling species. Specimens to about 2 kg often taken in freshwater. Voracious predator feeding on crustaceans, fishes, frogs and insects.

Adult, QM, Bruce Cowell

Juvenile, QM, Bruce Cowell

Moses Perch
Lutjanus russelli

Identification: To 45 cm, common at 25 cm. Large, black, oval spot on upper sides situated mainly above lateral line. Juveniles with 4 to 7 broad orange to bronze stripes on sides, fading and narrowing with age.

Habitat and Range: Offshore and coastal reefs and estuaries. Young specimens common in mangrove-lined estuaries and coastal reefs; large fish usually occupy deeper offshore reefs. Shark Bay, WA, to Sydney, NSW; tropical Indo-west Pacific.

QM, Bruce Cowell

QM, Bruce Cowell

Thread-finned Silverbiddy
Gerres filamentosus

Identification: To about 30 cm, common at 18 cm. Brilliant silver with about 10 vertical dark bars, often broken into rows of spots. Mouth small, protractible into downward directed tube; scales small to moderate in size, but conspicuous.

Habitat and Range: Coastal waters, estuaries and lower freshwater reaches, on sandy or muddy bottom. Shark Bay, WA, to Moreton Bay, Qld; tropical Indo-west Pacific.

Notes: Common in local estuaries, also in freshwater rivers.

Juvenile, QM, Bruce Cowell

Brown Sweetlips
Plectorhinchus gibbosus

Identification: To 75 cm. Dark grey-brown to charcoal-grey; adults with large lips; dorsal spines 14, rarely 13. Juveniles reddish-brown with caudal fin transparent to whitish.

Habitat and Range: Rocky reefs and estuaries. Juveniles often found well upstream in estuaries, among mangroves or seagrass beds. Point Quobba, WA, to Sydney, NSW; tropical Indo-west Pacific.

QM, Bruce Cowell

Barred Grunter Bream
Pomadasys kaakan

Other Name: Spotted Javelinfish

Identification: To 66 cm. Silver, tinted with bronze; 7–9 regular, dark vertical bars on upper body, bars solid in smaller specimens, consisting of rows of spots or occasionally almost completely faded in large adults; no dark blotch on operculum or dorsal fin.

Habitat and Range: Coastal reefs, bays and estuaries to lower tidal freshwater reaches. Shark Bay, WA, to Moreton Bay, Qld; tropical Indo-west Pacific.

Notes: Edible angling fish. When captured, emits grunting sound by grinding strong pharangeal plates in throat, used to crush molluscs and small crabs.

Yellow-finned Bream
Acanthopagrus australis

Identification: To 66 cm, common at 35 cm. Silvery; back and upper sides tinted olive-green or brassy; often with vague horizontal streaks. Ventral, pectoral and anal fins bright yellow; black spot at upper base of pectoral fin; second anal spine not greatly enlarged.

Habitat and Range: Coastal waters, estuaries and lower freshwater reaches. Cairns, Qld, to Gippsland Lakes, Vic.

Notes: Edible angling fish. Better known from southern waters, but often occurs in schools with Pikey Bream (see below).

QM, Bruce Cowell

Pikey Bream
Acanthopagrus berda

Identification: To 56 cm. Head and body dusky silver to charcoal-grey; second anal spine enlarged.

Habitat and Range: Coastal waters, estuaries and lower freshwater reaches. In mangrove creeks, also penetrates into freshwater. Northern WA to Caloundra, Qld, uncommon south of Yeppoon; tropical Indo-west Pacific.

Notes: Edible angling fish.

QM, Bruce Cowell

Seven-spot Archerfish
Toxotes chatareus

Identification: To about 45 cm, common at 18 cm. Single dorsal fin with 5 spines, situated at rear of back; 6 or 7 irregular black spots or vertically elongated black blotches on sides.

Habitat and Range: Estuaries, freshwater rivers and creeks, well into upper reaches. Coastal rivers, Derby, WA, to Proserpine, Qld; India to northern Australia.

Notes: Renowned for ability to dislodge insects from overhanging vegetation by accurately squirting jets of water through opposing grooves in roof of mouth and tongue. Small groups often seen at surface beneath shading branches.

QM, Bruce Cowell

QM, Bruce Cowell

Mangrove Archerfish
Toxotes jaculatrix

Identification: To 20 cm. Single dorsal fin with 4 or 5 spines, situated at rear of back; 4 or 5 solid, wedge-like black bars on upper sides. Smaller fish have lemon-yellow hue above.

Habitat and Range: Estuaries and tidal freshwater reaches, near mangroves. Derby, WA, to Hinchinbrook I., Qld; India to western Pacific.

Juvenile, QM, Bruce Cowell

Diamondfish
Monodactylus argenteus

Identification: To about 28 cm. Silvery, diamond-shaped body with small scales; dorsal and anal fins black-tipped; vertical black bars through eye and rear of operculum, fade with age. Small juveniles sooty-grey to black.

Habitat and Range: Reefs, coastal waters, estuaries and lower freshwater reaches. Dampier, WA, to Jervis Bay, NSW; tropical Indo-west Pacific.

Notes: Juveniles often enter freshwater, prized by aquarists.

QM, Bruce Cowell

Juvenile, QM, Bruce Cowell

Striped Scat
Selenotoca multifasciata

Identification: To 41 cm. Silvery with series of vertical black bars; several faint horizontal lines low on sides; 12 dorsal spines. Juveniles with vertical bars continued below as rows of spots.

Habitat and Range: Bays, estuaries and lower freshwater reaches. Shark Bay, WA, to Sydney, NSW; New Caledonia to New Guinea.

Notes: Adults in harbours and near river mouths; juveniles in small shoals, frequently in freshwater. Numerous sharp, venomous spines can cause painful wounds.

Spotted Scat
Scatophagus argus

Identification: To 38 cm. Light greenish-brown to dark chocolate-brown, with numerous large black spots in vertical rows; 11 dorsal spines. Juvenile with pale vertical bands across body, upper part of bands often bright crimson-red.

Habitat and Range: Estuaries and lower freshwater reaches. Adults usually in mangrove creeks; juveniles commonly enter freshwater. Dampier, WA, to Eden, NSW; tropical Indo-west Pacific.

Notes: Small specimens prized by aquarists. Fin spines venomous.

Adult, QM, Bruce Cowell

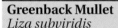
Juvenile, QM, Bruce Cowell

Greenback Mullet
Liza subviridis

Identification: To 38 cm. Hind tip of upper jaw bone visibly exposed, immediately behind and below rear corner of mouth; caudal fin slightly forked.

Habitat and Range: Bays, estuaries and tidal freshwater reaches. Exmouth Gulf, WA, to Clarence R., NSW; tropical Indo-west Pacific.

Notes: Most common mullet in northern Australia.

QM, Bruce Cowell

Diamond-scaled Mullet
Liza vaigiensis

Identification: To 55 cm. Caudal fin yellowish, square-cut; scales large, with dark edges giving net-like pattern; pectoral fins dusky to black; ventral and anal fins bright yellow in juveniles, whitish in adults.

Habitat and Range: Islands, bays and estuaries. Exmouth Gulf, WA, to Hervey Bay, Qld; tropical Indo-west Pacific.

Notes: Netted in shallow tropical waters. Young fish with black pectorals, often found in tidal rock pools.

Juveniles, QM, Bruce Cowell

QM, Bruce Cowell

Sea Mullet
Mugil cephalus

Identification: To 90 cm. Caudal fin forked; pectoral fins short; fins semi-transparent to dusky, not yellowish; anal fin soft rays 8; rear tip of upper jaw not exposed when mouth is closed.

Habitat and Range: Coastal waters, estuaries, freshwater rivers and creeks, extending to upper reaches. Mainland Australia, all river systems, uncommon north of Townsville, Qld; worldwide.

Notes: Harvested by nets in subtropical and temperate Australia, cultured in many countries. Lives in freshwater for long periods, but must return to sea to spawn.

QM, Bruce Cowell

Crimson-tipped Flathead Gudgeon *Butis butis*

Identification: To 18 cm. Light greyish-brown to almost black; often crimson edges to dorsal, anal and upper caudal fins; pectorals with red-edged black spot at base. Ventral fins not joined at base; head broadly flattened; eyes widely separated; mouth large, just reaching level of eye.

Habitat and Range: Estuaries and lower freshwater reaches of rivers and creeks. Common in mangrove creeks on roots and fallen branches where it rests upside down. Shark Bay, WA, to Tweed R., NSW; tropical Indo-west Pacific.

QM, Bruce Cowell

Brown Cheek-spine Gudgeon
Eleotris fusca

Identification: To 18 cm, common at 10 cm. Grey-brown to almost black; numerous fine, dark horizontal lines along scale rows; fins finely speckled, dorsal fins with faint, irregular brown streaks. Lower rear angle of cheek with strong downward curved spine, usually obscured by skin.

Habitat and Range: Lower freshwater reaches of rivers and creeks. Patchy distribution, Silver Plains (Cape York) to Johnstone R., Qld; tropical Indo-west Pacific.

Ebony Cheek-spine Gudgeon
Eleotris melanosoma

Identification: To 17 cm, common to 8 cm. Chocolate-brown to black, with fine horizontal lines along scale rows; fins speckled, small spots on dorsal fins forming horizontal rows. Lower rear angle of cheek with downward curved spine, obscured by skin.

Habitat and Range: Lower freshwater reaches of rivers and creeks. Cape York to Moreton Bay, Qld; common in Wet Tropics, rare south of Herbert R.

Juvenile, QM, Bruce Cowell

Empirefish
Hypseleotris compressus

Other Name: Carp Gudgeon

Identification: To 11 cm. Breeding male orange-red on lower sides and belly; dorsal and anal fins red with black band near edge; second dorsal fin with pale spots near base. Female and juveniles olive-brown with mostly transparent fins. Second dorsal rays 9–10.

Habitat and Range: Upper brackish reaches of estuaries and throughout almost all coastal freshwater systems. Murchison R., WA, to Towamba R., NSW; southern New Guinea.

Similar Species: Firetail Gudgeon (*H. galii*), from southern Qld, translocated into Tinaroo Dam. Another undescribed species known as far north as Tully.

QM, Bruce Cowell

Purple-spotted Gudgeon
Mogurnda adspersa

Identification: To 13 cm. Broad, diffuse, bluish band along sides, band overlaid with tan, orange and purple spots. Dorsal and anal fins dusky with tan and red spots; dorsal fins with yellow or orange edges.

Habitat and Range: Freshwater rivers, creeks, gullies and impoundments. Coastal drainages, Stewart R. (Cape York), Qld, to Clarence R., NSW, Murray-Darling Basin.

Similar Species: Northern Trout Gudgeon (*M. mogurnda*), to 17.5 cm with sparse rusty-brown spots on sides. Fitzroy R., WA, to Herbert R., Qld.

QM, Bruce Cowell

M. mogurnda, QM, Bruce Cowell

QM, Bruce Cowell

Snakehead Gudgeon
Ophieleotris aporos

Other Name: Mud Cod.

Identification: To about 40 cm. Head wedge-shaped, flattened. Dark greenish-brown, often with vague bands. Several dark reddish-brown lines radiating across cheek and operculum from eye. Bright reddish-orange variety also in area.

Habitat and Range: Lower reaches of coastal freshwater rivers, creeks and swamps, in shaded areas. Cape York to Proserpine, Qld; tropical Indo-west Pacific.

Juvenile, QM, Bruce Cowell

Spangled Gudgeon
Ophiocara porocephala

Identification: To 32 cm. Dark brown to black with scattered white or yellow spots on body; anal and ventral fins dusky yellowish, second dorsal and caudal fins with white or yellow spots and yellowish edges. Smaller specimens with narrow creamy-white saddles at front and rear of second dorsal fin, extending to lower sides.

Habitat and Range: Estuaries and lower freshwater reaches of rivers and creeks. Cairns to Maryborough, Qld; tropical Indo-west Pacific.

QM, Bruce Cowell

O. nullipora, Gunther Schmida

Aru Gudgeon
Oxyeleotris aruensis

Identification: To about 6.5 cm. Series of irregular, dusky curved bars on sides; black blotches above pectoral fin base and on upper base of caudal fin. Second dorsal rays 13–15; pectoral rays 13–16.

Habitat and Range: Small, flowing freshwater streams. Jardine R. (Cape York), and Mulgrave R. to Murray R., Qld; southern New Guinea.

Notes: Differs from Cape York and New Guinea specimens; may be distinct species.

Similar Species: Poreless Gudgeon (*O. nullipora*), only 4 cm; Gulf of Carpentaria drainages and Cape Flattery south to Tully, Qld.

Coastal Sleepy Cod
Oxyeleotris gyrinoides

Identification: To 32 cm. Brown with thin darker lines along scale rows; lips, cheeks and underside of head with pale bars and spots; dark lines radiating between and from rear of eyes; all fins strikingly speckled. Juveniles abruptly pale on back with broad black blotch across caudal fin. Second dorsal rays 9; pectoral rays 18–19.

Habitat and Range: Clear, flowing, coastal freshwater creeks and rivers. Patchy distribution, Cape York, to Herbert R., Qld; Sri Lanka to Philippines.

QM, Bruce Cowell

Sleepy Cod
Oxyeleotris lineolatus

Identification: To 40 cm. Head and body grey-brown to dark chocolate-brown without obvious markings; dorsal and caudal fins spotted; anal, pectoral and ventral fins unspotted, dusky or clear to whitish. Juveniles abruptly pale creamish-tan above. Second dorsal fin rays 9–10; pectoral rays 17–18.

Habitat and Range: Slow flowing or still freshwater creeks, rivers, lagoons and impoundments, usually near rocks, logs or aquatic plants. Tinaroo Dam in TNQ; Ord R., WA, to Fitzroy R., Qld; southern New Guinea.

Large juvenile, Gunther Schmida

Western Sleepy Cod
Oxyeleotris selheimi

Identification: To 48 cm. Head and body dark brown, marbled with pale tan; narrow, whitish, zig-zag band along sides at level of lower pectoral fin base; all fins spotted. Juveniles pale creamish-tan on back. Second dorsal fin rays 10; pectoral rays 18.

Habitat and Range: Freshwater rivers, creeks and impoundments. Kimberley region, WA, to Cape York, Qld. In TNQ, Barron, Annan and Normanby Rs. Translocated from Mitchell R., Qld, during 1950s.

QM, Bruce Cowell

Adult, QM, Bruce Cowell

Juvenile, QM, Bruce Cowell

Roman Nose Goby
Awaous acritosus

Identification: To about 18 cm. Light brown to creamy-white, irregular brown blotches on back, row of 8–10 dusky to black blotches on side. Mouth slightly underslung, especially in large specimens; ventrals joined, forming single fin.

Habitat and Range: Buries to eye level in clear, flowing, coastal freshwater rivers and creeks with sandy substrate. Pascoe R. to Pioneer R., Qld, uncommon south of Herbert R.; southern New Guinea.

QM, Bruce Cowell

Puntang Goby
Exyrias puntang

Identification: To 16 cm. Olive-brown above with numerous bluish-silver spots on sides; fins with rows of conspicuous reddish-brown to black spots. Caudal fin longer than head, rounded to bluntly pointed; first dorsal fin with anterior rays elongated in males.

Habitat and Range: Coastal lagoons, estuaries and lower reaches of freshwater streams. Patchy, Cape York to Proserpine, Qld; tropical western Pacific to Sri Lanka.

QM, Bruce Cowell

Chin-barbel Flathead Goby
Glossogobius bicirrhosus

Identification: To about 7.5 cm. Greenish-brown to semi-transparent; dark edges to scales; several brown blotches on back; 4–5 dusky blotches along side. Series of fine barbels on chin below lower lip.

Habitat and Range: Estuarine, also enters lower reaches of freshwater creeks. Patchy, Cape York to Townsville, Qld; tropical western Pacific to Indonesia.

Mangrove Flathead Goby
Glossogobius biocellatus

Identification: To about 10 cm. Body mottled dark brown to black, thin dusky lines along sides; caudal fin speckled above, lower edge with black bars; anal and ventral fins dusky to black. Ventral fins joined, forming single fin.

Habitat and Range: Estuaries and lower freshwater reaches of rivers and creeks, usually near mangroves. Cape York to Southport, Qld; tropical Indo-west Pacific.

QM, Bruce Cowell

Celebes Flathead Goby
Glossogobius celebius

Identification: To about 14 cm. Several indistinct dark saddles across back and 5 rectangular black blotches along middle of sides. Profile of snout broadly rounded.

Habitat and Range: Lower freshwater reaches of clear flowing coastal rivers and creeks. Pascoe R. to Hinchinbrook I., Qld; tropical western Pacific to Indonesia.

QM, Bruce Cowell

Circumspect Flathead Goby
Glossogobius circumspectus

Identification: To 12 cm. Diffuse dark blotches along middle of sides; no obvious cross-bands; ventral and anal fins semi-transparent.

Habitat and Range: Estuaries and tidal freshwater reaches. Broome, WA, to Burnett R., Qld; tropical western Pacific.

QM, Bruce Cowell

Common Flathead Goby
Glossogobius giurus

Identification: To 25 cm. Five to six broad, diffuse bands across back; 5 round to squarish black blotches along middle of sides. Snout flattish, bump behind upper lip.

Habitat and Range: Freshwater rivers and creeks, from lower tidal waters to upper reaches. Fortesque R., WA, to Fitzroy R., Qld; widespread tropical Indo-west Pacific.

GR Allen

Gunther Schmida

Mulgrave Goby
Glossogobius sp.

Identification: To 8 cm. Eight or nine irregular black blotches on sides; first dorsal fin speckled with distinct black spot near rear base; second dorsal fin with rows of black dots on lower half; ventral and anal fins dusky to black. Single ventral fin.

Habitat and Range: Clear flowing, coastal freshwater streams with gravelly substrate. Restricted to Russell–Mulgrave R. drainage and several creeks near Mossman, Qld.

QM, Bruce Cowell

Netted-cheek Goby
Mugilogobius notospilus

Identification: To about 4 cm. Head and snout short, rounded; cheeks bulbous, marked with patchwork of yellow on dark grey-brown; usually 2 small black spots on caudal fin base.

Habitat and Range: Flowing, coastal freshwater streams. Cooktown to Hinchinbrook I., Qld; Indonesia to New Guinea.

QM, Bruce Cowell

Speckled Goby
Redigobius bikolanus

Identification: To 4 cm. Four short black bars on lower body between origin of anal fin and caudal fin base; two black spots on caudal fin base. Mature male with enlarged head and mouth.

Habitat and Range: Estuaries and lower freshwater reaches of rivers and creeks. Pascoe R. to Brisbane, Qld; tropical western Pacific.

Black-bar Goby
Redigobius baleatus

Identification: To 4 cm. Two conspicuous black bars, through centre of first dorsal fin to belly and from eye diagonally across operculum. Mature male, first dorsal fin bright yellow.

Habitat and Range: Estuaries and lower tidal freshwater reaches of rivers and creeks. Cape York to Burdekin R., Qld; Sri Lanka to Philippines.

QM, Bruce Cowell

Spot-fin Goby
Redigobius chrysozona

Identification: To 4 cm. Light grey-brown with sparse darker mottlings; short dusky bar from middle of eye to rear of mouth. First dorsal fin with jet black spot in centre, often surrounded by yellow or orange in male.

Habitat and Range: Upper estuaries and lower freshwater reaches of rivers and creeks. Pascoe R., to Hinchinbrook I., Qld; Indonesia to Philippines.

GR Allen

Scaleless Goby
Schismatogobius sp.

Identification: To 5 cm. Head and body scaleless; short blunt snout. Three dark brown bands across back and upper sides; four irregular dark blotches along middle of sides adjacent to corners of upper bands; dorsal, caudal and pectoral fins speckled.

Habitat and Range: Clear, flowing, freshwater creeks and rivers on gravelly substrate. Several streams between Endeavour R., and Liverpool Ck. (Tully), Qld.

Gunther Schmida

QM, Bruce Cowell

Stiphodon allen, GR Allen

Blunt-nose Goby
Sicyopterus sp.

Identification: To at least 14 cm. Head and body cylindrical; dark reddish-brown back and sides; creamish-white belly. Snout bluntly rounded; mouth large, situated low on head; eyes small and broadly separated; scales small.

Habitat and Range: Clear, fast flowing freshwater streams. Known only from Barron, Daintree and Bloomfield Rs, Qld, but probably more widespread in Wet Tropics.

Similar Species: Neon Goby (*Stiphodon allen*), smaller, known only from specimens taken in pebbly riffles of Harvey Ck and Mulgrave R., Qld.

Teardrop Goby
Stenogobius psilosinionus

Identification: To 10 cm. Snout short, head roundish; distinct black bar below eye. About 6 or 7 faint dark bars on body, extending to belly. Middle of back unscaled or with naked patches.

Habitat and Range: Estuaries and lower freshwater reaches of coastal streams. Cairns to Hinchinbrook I., Qld; southern New Guinea.

QM, Bruce Cowell

Shadow Goby
Yongeichthys nebulosus

Identification: To 18 cm. Head and back to dorsal fin scaleless; body scales large; 3 or 4 large dark brown to black blotches on sides; dorsal and caudal fins have small brown spots.

Habitat and Range: Coastal waters, bays and estuaries, occasionally in tidal freshwater reaches. Shark Bay, WA, to Townsville, Qld; tropical Indo-west Pacific.

QM, Bruce Cowell

Common Mudskipper
Periophthalmus argentilineatus

Identification: To 9.5 cm. Eyes protruding; dorsal fins separate, both with black band near outer edge. First dorsal fin with 11–16 rays and numerous small white spots below black band; membrane uniting ventral fins much reduced or absent.

Habitat and Range: Muddy shorelines of bays, estuaries and tidal freshwater reaches. Carnarvon, WA, to Hervey Bay, Qld; tropical Indo-west Pacific.

Notes: Common on mangrove-lined, mudbanks exposed at low tide. Occasionally on logs, branches and rocks in lower reaches of freshwater streams. Retreats to safety of water when threatened.

QM, Bruce Cowell

Spotted Tongue Sole
Paraplagusia bilineata

Identification: To 40 cm. Hook-like extension to upper jaw extending to rear edge of eye; upper edge of lower jaw fringed with row of branched tentacles; 'eyed' side with 3 lateral lines and numerous, small, irregular-oval pale blotches.

Habitat and Range: Coastal waters and estuaries, on silty sand or muddy substrate. Geraldton, WA, to northern NSW; tropical Indo-west Pacific.

Notes: Larger specimens on trawl grounds; juveniles common on tidal flats and beaches. Capable of burying rapidly into soft bottoms, leaving only eyes protruding.

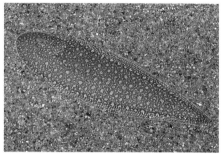
QM, Bruce Cowell

Milk-spotted Toadfish
Chelonodon patoca

Identification: To 38 cm, common at 18 cm. Skin with dense patches of minute spines on back and belly; nasal opening with 2 short flaps; greyish to greenish-brown with numerous close-set white spots; 4 broad dusky bands across back.

Habitat and Range: Bays and estuaries, occasionally entering tidal freshwater reaches. Onslow, WA, to Maroochy River, Qld; tropical Indo-west Pacific.

Notes: Flesh poisonous. Usually found on shallow, muddy tidal flats.

QM, Bruce Cowell

Introduced Fishes

The following four introduced species are all live-bearing fishes, widespread between Brisbane and Cairns.

Male, QM, Bruce Cowell

Mosquitofish
Gambusia holbrooki

Identification: Males to 3.5 cm, females to 6 cm. Head flattened above; single dorsal fin; tail finely speckled. Male with anal fin modified to form copulatory organ. Mature female with rear part of abdomen dark.

Notes: Native to central America.

Male, QM, Bruce Cowell

Guppy
Poecilia reticulata

Identification: Male to 3 cm, female to 5.5 cm. Fins clear, without speckling. Male usually has brightly coloured blotches and several blackish spots on body and caudal fin base. Female plain with net-like pattern on scales. Many aquarium-bred varieties with brighter colours and fancy fins.

Notes: Native to north-western South America.

QM, Bruce Cowell

Swordtail
Xiphophorus helleri

Identification: To about 8.5 cm. Dark line along lower body between rear of anal fin base and caudal fin. Male with copulatory organ, lower rays of caudal fin produced to form a long black-edged 'sword'. Aquarium-bred varieties usually red; feral specimens mostly green with several reddish-brown lines along sides.

Notes: Native to Central America.

QM, Bruce Cowell

Platy
Xiphophorus maculatus

Identification: To 6.5 cm. Male with copulatory organ, but sexes similar. No dark line on lower body as in Swordtail (see above). Aquarium-bred fish red, orange, yellow or black speckled; feral specimens usually greenish-brown, often with large black blotch near caudal fin base.

Notes: Native to Central America.

Tilapia
Oreochromis mossambica

Other Name: Mozambique Mouthbrooder

Identification: To about 40 cm, common at 25 cm. Single nostril each side of snout; dorsal spines 15–17, dorsal rays 10–13; teeth in fine, brushlike band. Adult, silvery-olive to dark grey-brown, mottled with dusky flecks. Juvenile, silver-grey with dusky bars, black spot at front of soft dorsal fin base and 3–4 dark spots on sides. Mature male, blackish, lower half of head light grey; enlarged jaws; head profile concave at snout; dorsal and caudal fins with red edges.

Habitat and Range: Slow flowing or still freshwater to brackish rivers, creeks, drains, lagoons and impoundments. Gascoyne R., WA, Cairns, Innisfail, Townsville and Brisbane areas, Qld. Native to south-east Africa.

Notes: Declared noxious under *Fisheries Act*. Male builds nest in coarse, sandy substrate. Female mouthbroods eggs, larvae and small fry. Should never be maintained, or released into waterways.

Adult male, QM

Large juvenile, QM, Bruce Cowell

Niger Cichlid
Tilapia mariae

Identification: To 30 cm. Single nostril each side of snout; dorsal spines 15–16, dorsal rays 12–15; teeth fine, in several rows. Adult, greenish-yellow to brown with 5–6 conspicuous black spots along sides, usually a dark blotch on operculum. Spots may vary in number and intensity according to mood. Juvenile, up to 8 or 9 vertical black bars on head and body, dusky spot at base of anterior, soft dorsal rays.

Habitat and Range: Brackish upper estuaries and freshwater rivers, creeks and lagoons. Cairns and Johnstone R., Qld. Native to west Africa.

Notes: Declared noxious under *Fisheries Act*. Guards eggs and fry like Tilapia (see above), but does not mouthbrood.

Adult, QM, Bruce Cowell

Juvenile, QM, Bruce Cowell

White-lipped Treefrog. Bruce Cowell

FROGS

Sixty-one species of native frogs (27 endemic) are found in Tropical North Queensland. Most of this coastal region, between Cooktown and Sarina, falls within three biogeographic zones well known for high frog biodiversity.

The Wet Tropics (Cooktown to Rollingstone) has 50 native frog species — 42 per cent of Queensland's frog fauna. Of these, 22 species are not found anywhere else in Australia. The Central Queensland Coast Biogeographic Region (Proserpine to Sarina) has 27 native species (with three restricted to the area) and the coastal section of the Northern Brigalow Belt (Rollingstone to Proserpine) supports 21 species (with one restricted). A fourth area, which encompasses Mareeba to the west of Cairns, lies in the eastern edge of the Einasleigh Uplands Biogeographic Region.

All five Australian frog families — Treefrogs (Hylidae), Southern Frogs (Myobatrachidae), Narrow-mouthed Frogs (Microhylidae), True Frogs (Ranidae) and the introduced Toads (Bufonidae) — are found in TNQ. Only eastern Cape York and the Northern Territory support a similar number of families.

In TNQ, as in other parts of Australia, frogs are 'popular'. Some, like Green Treefrogs, are frequently seen in the home and urban environment, while others are not so easy to locate. In the past decade, frogs have received considerable media attention because populations of several species have declined dramatically, a matter of concern for anyone interested in maintaining Australia's biodiversity. The 'disappearing frog' phenomenon is not confined to TNQ. Species have declined elsewhere in Australia and also in North and South America, eastern Europe and Russia.

Ironically, some of the 'disappearing frogs' include species from well-protected or relatively pristine habitats, not affected by land-clearing or habitat modification.

Among them are populations of the Waterfall Frog, Armoured Waterfall Frog, Common Mistfrog, Mountain Mistfrog, Australian Lacelid, Sharp-snouted Day Frog, Eungella Day Frog, Northern Tinker Frog and the Northern Gastric-brooding Frog. These frogs were considered 'safe' in relatively inaccessible and upland rainforest conservation reserves.

In the coastal lowlands, drainage of swamps, modification of the water table and watercourses for sugar cane and real estate expansion have had significant impacts on frog habitat. This is especially so in paperbark swamps and low-lying areas with ephemeral waters. Many are endangered ecosystems. Limited information is available on frog distributions within this coastal area.

Tadpoles are obvious in streams and ponds throughout TNQ. Many species, such as the Northern Gastric-brooding Frog, the Nursery-frogs and Whistling-frogs do not have free-swimming tadpoles, but develop young in the stomach or in eggs laid on moist earth. Some stream tadpoles possess large mouth parts which enable them to attach, sucker-like, to rocks or debris in fast flowing streams. Others have smaller mouths and prefer pools where the water flow is slower. Identification of tadpoles is difficult and those of many species have not been described.

To enable non-specialists to identify frogs, the species described here are grouped according to broad similarities in appearance. However, two groups of frogs are particularly difficult to distinguish by external features. Narrow-mouthed frogs (Family Microhylidae) and some toadlets (genus *Uperoleia*) are small (to about 30 mm), brown or brownish-grey with highly variable colour patterns. They also tend to be difficult to find. For this reason, the species accounts do not dwell on colour and form, but focus on call, which is usually a reliable method of identification. The length in each description is an approximate size. For more information, readers should consult *Reptiles and Amphibians of Australia* by H.G. Cogger (Reed, New Holland) or *Field Guide to Australian Frogs* by J. Barker, H.C. Grigg & M.J. Tyler (Surrey Beatty & Sons).

Keith R McDonald

Green Treefrogs

Small to large (25–100 mm); bright green to olive; expanded discs on fingers and toes.

QM

Common Green Treefrog
Litoria caerulea

Identification: Length 100 mm. Robust with moderately long legs. Green to olive-brown; white belly; sometimes a row of white dots from corner of mouth to mid-body. Raised glandular area between eyes; snout short and rounded. Fingers webbed at base, toes three-quarter webbed.

Habitat and Range: All habitats, except dense rainforest. Common in suburban areas, sheltering in toilets, bathrooms, gardens, etc. Northern and eastern Australia; southern New Guinea.

Mating Call: Repeated deep 'crawk crawk'.

Eggs: Brown; laid in jelly mat on water surface, sink to bottom of pool.

QM

White-lipped Treefrog
Litoria infrafrenata

Identification: Length to 140 mm. Green; white stripe on lower jaw; in breeding season may have salmon-pink on arms and legs. Long slender legs, flattened head, prominent snout. Fingers one-third to half webbed, toes almost fully webbed.

Habitat and Range: Common in coastal lowlands, especially paperbark swamps, occasionally in open forests to 600 m; suburban areas. Cape York to Rollingstone, Qld; New Guinea (including New Britain).

Mating Call: Repeated, deep 'worrk'.

Eggs: Brown; laid in clear jelly clump on water surface, in permanent and temporary summer pools.

Orange-thighed Treefrog
Litoria xanthomera

Identification: Length 60 mm. Green; reddish-orange eyes; bright orange on limbs and flanks; belly yellow-orange; hidden area of thighs orange. Fingers three-quarters webbed, toes fully webbed.

Habitat and Range: Rainforest, sometimes edge of wet eucalypt forest. Wet Tropics, Big Tableland to Bluewater Ra., Qld.

Mating Call: Series of rising 'waaarks', ending in trills. Forms large, noisy choruses during summer breeding season.

Eggs: Brown; laid in clear jelly mat on surface; sink to bottom or attach to vegetation.

Michael Anthony

Orange-eyed Treefrog
Litoria chloris

Identification: Length 60 mm. Green; reddish-orange eyes; bright yellow on limbs and flanks; belly yellow; hidden area of thighs purple. Fingers three-quarters webbed, toes fully webbed.

Habitat and Range: Rainforest and wet forest. Conway and Clarke Ra., Miriam Vale, Qld, to NSW.

Mating Call: Similar to Orange-thighed Treefrog (see above).

Eggs: Similar to Orange-thighed Treefrog.

QM, Bruce Cowell

Graceful Treefrog
Litoria gracilenta

Identification: Length about 45 mm. Bright green; burnt-orange eyes; yellow belly; back of thighs maroon or purplish-brown. Light cream stripe from nose, along head, over eye bulge to forearm; Fingers three-quarters webbed, toes fully webbed.

Habitat and Range: Common in open forest, woodland; sometimes in gardens with good vegetation cover. Cape York, Qld, to Gosford, NSW; southern New Guinea.

Mating Call: Long, growl-like 'aaarrrc' repeated frequently. Forms noisy choruses during summer breeding season.

Eggs: Brown; laid in clear jelly clump on water surface.

QM

Bruce Cowell

Eastern Dwarf Treefrog
Litoria fallax

Identification: Length 25 mm. Robust. Green or brown to olive-brown, sometimes scattered dark spots on back; belly white; back of thighs dull orange. White stripe from jaw to forearm; bronze stripe from nostril to eye. Fingers with little webbing, toes three-quarters webbed.

Habitat and Range: Suburban gardens, temporary and permanent waterholes in open forests; dams in agricultural areas. Daintree R., Qld, to south of Sydney, NSW.

Mating Call: Long 'wreeek' followed by one or two 'pips'.

Eggs: Light brown; laid in small clumps on water surface, attach to reeds and other vegetation.

QM

Northern Dwarf Treefrog
Litoria bicolor

Identification: Length 30 mm. Slender. Green or fawn, sometimes with broad brown band running down back; belly white; back of thighs and groin dull orange or yellow. Brown or bronze head stripe extends from nostril to about mid-body. Fingers with little webbing, toes three-quarters webbed.

Habitat and Range: Various habitats, but not rainforest. Breeds in permanent, semi-permanent and temporary pools with grasses, lilypads or sedges. Northern Australia to Bowen, Qld; New Guinea.

Mating Call: High pitched 'wreeeeeek' lasting less than a second and two pips merging with first part of call.

Eggs: Brown; laid in clear jelly mat on water surface.

Similar Species: Eastern Dwarf Treefrog (see above).

Rocketfrogs

Medium-sized (to 60 mm); pointed snout, long legs; small discs on fingers and toes.

Striped Rocketfrog
Litoria nasuta

Identification: Length about 45 mm. Light to dark brown; stripes on back enclosing warts and longitudinal skin ridges; belly white; back of thigh yellowish with brown stripes. Dark head stripe from nostril ending abruptly behind ear, enclosing ear; pale bar in front of eye. Fingers unwebbed, toes half webbed.

Habitat and Range: Grassland, pasture, swamps, open forest, woodland. Northern Australia, coastal northern WA to Gosford, NSW; New Guinea.

Mating Call: A few 'clucs', followed by a rapid series of 'weks' lasting for several seconds, finally ending in a few 'clucs'.

Eggs: Laid in clumps on water's edge.

QM

Tawny Rocketfrog
Litoria nigrofrenata

Identification: Length 45 mm. Back fawn to light brown; back of thigh dark with pale horizontal blotches; shins with distinctive black border to pale upper surface. Head stripe extends from nostril, ends abruptly behind ear, broken by vertical bar in front of eye, encloses ear. Fingers unwebbed, toes half webbed.

Habitat and Range: Open forest and woodland, particularly grassy, inundated areas in summer. Cape York to Mount Molloy, Qld; New Guinea.

Mating Call: Similar to Striped Rocketfrog (see above).

Eggs: Laid in clumps in vegetation on water's edge.

Michael Anthony

QM

Broad-palmed Rocketfrog
Litoria latopalmata

Identification: Length 40 mm. Grey to brown above, sometimes with darker blotches; lower jaw mottled; back of thigh pale with dark speckling. Head stripe extends from nostril to behind ear, broken by pale vertical bar in front of eye, encloses ear. Discs slightly wider than digits. Fingers unwebbed, toes three-quarters webbed.

Habitat and Range: Upland wet open forest. Patchy distribution, Wet Tropics, Clarke Ra., also Rockhampton, Qld, to mid-NSW, west to desert areas of Qld, NSW, SA.

Mating Call: Similar to Striped Rocketfrog (see p. 175).

Eggs: Laid in clumps in vegetation on water's edge.

QM

Bumpy Rocketfrog
Litoria inermis

Identification: Length 35 mm. Grey or brown with darker patches on back and numerous small warts; back of thigh pale or yellowish with dark mottling; some mottling on legs. Indistinct head stripe from nostril ending abruptly behind ear with pale bar in front of eye. Fingers unwebbed, toes half to three-quarters webbed.

Habitat and Range: Grassy open forest, woodland, especially around summer rain-filled pools. Northern Australia to Maryborough, Qld.

Mating Call: Similar to Striped Rocketfrog (see p. 175).

Eggs: Brown; laid in clumps in shallow water.

Similar Species: Broad-palmed Rocketfrog (see above).

Stony-creek Frog
Litoria lesueuri

Identification: Male 45 mm, female to 65 mm. Light grey to brown; back of thigh yellow and black, groin yellow with black patch. Narrow head stripe from nostril through eye passing over ear, ending in tear-drop shape above forearm. Breeding male lemon-yellow at night. Discs slightly wider than digits. Fingers unwebbed, toes three-quarters webbed.

Habitat and Range: In streams in various habitats. Eastern Australia, Cooktown, Qld, to Vic.

Mating Call: Soft whirring.

Eggs: Dark brown; laid as clump in sandy depression made by frog, or small rock pool.

QM, Bruce Cowell

Small Treefrogs

Small (to 40 mm); brown; expanded discs on fingers and toes.

Little Red Frog
Litoria rubella

Identification: Length 40 mm. Dumpy with blunt snout and short legs. Light grey, fawn, brown or reddish-brown with two darker patches on lower back; belly white, groin lemon-yellow. Broad, dark band extends along head and body. Breeding male has dark throat. Fingers have little webbing, toes half to two-thirds webbed.

Habitat and Range: All habitats, except rainforest. Common in houses in northern Australia. Breeds in summer rain-filled pools. Northern two-thirds of Australia, including deserts; New Guinea.

Mating Call: High pitched, repeated 'kreeee'.

Eggs: Small, brown mass laid as a mat on water surface.

QM

QM

Javelin Frog
Litoria microbelos

Identification: Length 15 mm. Delicate with sharp snout. Brown or light brown, sometimes with lighter area on back; scattered warts on back, head and legs; belly white or light brown. Fingers unwebbed, toes have only a trace of webbing.

Habitat and Range: Tall grass near swamps, summer rain-filled depressions and pools. Eastern Cape York, to Rollingstone, Qld; far northern NT and WA.

Mating Call: Insect-like, high-pitched buzz. Males call while perched on grass stems and leaves.

Eggs: Unknown.

QM

Whirring Treefrog
Litoria revelata

Identification: Length 35 mm. Blunt snout and moderately long legs. Cream-brown to red-brown on back sometimes with broad, brown stripe; groin and back of thigh orange with black spots. Dark stripe along head to forearm with pale stripe along upper jaw. Fingers have only trace of webbing, toes half webbed.

Habitat and Range: Around pools in pastures, on rainforest edges. Southern uplands of Atherton Tablelands and Clarke Ra.; also Border Ra., south of Brisbane, Qld.

Mating Call: Series of high-pitched whirrings. Calls from reeds and grass near water.

Eggs: Unknown

Conservation Status: Rare.

Medium-sized Treefrogs

Length to about 60 mm; large discs on fingers and toes.

Northern Laughing Treefrog
Litoria rothi

QM

Other Name: Roth's Treefrog

Identification: Length 60 mm. Grey, whitish or mottled brown with small, iridescent green spots on back; belly off-white with brown flecks on throat; upper half of eye maroon; back of thigh black with a few yellow blotches; yellow can extend onto inner toe webbing. Colour of individuals may vary on same day. Fingers half webbed, toes nearly fully webbed.

Habitat and Range: Open forest, woodland, paperbark swamps. Northern Australia to Gympie, Qld.

Mating Call: Series of notes like maniacal laugh. Calls from vegetation around pools.

Eggs: Brown; laid in clumps on water surface.

Stream Frogs

Small to large (25–100 mm); some with expanded discs on fingers and toes; common near waterfalls, riffles or pools in rainforest streams. Many have had unexplained population declines.

Green-eyed Treefrog
Litoria genimaculata

QM, Jeff Wright

Identification: Male 40 mm, female 65 mm. Blunt head and long legs. Colour varies, grey-brown, reddish-brown or silvery with dark brown mottling, sometimes with green blotches resembling lichen. Eye silver with upper quarter green. Hind edge of arm and leg serrated. Fingers half webbed and toes nearly fully webbed.

Habitat and Range: Rainforest streams and adjacent vegetation. Wet Tropics, Qld; New Guinea.

Mating Call: Repeated single 'tocs'. Calls from vegetation near streams.

Eggs: Dark brown; laid in clump in shallow water.

Conservation Status: Rare.

QM

Australian Lace-lid
Nyctimystes dayi

Identification: Male 35 mm, female 55 mm. Blunt head, long legs and prominent eyes. Dark or light brown, sometimes with creamish, irregular blotches; belly off-white. Eyelid with distinct venation not found in any other Australian frog. Fingers half webbed, toes nearly fully webbed.

Habitat and Range: Near streams in spring and summer. Wet Tropics, Qld.

Mating Call: Short, sharp 'ee' or longer, drawn out 'eeeeee'. Males call from rocks and vegetation near running streams.

Eggs: Large, pale; laid under and on rocks in streams.

Conservation Status: Endangered.

QM

Waterfall Frog
Litoria nannotis

Identification: Male 47 mm, female 53 mm. Robust. Back slate-grey, grey-brown or dull green with dark markings; belly white. Ear indistinct. Fringe to rear edge of arm and legs. Male has raised spines on nuptial pad. Fingers about one-third webbed, toes nearly fully webbed.

Habitat and Range: Waterfalls and cascades in rainforest streams; occasionally water-falls in nearby wet forest. Wet Tropics, Qld.

Mating Call: Short, harsh growl.

Eggs: Large, pale; in mass under rocks.

Conservation Status: Endangered.

Similar Species: Armoured Frog (*L. lorica*), slightly smaller (male 30 mm, female 35 mm); endangered; Thornton Peak and McDowell Ra., Qld.

Mountain Mistfrog
Litoria nyakalensis

Identification: Length 30 mm. Robust. Back olive-brown, slate-grey or brown; belly off-white with reddish tinge to hind limbs. Male has large forearm; coarse spines on nuptial pads. Ear small and indistinct. Fingers slightly webbed, toes nearly fully webbed.

Mike Trennery

Habitat and Range: Upland rainforest streams. Wet Tropics, McDowell Ra. (near Thornton Peak), to Carron Ck (Kirrama Ra.) Qld.

Mating Call: Slow growl from males calling over riffles.

Eggs: Large, pale; laid under rocks in riffles.

Conservation Status: Endangered.

Common Mistfrog
Litoria rheocola

QM, Jeff Wright

Identification: Male 30 mm, female 35 mm. Back slate-grey or brown with irregular darker markings; pale triangle between eyes and snout; belly white. Fingers one-third webbed, toes nearly fully webbed.

Habitat and Range: Rainforest streams. Wet Tropics, Qld.

Mating Call: Series of 'wreeek wreeeks'. Males call from rocks and streamside vegetation.

Eggs: Large, cream; laid in clump under rocks in stream.

Conservation Status: Endangered.

Northern Gastric-brooding Frog
Rheobatrachus vitellinus

QM, Bruce Cowell

Identification: Male 50 mm, female 60 mm. Back brown with irregular darker markings; chest white; lower belly and underside of legs yellow. Eyes prominent. No discs; fingers unwebbed, toes fully webbed.

Habitat and Range: Rainforest streams. Clarke Ra., Qld.

Mating Call: Rapid series of notes similar to Spotted Marshfrog (see p. 185). Males call from rocky areas within streams September-December.

Eggs: Large, cream. Female carries tadpoles (with no mouthparts) in stomach where they develop to froglets before being expelled through mouth.

Conservation Status: Endangered; not located since 1985.

QM

Sharp-snouted Dayfrog
Taudactylus acutirostris

Identification: Male 25 mm, female 30 mm. Snout profile wedge-shaped. Back yellowish-brown to dark chocolate-brown, sometimes with 'V' or 'W' markings; broad band, with pale line above, along side of body. Belly off-white with dark spots and marking; legs olive-yellow below and in hidden area of thigh. Discs slightly larger than digits; fingers and toes unwebbed.

Habitat and Range: Upland rainforest streams. Wet Tropics, Qld.

Mating Call: High pitched 'tink tink' or a drawn out 'eek eek eek'.

Eggs: Large, pale brown; in clump attached to underside of rocks or below water line.

Conservation Status: Endangered; population declines since early 1990s.

Eungella Dayfrog
Taudactylus eungellensis

Identification: Male 27 mm, female 32 mm. Snout profile rounded. Back yellowish-tan to dark chocolate-brown; most animals have dark 'X' markings on back; legs barred; belly off-white to cream. Ear hidden. Fingers and toes unwebbed.

Habitat and Range: Upland rainforest streams. Clarke Ra., Qld.

Mating Call: Gentle rattling sound that may be difficult to hear over water noise.

Eggs: Large, pale brown; in clump attached to underside of rocks.

Conservation Status: Endangered; population declines in mid-1980s.

Environmental Protection Agency

Liem's Tinkerfrog
Taudactylus liemi

Identification: Length 25 mm. Robust body, short rounded snout. Back reddish-brown, dark brown or yellowish-brown with irregular, darker markings; belly cream. Ear hidden. Discs slightly wider than digits; fingers and toes unwebbed.

Habitat and Range: Rainforest streams. Clarke Ra., Qld.

Environmental Protection Agency

Mating Call: Loud, tinking tapping. Calls from within boulder heaps with seepage, alongside streams with seepage.

Eggs: Large, pale cream.

Conservation Status: Rare.

Northern Tinkerfrog
Taudactylus rheophilus

Mike Trennery

Identification: Length 28 mm. Robust with short snout. Back reddish-brown, dark brown or yellowish-brown with irregular darker markings; belly white with brownish marks. Pale grey streak from head to groin. Discs slightly wider than fingers and toes; no webbing.

Habitat and Range: Mountain-top streams (above 900 m) in rainforest. Four separate populations in Wet Tropics, Qld.

Mating Call: Soft metallic, tapping 'ink ink ink' or gentle rattling sound.

Eggs: Large, pale cream.

Conservation Status: Endangered.

Northern Barred-frog
Mixophyes schevilli

M. schevilli, QM, Jeff Wright

Identification: Length 100 mm. Robust. Back light brown to chocolate-brown with large, dark, irregular shaped blotches; belly white. Dark stripe from snout, over ear to shoulder. Hind limbs with narrow, irregular bands. Pupil vertical. No discs; fingers unwebbed, toes nearly fully webbed.

Habitat and Range: Rainforest pools and streams. Wet Tropics, Qld.

Mating Call: Deep 'waark' or 'gruump'.

Eggs: Large, light brown; laid on soil under banks above water.

Similar Species: Great Barred-frog (*M. fasciolatus*); Clarke Ra., Gin Gin, Qld, to north-eastern NSW.

M. fasciolatus, QM, Gary Cranitch

Marsh Frogs

Medium to large (45–70 mm); striped or spotted; no finger or toe discs; snout profile rounded.

QM, Gary Cranitch

Tusked Frog
Adelotus brevis

Identification: Male 40 mm, female to 35 mm. Back brown with irregular darker markings, sometimes with mid-back stripe; belly mottled black and white; red in groin and on legs. Male, broader head, larger than female. Vestigial webbing on toes and fingers; female has fringe of webbing on second finger.

Habitat and Range: Rainforest, wet forest, woodland. Declines in some upland populations noted. Clarke Ra., Rockhampton, Qld, to north-eastern NSW.

Mating Call: 'Docuk'. Submerged males call from under leaf litter or cavities under banks and rocks.

Eggs: Pale grey; laid in foam nest on water surface under vegetation.

QM

Brown-striped Frog
Limnodynastes peroni

Identification: Male 40 mm, female to 65 mm. Pointed snout. Back has light and dark brown stripes, sometimes with reddish tinge; white or yellow raised fold below eye to arm; belly white. Male has yellowish throat with brown mottling. Fingers and long toes unwebbed.

Habitat and Range: Farmland and moist forest. Wet Tropics, Mackay area, Rockhampton, Qld, south to Tas., SA.

Mating Call: Sharp, explosive 'toc'. Submerged males call from beneath overhanging vegetation.

Eggs: Small, dark brown; laid in foam nest on water surface under vegetation.

Spotted Marshfrog
Limnodynastes tasmaniensis

Identification: Length to 45 mm. Greyish to pale brown on back with scattered, darker brown blotches; belly white. Broad head stripe extending from nostril to base of arm; white or yellow, raised fold below eye to arm. Male has yellowish throat with light brown wash. Fingers and toes long, unwebbed.

Habitat and Range: Grassy open forest and woodland with shallow waterholes and permanent pools filled by summer rain; frequently around dams on farms. Coastal areas to deserts; eastern Australia, west of Atherton Tableland, Qld, to southern areas.

Mating Call: Rapid series of 'uk uk uks'. Males call partly submerged beneath overhanging vegetation.

Eggs: Small, brown; laid in foam nest on water surface under vegetation.

QM

Marbled Marshfrog
Limnodynastes convexiusculus

Identification: Length 55 mm. Pointed snout, short legs. Back brown or dark olive with numerous irregular blotches; white belly; dark blotch below eye. Irregular head stripe from snout to forearm bordered below by raised fold from below eye to arm. Male may have brown wash on throat. Fingers unwebbed, only a trace of webbing at base of toes.

Habitat and Range: Grassy open forest, woodland and grassland near temporary, summer pools or permanent waterholes. Northern Australia to Miriam Vale, Qld.

Mating Call: Single, sharp 'plonk' that can be heard for a considerable distance. Males call partly submerged under overhanging grass.

Eggs: Dark brown; laid in white foam nest on water surface, concealed by overhanging vegetation.

QM

Burrowing Frogs

Medium to large (40–75 mm); blunt-headed, short legs with digging tubercle on sole of foot.

QM

Ornate Burrowing-frog
Limnodynastes ornatus

Identification: Length 45 mm. Rotund, blunt nose, short legs. Colour varies, irregular blotches of browns, reddish-browns, greys and dull yellows, sometimes with 'butterfly' patch on back or mid-back stripe; some animals uniformly coloured. Small warts on back, sometimes tipped with orange; belly smooth, white. Fingers unwebbed, toes with slight webbing.

Habitat and Range: Common, particularly after rain. Widespread in various habitats, except rainforest. Northern and eastern Australia from wet coastal fringes to semi-arid environments.

Mating Call: Males give a deep 'unk', repeated at short intervals while floating on water.

Eggs: Dark brown; laid in foam nest floating on water. Nest breaks down rapidly to form a mat, especially under warm conditions.

Bruce Cowell

Scarlet-sided Pobblebonk
Limnodynastes terraereginae

Identification: Length to 75 mm. Robust, rotund. Back brown or brownish-grey with irregular, yellowish or reddish-yellow sides and upper arm; bright red groin and hidden surface of thigh; white or yellow, raised fold below eye to arm; belly white or creamy. Raised gland on surface of lower leg. Fingers unwebbed, toes with trace at base.

Habitat and Range: Riverine flats in grassy open forest near temporary summer pools or permanent waterholes. Tip of Cape York, Qld, to northern central NSW.

Mating Call: Deep, highly resonant 'bonk'. Males call partly submerged under leaf litter or overhanging vegetation.

Eggs: Dark brown; laid in white foam nest on water surface, concealed or partly concealed by leaf litter and overhanging vegetation.

Green-striped Frog
Cyclorana alboguttata

Identification: Length 65 mm. Narrow head, snout pointed. Back brown, olive or pale green with green stripe on back and raised brown warts; belly off-white with dull mottling. Prominent skin fold on back. Fingers unwebbed, toes half-webbed.

Habitat and Range: Around pools in inundated grassland and woodland. North-eastern NT, eastern Qld, to northern central NSW.

Mating Call: Rapid, quacking 'wuck'.

Eggs: Unknown.

QM

Eastern Snapping-frog
Cyclorana novaehollandiae

Identification: Length 100 mm. Robust, broad head, wide mouth. Back brown, grey or dull yellow with dark mottling; back of thigh variegated grey; belly white; throat sometimes flecked brown. Dark stripe from nostril to behind ear; sometimes dark bar under eye. Fingers unwebbed, toes one-quarter to one-third webbed. Juveniles bright green, two white stripes on back.

Habitat and Range: Inundated grassland, grassy open forest and woodland. Cape York, Qld, to northern central NSW.

Mating Call: Deep repeated 'whonk'. Males call from banks of pools.

Eggs: Brown; laid in clump on surface of ephemeral waters.

QM, Bruce Cowell

Superb Collared-frog
Cyclorana brevipes

Identification: Length 40 mm. Rotund, short legs. Back pale, mottled dark and light brown; pale stripe behind eye bulge; dark head stripe from snout to behind ear. Fingers unwebbed, toes slightly webbed.

Habitat and Range: Inundated grassland, woodland and open forest. Cape York, Qld, to northern central NSW.

Mating Call: Long bleating 'waaa', like a sheep. Males call from near ponds.

Eggs: Brown; laid in clear jelly clump on water surface.

QM

Environmental Protection Agency

Northern Spadefoot
Notaden melanoscaphus

Identification: Length 50 mm. Rotund, small head, narrow mouth. Back slate or pale grey, dark blotches mottled; belly white. Short, robust legs; dark tubercle on sole of foot. Fingers and toes unwebbed.

Habitat and Range: Inundated grassland, grassy open forest and woodland. Northern Australia. Separate population in coastal plains near Townsville, Qld.

Mating Call: Owl-like 'whoop whoop'. Males call while floating in water.

Eggs: Dark brown; spread on water surface.

Woodfrogs

Medium-sized (about 60 mm); grey or brownish; pointed head; no finger or toe discs, fingers unwebbed, toes nearly fully webbed.

Bruce Cowell

Australian Woodfrog
Rana daemeli

Identification: Length 60 mm. Prominent snout and long legs. Back brown or grey-brown with some mottling; legs and arms barred brown. Ear obvious. Skin fold from behind eye to bottom of back. Gland at corner of jaw. Toes three-quarters webbed.

Habitat and Range: Lowland permanent or stream pools, occasionally to 600 m. North-east Arnhem Land, NT; Cape York, to Rollingstone, Qld; New Guinea.

Mating Call: Series of reedy quacks.

Eggs: Dark brown; laid in large mass of clear jelly on surface, sink to bottom.

Froglets

Small (20–30 mm); grey or greyish-brown; no discs; unwebbed fingers and toes.

QM, Jeff Wright

Chirping Froglet
Crinia deserticola

Identification: Length 18 mm. Pale grey with darker markings; legs barred; belly white.

Habitat and Range: Edges of temporary and permanent pools from arid to coastal, moist open forest and woodland. NT, Cape York to Childers (near Bundaberg), west to arid zone, Qld; northern SA.

Mating Call: Short, high-pitched 'eeh', repeated in a series, followed by three or four rapid 'eeh eeh eehs'.

Eggs: Small, brown; laid on submerged vegetation in pools.

Torrid Froglet
Crinia remota

Identification: Length 18 mm. Brown or grey, sometimes with broad back stripe and warts on back; legs barred; belly white.

Habitat and Range: Paperbark swamps and inundated grassland. Northern Australia, Cape York to Rollingstone, Qld; southern New Guinea.

Mating Call: Series of rapid taps.

Eggs: Unknown.

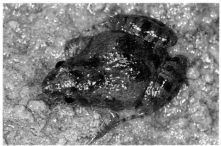

QM, Bruce Cowell

Toadlets and Broodfrogs

Small (20–30 mm); coppery-brown or brownish-grey. Toadlets with red or orange groin and hidden area of thigh. Broodfrogs with black and white marbling on belly. No discs on fingers and toes; unwebbed or only a trace of webbing.

Magnificent Broodfrog
Pseudophryne covacevichae

Identification: Length 25 mm. Squat; rufous brown or coppery back; dark flanks with canary-yellow patches on upper arm and between legs; belly marbled black and white. Fingers unwebbed, toes with trace of webbing at base.

Habitat and Range: Restricted to seepage areas in headwaters of gullies in open forest and woodland. Ravenshoe, Qld.

Mating Call: Slow, squelch-like 'aark', sometimes with rapid 'yeerks' when disturbed.

Eggs: Large, pale brown; laid at base of tussocks or leaf debris in summer seepage area; sometimes attended by males.

Conservation Status: Vulnerable.

Similar Species: Great Brown Broodfrog (*P. major*); found in separate populations west of Bowen and Mackay, Qld; also south to Qld–NSW border.

P. covacevichae, QM, Jeff Wright

P. major, QM, Jeff Wright

U. altissma, QM, Jeff Wright

U. fusca, QM

Tableland Toadlet
Uperoleia altissma

Identification: Length 25 mm. Squat. Grey-brown back with darker brown mottling; raised glands with yellowish tinge on sides of back and flanks; sometimes numerous tubercules on back; red-orange flash in groin and behind knee; belly grey. Fingers unwebbed, toes with webbing at base.

Habitat and Range: Open forest and woodland of western Atherton and Windsor Tablelands, Qld.

Mating Call: Rasping, squelch-like click.

Eggs: Brown; laid in clump in shallow water.

Similar Species: Dusky Toadlet (*U. fusca*); mating call a squelch-like click; Clarke Ra., Bulburin to Qld–NSW border. Stonemason Toadlet (*U. lithomoda*); mating call a single, explosive click like a hammer tap; Cape York to west of Townsville, Qld. Mimic Toadlet (*U. mimula*); call a squelch-like click; Torres Strait to Bowen, Qld.

Narrow-mouthed Frogs

Small to medium (15–35 mm); brownish to grey-brown; in rainforest leaf litter. In TNQ, restricted to Wet Tropics; also found in Cape York, Qld, Arnhemland, NT; New Guinea.

QM, Jeff Wright

Rattling Nursery-frog
Cophixalus hosmeri

Identification: Length to 15 mm. Grey or brown with mottling on back; dark brown on side of head; faint pale area just above groin, may be more obvious in darker specimens. Belly pale or with pale spots; throat of male darker. No discs; fingers and toes unwebbed.

Habitat and Range: Rainforest. Carbine Tableland, Thornton Peak uplands, Qld.

Mating Call: Fast tapping, like a marble on a tile.

Eggs: Large, pale; laid in moist area under leaf litter, logs and vegetation. No free-swimming tadpole. Development takes place in egg, fully developed froglet emerges.

Conservation Status: Rare

Buzzing Nursery-frog
Cophixalus bombiens

Identification: Length to 15 mm. Grey and brown mottling on back, limbs and sides; faint, pale area just above groin; belly light with pale brown markings. Discs slightly broader than fingers and toes; no webbing.

Habitat and Range: Northern rainforest of Wet Tropics. Shipton's Flat to Carbine Tableland, Qld.

Mating Call: Insect-like buzz.

Eggs: Similar to Rattling Nursery-frog (see p. 190).

Conservation Status: Rare.

Deborah Pergolotti

Tapping Nursery-frog
Cophixalus concinnus

Identification: Length to 26 mm. Robust. Brown back, side of head dark brown; faint pale area above groin; belly pale. Discs slightly larger or equal to fingers and toes; no webbing.

Habitat and Range: Three separate populations on Carbine Tableland, Thornton Peak uplands, Mt Finnigan uplands, Qld.

Mating Call: Tapping sound; similar to Rattling Nursery-frog (see p. 190), but slower.

Eggs: Similar to Rattling Nursery-frog.

Conservation Status: Rare.

QM, Jeff Wright

Northern Tapping Nursery-frog
Cophixalus exiguus

Identification: Length to 15 mm. Grey or brown with mottled back; dark brown on side of head; faint pale area above groin, may be more obvious in darker specimens; belly pale or with paler spots. Throat of male darker. No discs; fingers and toes unwebbed.

Habitat and Range: Rainforest centred on Mt Finnigan, Qld.

Mating Call: Similar to Rattling Nursery Frog (see p. 190).

Eggs: Similar to Rattling Nursery-frog.

Conservation Status: Rare.

Environmental Protection Agency

Deborah Pergolotti

Creaking Nursery-frog
Cophixalus infacetus

Identification: Length to 17 mm. Back brown with dark brown markings and faint 'W' on upper back; darker area on side of head; sides mottled; belly lightly mottled. Discs slightly wider than digits; fingers and toes unwebbed.

Habitat and Range: Rainforest on eastern slopes of coastal ranges. Cairns to Herbert Valley, Qld.

Mating Call: Creaking, like opening a door with rusty hinge.

Eggs: Similar to Rattling Nursery-frog (see p. 190).

Conservation Status: Rare.

Environmental Protection Agency

Mt Elliot Nursery-frog
Cophixalus mcdonaldi

Identification: Length to 20 mm. Robust. Greyish-brown to dark brown; faint pale area above groin; side of head dark; belly pale or creamy-yellow. Discs slightly wider than digits; fingers and toes unwebbed.

Habitat and Range: Known only from rainforest above 900 m on Mt Elliot, Qld.

Mating Call: Buzzing sound.

Eggs: Similar to Rattling Nursery-frog (see p. 190).

Conservation Status: Rare.

Michael Anthony

Mountain-top Nursery-frog
Cophixalus monticola

Identification: Length to 21 mm. Red-brown to yellow-brown, sometimes darker mottling on back; two pale areas above groin; may have mid-back band; belly yellow, reddish-brown or white; throat darker. Discs equal to or not much wider than digits; fingers and toes unwebbed.

Habitat and Range: Rainforest. Carbine Tableland and Thornton Peak uplands above 1000 m, Qld.

Mating Call: Short trill.

Eggs: Similar to Rattling Nursery-frog (see p. 190).

Conservation Status: Rare.

Bellenden Ker Nursery-frog
Cophixalus neglectus

Identification: Length to 28 mm. Robust. Greyish-brown to dark brown; faint pale area above groin; side of head dark; belly pale or creamy-yellow. Discs slightly wider than fingers and toes; no webbing.

Habitat and Range: Two isolated populations in rainforest above 800 m on Mt Bellenden Ker and Mt Bartle Frere.

Mating Call: Buzzing sound.

Eggs: Similar to Rattling Nursery-frog (see p. 190).

Conservation Status: Rare.

QM, Jeff Wright

Common Nursery-frog
Cophixalus ornatus

Identification: Length to 25 mm. Variable back pattern, generally grey to brown with pale blotch above groin; sometimes dark 'W' shape on upper back; narrow or broad stripe from snout down centre of back; pale belly finely spotted grey to brown. Large finger and toe discs; disc on third finger larger than disc on fourth toe; no webbing.

Habitat and Range: Rainforest, but sometimes in adjacent wet eucalypt forest. Carbine Tableland to Bluewater Ra., Qld.

Mating Call: Short 'beep', similar to car horn. Calls from vegetation above ground, rarely higher than 2 m.

Eggs: Similar to Rattling Nursery-frog (see p. 190).

QM, Jeff Wright

Black Mountain Boulder-frog
Cophixalus saxatalis

Identification: Male 30 mm, female 40 mm. Male brown with darker brown blotches; female canary-yellow; pale belly finely spotted grey to brown. Large discs on finger and toes; disc on third finger larger than disc on fourth toe; no webbing.

Habitat and Range: Boulder fields of Black Mtn NP, Qld.

Mating Call: Rattling sound.

Eggs: Unknown.

Conservation Status: Rare.

Female, QM, Gary Cranitch

S fryi, QM

Northern Whistling-frog
Sphenophryne fryi

Identification: Length to 35 mm. Back brown, brownish-orange or grey with dark side to head; belly off-white to creamish with light speckles, sometimes darkly mottled. Discs small, not much wider than digit; fingers and toes unwebbed.

Habitat and Range: Rainforest. Wet Tropics, Big Tableland to north of Tinaroo Dam.

Mating Call: Series of whistle-like notes 'piip piip piip'.

Eggs: Similar to Rattling Nursery-frog (see p. 190).

Conservation Status: Rare.

Similar Species: Robust Whistling-frog (*S. robusta*), rainforests above 360 m; Bluewater Ra. to southern Lamb Ra., Qld. Call high pitched whistle-like couplets.

S. robusta, Environmental Protection Agency

QM, Jeff Wright

White-browed Whistling-frog
Sphenophryne pluvialis

Identification: Length to 30 mm. Grey-brown or brown back with pale streak from nose along head and over eye bulge. Underside of throat mottled grey; belly mottled pale grey, sometimes with yellow or cream spots, or yellowish-green on lower abdomen; red eye. Discs slightly wider than digits; fingers and toes unwebbed.

Habitat and Range: Rainforest. Big Tableland to Wallaman Falls (Seaview Ra.), Qld.

Mating Call: Series of high pitched, rapid whistle-like notes. Can be confused with Northern Whistling-frog (see above).

Eggs: Similar to Rattling Nursery-frog (see p. 190).

CANE TOAD

The Cane Toad is common throughout Tropical North Queensland. The toad, a native of Central and South America, was introduced to TNQ in 1935, in a failed attempt to control cane beetles. It has since spread down the east coast to northern New South Wales, west into the Gulf country and the north-eastern Northern Territory. It has as also been introduced into several Pacific islands, including New Guinea.

The Cane Toad is a generalist, existing in many diverse habitats and environments, and eats a wide variety of food, hence its broad distribution. In TNQ, it breeds mainly in spring and summer, but has been known to reproduce when unseasonal warm, moist conditions occur. The toad is toxic to a number of native and domestic animals. It also competes with native fauna for shelter, food and breeding sites and is considered a threat to the environment. **Keith R McDonald**

Cane Toad
Bufo marinus

Identification: Large, up to 20 cm, but mainly 10–15 cm. Large glands (which secrete toxin) behind ears; bony ridge from snout to eye; raised area above eye. Back warty with leathery skin; underside white mottled brown or grey. No toe discs, but full webbing; no webbing on fingers.

Habitat and Range: Wide ranging from beach dunes, woodland and forest to grassland and swamps; also disturbed areas of rainforest, especially roads and walking tracks. Occurs infrequently in upland, undisturbed rainforest. North-eastern NT to eastern and northern Gulf of Carpentaria, Qld, south to northern NSW.

Mating Call: Continuous, melodious 'warble', sounds like a small petrol engine. Calls from water or banks of permanent or temporary bodies of water.

Eggs: String of dark pigmented eggs laid on bottom of pools. One female can lay up to 30,000 eggs each season.

Tadpoles: Swim and feed in schools; black with rotund bodies, short tails. Juvenile toads grey to dark grey with burnt orange tips to warts and mottled grey underside.

Similar Species: Marsh Frogs (see pp. 184–85), Toadlets (see p. 190) and Eastern Snapping-frog (see p. 187).

Notes: Some native animals, such as Freshwater Snakes, water rats and crows, appear to prey on toads by flipping them over and eating stomach, thus avoiding toxic glands on back.

Bruce Cowell

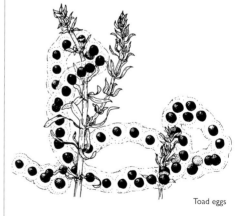

Toad eggs

Krefft's Short-necked Turtle, John Cann

FRESHWATER TURTLES

Freshwater turtles are common in most rivers, creeks and lagoons of Tropical North Queensland. Although they spend most of their lives in water, they are often seen basking on logs or rocks. Basking turtles tend to be shy and will retreat rapidly to the water if disturbed. Turtles leave the water to breed and disperse during heavy rains.

Most freshwater turtles grow slowly and are long-lived. Although sexual maturity occurs between 4 and 14 years, it may take a turtle 70 years to grow to maximum size.

There is little doubt that turtle populations have suffered declines due to human activities, such as water pollution and the draining of swamps and lagoons. Populations are further diminished by the effects of introduced predators, such as foxes, which destroy turtle nests and consume the eggs.

Most Australian freshwater turtles belong to the family Chelidae. These turtles are easily recognised by their webbed, clawed feet and ability to fold their necks sideways, for protection, between a bony carapace (top of shell) and plastron (underside). They occur only in South America, Australia, New Guinea and eastern Indonesia.

John Cann, Patrick Couper and Heather Janetzki

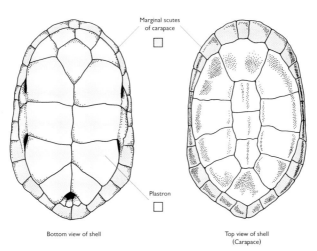

Marginal scutes of carapace

Plastron

Bottom view of shell

Top view of shell (Carapace)

Shell of Eastern Snake-necked Turtle

Chelodina longicollis, John Cann

Eastern Snake-necked Turtle
Chelodina longicollis
New Guinea Long-necked Turtle
Chelodina novaeguineae

Identification: Carapace to 30 cm; broadly oval, expanded at rear; brown to black with darker mottling. Plastron wide at front; cream. Neck about as long as carapace. *C. longicollis*, width of front lobe of plastron broad, overlaps inner edges of marginal scutes of carapace; dark edging between plates of plastron. *C. novaeguineae*, front of plastron extends only as far as inner edges of marginal scutes of carapace.

Habitat and Range: Lagoons. *C. longicollis*, patchy distribution from Ayr, Qld, to Adelaide, SA; *C. novaeguineae*, Cape York to Proserpine, Qld; New Guinea.

Nesting: *C. longicollis*, late September–December, *C. novaeguineae*, April–August; 8–24 hard-shelled eggs (32 x 33 mm), hatch after 120 days.

Notes: Where two species overlap (Ayr–Proserpine), hybridisation occurs. Feed on small aquatic animals. Can migrate overland, sometimes several kilometres, following rain; may bury in mud or loose soil and aestivate during dry times.

John Cann

Saw-shelled Turtle
Elseya latisternum

Identification: Carapace to 28 cm; broadly oval, expanded at rear; brown to dark brown, sometimes with darker blotches. Hind edge strongly serrated in hatchlings, but reduced or lost in adults. Plastron yellowish with dark-edged scales. Neck short, spiny.

Habitat and Range: Rivers, steams. Coastal, Cape York, Qld, to northern NSW; believed to be introduced to Lake Eacham, Atherton Tablelands.

Nesting: September–January; 9–17 hard-shelled eggs (33 x 22 mm), hatch after 60 days; several clutches can be laid each season.

Notes: Feeds on aquatic insects, fish, tadpoles and frogs; one of few native animals which successfully preys on Cane Toad.

Snapping Turtles
Elseya dentata complex

Identification: Carapace to 45 cm; broadly oval, expanded at rear, serrated in young specimens (degree of serration varies between drainage systems); brown to dark brown (black in large adults). Plastron yellowish to black. Neck short, thick in adults, with conspicuous rounded bumps. Several distinct forms; best distinguished by range. Adult female *E. irwini* has white head with cream to yellow, horny sheath on crown.

Elysea irwini, John Cann

Habitat and Range: Large rivers and associated lagoons. In Qld, from Cairns to Gympie. *E. irwini* in Burdekin drainage; distinct forms of *E. dentata* in Johnstone R. and Fitzroy drainage.

Nesting: April–September; 5–15 hard-shelled eggs (50 x 29 mm), hatch after 150 days; can lay more than one clutch each season.

Notes: Feed on small aquatic animals, carrion, algae and seeds, fruit and leaves of waterside vegetation.

Krefft's Short-necked Turtle
Emydura krefftii

Identification: Carapace to 34 cm; broadly oval, expanded at rear; often serrated in juveniles; olive-brown to black. Plastron creamish, or tinged with dark brown. Neck short with low rounded bumps. Face with yellowish streak extending back from eye (may be obscure or absent in large adults), also streak along lower jaw.

John Cann

Habitat and Range: Rivers, creeks and associated pools and lagoons. Eastern Qld from Princess Charlotte Bay (Cape York), to Gympie, Qld.

Nesting: September–January; 4–16 hard-shelled eggs (34 x 20 mm), hatch after 80 days; several clutches may be laid each season.

Esuarine Crocodile, QM, Bruce Cowell

CROCODILES

The Estuarine Crocodile belongs to an ancient group whose ancestors were around in the time of the dinosaurs and survived the break up of continents and even the Ice Ages. Today, this crocodile is found from India, through south-east Asia to northern Australia. Estuarine Crocodiles occur within all river systems of Tropical North Queensland, including the upper reaches of large rivers. They can be seen in tidal areas and in freshwater swamps, lagoons and impoundments of the coastal lowlands.

Throughout the region, crocodile warning signs have been erected near access points to rivers, creeks and swamps, anywhere that Estuarine Crocodiles pose a potential danger. Problem crocodiles are removed by the Environmental Protection Agency to crocodile farms and zoos or translocated to other, less accessible areas.

The Freshwater Crocodile (*Crocodylus johnstoni*) occurs within TNQ as two introduced populations in coastal streams near Townsville and Giru. There is a natural population in the upper Herbert River where it was first collected by Sub-inspector Johnstone for the Australian Museum. **Keith R McDonald**

Estuarine Crocodile
Crocodylus porosus

Other Name: Saltwater Crocodile.

Identification: Adult rarely exceeds 5 m; male larger than female. Broad snout; powerful tail for swimming. Enlarged scales in two rows on neck. (Freshwater Crocodile has narrow snout, single row of neck scales and rarely exceeds 2.5 m.)

Habitat and Range: Coastal rivers, swamps and billabongs; sometimes seen in open sea and on coastal beaches. Northern Australia from Kimberley region, WA, to Rockhampton, Qld; India and south-east Asia.

Mating: During breeding season (November–March) males call, noisily exhale air, and perform complex series of mating rituals with females.

Nest and Eggs: About 60 hard-shelled eggs laid in large mound of vegetation and soil near brackish or freshwater. Female guards nest, sometimes from nearby wallow. Incubation takes about 3 months. Hatchlings found in creches, sometimes guarded by adult.

QM, Bruce Cowell

Food: Juvenile feeds on insects, crustaceans and fish. Adult eats crustaceans, fish, mammals and birds. Many prey animals taken from near water's edge as they come to feed or drink.

Conservation Status: Vulnerable. Population declines due to loss of most breeding habitat, removal of adult crocodiles and slow recovery from earlier exploitation. Declared Protected in 1974.

Notes: Previously hunted for skins, which make excellent leather hides. Now farmed in captivity for skin and meat, with most being exported.

Boyd's Forest Dragon, QM, Jeff Wright

LIZARDS

Many species of lizards are common in Tropical North Queensland and are seen frequently, even in town and city gardens. Well-established in these areas are nocturnal geckoes, such as the Tree Dtella and Asian House Gecko, and a variety of other lizards, including Rainbow, Striped, and Sun Skinks.

Of the 102 species of lizards known from TNQ, 18 are of conservation concern. Sixteen are 'rare', usually by virtue of their narrow ranges. Some of these (the Mt Bartle Frere skinks, *Eulamprus frerei* and *Techmarscincus jigurru*) are known from only single localities. Two species are listed as 'vulnerable'. The pygopodid, *Delma labialis*, and the Yakka Skink, *Egernia rugosa*, are patchily distributed in TNQ's open forested areas. Although some species already seem to be rare, prospects for preserving TNQ's lizard diversity are relatively good when compared with those for lizard species from the Brigalow Belt to the near west.

Although they are seen often and sometimes easily caught for close examination, lizards are not always easily identified. The species accounts which follow will help with identification. They are arranged by family (geckos, legless lizards, skinks, dragons and goannas) and, within each, alphabetically by Latin name. The identification data for each is not exhaustive. Rather, it focuses on features which are key to recognising each species. Reliance on limb length and number of digits has generally been avoided in the descriptions, except for those of some skinks, where they vary from the conventional 'well-developed fore and hindlimbs with five digits on each'.

The locality records are based on specimens in the Queensland Museum reference collection and published data. While these give a good indication of species distributions, they do not provide a complete picture. New occurrences (based on specimens not just sightings) are always welcomed by the Herpetology Section of the Queensland Museum.

The following features and abbreviations have been used: snout to vent length (SVL); midbody scale rows (the number of scales encircling the body half way between the fore and hindlimbs).

Patrick Couper, Jeanette Covacevich, Heather Janetzki & Keith McDonald

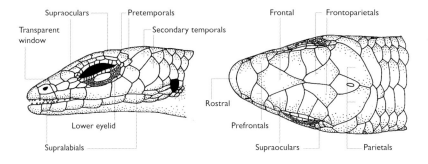

Geckos

A gecko is easily recognised by its large, lidless eyes and soft, 'velvety' skin, which may be interspersed with small 'spines'. One hundred and eight species are known from Australia. Geckos are nocturnal. Most species prefer drier habitats and some readily colonise human dwellings.

QM

Chameleon Gecko
Carphodactylus laevis

Identification: SVL 130 mm. Limbs long, slender. Tail carrot-shaped. Body light to dark brown with small black flecks. Broad, black, facial streak from nostril to eye. Original tail dark with 4 or 5 narrow, white bands; regrown tail speckled, unbanded.

Habitat and Range: Rainforest. TNQ only, Big Tableland to Kirrama.

Michael Anthony

Ring-tailed Gecko
Cyrtodactylus louisiadensis

Identification: SVL 130 mm. Tail long, slender. Body pale olive to brown with broad, chocolate-coloured bands, first forming a 'collar' between eyes. Original tail boldly banded.

Habitat and Range: Open forest, rainforest. TNQ, Cooktown to Mount Molloy. Australia, McIlwraith Ra. (Cape York); Cape Melville to Mount Molloy, Qld.

QM, Bruce Cowell

Diplodactylus steindachneri

Identification: SVL 55 mm. Tail cylindrical. Body tan to dark brown with large, pale blotches with darker edges; foremost blotch connected to eyes forming Y-shaped marking on nape.

Habitat and Range: Dry open forest. TNQ, near Mareeba. Australia, semi-arid Qld and NSW.

Tree Dtella
Gehyra dubia

Identification: SVL 80 mm. Tail smooth, cylindrical; base flattened. Body grey to brown, usually with darker blotches and pale spots; pattern barely discernible at night. Inner digit on each limb clawless.

Habitat and Range: Open forest; often on buildings. TNQ, Cooktown to Sarina, including continental islands. Australia, Cape York, Qld, to inland northern NSW.

Similar Species: Asian House Gecko, all digits clawed (see below).

QM, Bruce Cowell

Asian House Gecko
Hemidactylus frenatus

Identification: SVL 60 mm. Tail cylindrical, slightly flattened, small spines along edges. Body fawn to grey with pale flecks and darker mottling.

Habitat and Range: Coastal towns and cities. TNQ, Cooktown, Cairns, Townsville, Mackay. Northern Australia, Darwin, NT, to Brisbane, Qld. Introduced from south-east Asia.

Similar Species: Tree Dtella (see above).

QM, Gary Cranitch

Bynoe's Gecko
Heteronotia binoei

Identification: SVL 50 mm. Tail long, cylindrical. Back with scattered, enlarged scales. Body grey to brown, dark and pale flecked; broken bands usually present. Three scales enclosing base of each claw.

Habitat and Range: Open forest and woodland. TNQ, Cooktown to Sarina, including continental islands. Australia, all mainland states.

Similar Species: *N. cheverti*, 2 scales enclosing base of each claw (see p. 206).

Steve Wilson

QM, Gary Cranitch

Mourning Gecko
Lepidodactylus lugubris

Identification: SVL 50 mm. Tail long, cylindrical, slightly flattened, with flanges of small, spiny scales along edges. Body cream to fawn, dark flecks and W-shaped markings along back.

Habitat and Range: Mangroves, woodland, urban areas. TNQ, Cooktown to Bowen, some islands. Australia, Torres Strait to Bowen, Heron I., Qld.

Michael Anthony

Nactus cheverti

Identification: SVL 80 mm. Tail long, cylindrical. Back with scattered, enlarged, raised scales. Body brown to black, sometimes with darker blotches and broken bands.

Habitat and Range: Coastal forest. TNQ, Cooktown to Dunk I; also north to southern Princess Charlotte Bay (Cape York).

Similar Species: Bynoe's Gecko (see p. 205).

QM, Jeff Wright

Black Mountain Gecko
Nactus galgajuga

Identification: SVL 50 mm. Tail long, cylindrical. Rows of enlarged, raised scales on back. Body, tail and limbs purplish-brown with narrow cream bands.

Habitat and Range: TNQ only, Black Mtn NP.

Velvet Geckos

Oedura castelnaui

Identification: SVL 90 mm. Tail relatively long and moderately flattened. Body purplish with broad pale bands.

Habitat and Range: Dry forest and woodland. TNQ, Mareeba, Ravenshoe, Townsville areas; also north to tip of Cape York.

QM

Oedura coggeri

Identification: SVL 70 mm. Tail cylindrical, slightly flattened. Body orange to brown with numerous purple-edged, pale blotches that may form broken bands.

Habitat and Range: Woodland. TNQ, Palmer R. (near Cooktown) to Mt Garnet; also north to Lockhart R., (Cape York), Qld.

Michael Anthony

Oedura ocellata

Identification: SVL 80 mm. Tail cylindrical, slightly flattened. Body yellowish, mottled purple. Centre of back with pairs of dark-edged, pale spots, usually joined into larger U-shaped marking on nape.

Habitat and Range: Dry open forest, vine thickets, rainforest edges. TNQ, Mt Garnet to Eungella. Australia, also south to northern NSW.

QM, Jeff Wright

Oedura rhombifer

Identification: SVL 70 mm. Tail cylindrical. Body slender, grey to brown with broad, ragged-edged, vertebral stripe.

Habitat and Range: Woodland. TNQ, Mt Cook (Cooktown) to Pine Mtn (near Sarina), including continental islands. Northern Australia.

QM, Bruce Cowell

Leaf-tailed Geckos

Phyllurus isis, QM. Jeff Wright

Phyllurus nepthys, QM. Bruce Cowell

Phyllurus isis
Phyllurus nepthys
Phyllurus ossa

Identification: Tail flattened, carrot or leaf-shaped. Scattered spiny scales on body, limbs and tail. Body brownish with numerous dark blotches; tail with white bands.

P. isis, SVL to 76 mm, moderately spiny, two white bands at base of tail reduced to paired blotches; *P. nepthys*, SVL to 103 mm, very spiny, lower surface peppered with brown flecks; *P. ossa*, SVL to 89 mm, moderately spiny, lower surface not flecked, white bands at base of tail span full width.

Habitat and Range: Rainforest. TNQ only, *P. isis*, Mt Blackwood and Mt Jukes (near Mackay); *P. nepthys*, Clarke Ra.; *P. ossa*, Mt Dryander (near Proserpine) to Mt Ossa (near Mackay).

Phyllurus ossa, QM. Bruce Cowell

QM. Jeff Wright

Saltuarius cornutus

Identification: SVL 140 mm. Tail, broad and flat, leaf-shaped. Body brown to greenish; series of lichen-like blotches along back.

Habitat and Range: Rainforest. TNQ only, Big Tableland to Paluma.

Legless Lizards

Although superficially snake-like, legless lizards are most closely related to geckos. They occur only in Australia and New Guinea. Thirty-five species are known. They have no forelimbs and are easily recognised by their flap-like hindlimbs. These are held tightly against the body, adjacent to the vent. Legless lizards have broad fleshy tongues, external ear openings and tails that are greater than two and a half times the body length.

Delma labialis

Identification: SVL 100 mm. Tail cylindrical, about four times longer than SVL. Snout rounded. Body grey to reddish-brown; pale vertical bars on face and neck; thin dark line along each side of tail.

Habitat and Range: Open forest, woodland. TNQ only, Rollingstone to Mt Abbot, Magnetic I., South Molle I., Shaw I., Keswick I.

QM, Jeff Wright

Delma mitella

Identification: SVL 80 mm. Tail cylindrical, about three times longer than SVL. Snout rounded. Body brownish. Head olive with narrow, cream bands. Seven scales on head between rostral and frontal shields.

Habitat and Range: Open forest, rainforest edges. TNQ only, near Mareeba, Herberton, Paluma.

Similar Species: *D. tincta*, 5 scales on head between rostral and frontal shield (see below).

QM

Delma tincta

Identification: SVL 80 mm. Tail cylindrical, about three times longer than SVL. Snout rounded. Body grey to brown; head usually with dark bands, 2–3 narrow, cream spaces between bands.

Habitat and Range: Open forest. TNQ, Cooktown to Mackay, including continental islands. Northern Australia.

Similar Species: *D. mitella* (see above).

QM

Bruce Cowell

Burton's Legless Lizard
Lialis burtonis

Identification: SVL 290 mm. Tail cylindrical, two and a half times longer than SVL. Snout long, wedge-shaped. Body cream, grey, brown or black; sometimes with stripes or spots.

Habitat and Range: Open forest, woodland, grassland. TNQ, Cooktown to Sarina. Australia, all mainland states.

Common Scaly-foot
Pygopus lepidopodus

Identification: SVL 230 mm. Tail cylindrical, three times longer than SVL. Snout rounded. Dark bar usually below eye. Body grey to russet, often with numerous pale-edged dark dashes.

Habitat and Range: Heathland, woodland and eucalypt forest. TNQ, Shipton's Flat, Yungaburra, Herberton. Patchy distribution, eastern and southern Australia.

Steve Wilson

Skinks

This is the most diverse of Australia's reptile families, with 375 known species. These range in size from 30 mm to 300 mm (SVL) and have highly varied body forms and habits. Most have well developed fore and hindlimbs with 5 digits on each. Where limb length and digit number vary from this 'norm', information is provided in the species accounts. A skink is easily recognised by its overlapping body scales and large, symmetrical head scales.

A. brevicollis, QM. Bruce Cowell

Worm Skinks (*Anomalopus* spp.)

Anomalopus brevicollis
Anomalopus gowi

Identification: SVL 50–80 mm. Limbs absent. Lower eyelid movable, scaly. No ear opening. Tip of snout opaque. Body pale to rich brown with longitudinal rows of dark flecks; darker on head and tail-tip. Mid-body scale rows 18–22; scales smooth. *A. brevicollis* (usually three supraoculars, six supralabials, frontoparietals in contact); *A. gowi* (two supraoculars, usually five supralabials, separated frontoparietals).

Habitat and Range: Open forest, rainforest, vine thickets. *A. brevicollis*, TNQ, Mt Abbot, Finch Hatton; also west to Clemont (near Bowen) south to Theodore, Qld. *A. gowi*, TNQ only, Mt Garnet, Townsville area.

Verreaux's Skink
Anomalopus verreauxi

Identification: SVL 185 mm. Limbs very small. Three fingers, one toe. Lower eyelid movable, scaly. No ear opening. Body grey to brown; paler band across neck, obscure in large specimens. Midbody scale rows 18–23; scales smooth.

Habitat and Range: Open forest, rainforest, vine thickets. TNQ, Conway Ra., Clarke Ra.; east coast to north-eastern NSW.

QM

Thornton Peak Calyptotis
Calyptotis thorntonensis

Identification: SVL 35 mm. Limbs short. Lower eyelid movable, scaly. No ear opening. Body brown, with dark flecks; blackish stripe along upper flanks. Midbody scale rows 24; scales smooth.

Habitat and Range: Upland rainforest. TNQ only, Thornton Peak and adjacent mountains.

QM

Rainbow Skinks (*Carlia* spp.)

Carlia jarnoldae

Identification: SVL 40 mm. Four fingers, 5 toes. Lower eyelid movable, large transparent window. Ear opening horizontal, small pointed scale on front edge. Breeding male brown with black stripes; upper flanks black with small blue spots; lower flanks red to orange. Female brown, rows of dark flecks; flanks dark with white stripe. Midbody scale rows 26–33; back scales 6-sided with 3 strongly raised lines.

Habitat and Range: Dry eucalypt forest, heath. TNQ, Cooktown to Collinsville. Australia, also north to Heathlands (Cape York).

QM

Bruce Cowell

Carlia longipes

Identification: SVL 55 mm. Four fingers, 5 toes. Lower eyelid movable with small transparent window. Ear opening circular or vertical, pointed scales on front edge. Body brown, sides red; black stripe from nostril to just behind forelimb. Midbody scale rows 30–41; back scales with rounded hind edge, smooth or with moderately raised lines. Breeding male, white throat.

Habit and Range: Open forest, rainforest edges. TNQ, Cooktown to Hinchinbrook I. Australia, also Cape York, Qld, eastern Arnhem Land, NT.

Similar Species: *C. rostralis,* breeding male has black throat (see p. 214).

QM, Bruce Cowell

Carlia munda

Identification: SVL 40 mm. Four fingers, 5 toes. Lower eyelid movable with large transparent window. Ear opening horizontal, few small scales on upper edge. Body olive-brown, white line from under eye to top of ear and from below ear to beyond forelimb. Midbody scale rows 24–32; back scales with rounded hind edge, smooth or with moderately raised lines.

Habitat and Range: Open forest, woodland. TNQ, Palmer R. (near Cooktown) to Collinsville. Australia, northern WA, NT, northern and eastern Qld.

Carlia mundivensis

Identification: SVL 55 mm. Four fingers, 5 toes. Lower eyelid movable with small transparent window. Ear opening vertical, pointed scales around edges. Body olive-grey with darker blotches and pale speckling. Midbody scale rows 34–42; back scales 6-sided with 2 or 3 strongly raised lines.

Habitat and Range: Open forest, dry vine thickets. TNQ, Chillagoe to near Sarina; also south to Mount Morgan, Qld.

QM

Carlia pectoralis

Identification: SVL 52 mm. Four fingers, 5 toes. Lower eyelid movable with large transparent window. Ear opening vertical, one or two enlarged scales on front edge. Body grey-brown, back with black and white flecks. Breeding male has two red stripes between fore and hindlimbs. Midbody scale rows 23–34; back scales 6-sided with 3 strongly raised lines.

Habitat and Range: Open forest, woodland, dry vine thickets. TNQ, Mount Molloy to Sarina; also eastern Qld.

Similar Species: *C. vivax* 2 strongly raised lines on each back scale, (see p. 215).

QM, D Knowles

Carlia rhomboidalis
Carlia rubrigularis

Identification: SVL 60 mm. Four fingers, 5 toes. Lower eyelid movable with small, transparent window. Interparietal and frontoparietals fused to form single shield. Ear opening round, 1 to 3 large, pointed scales on front edge. Body brown; pale, indistinct stripe may run from behind eye to tail. *C. rhomboidalis*, chin bright blue, throat pink. *C. rubrigularis*, chin and throat pink. Midbody scale rows 28–38; back scales with rounded hind edge, smooth.

Habitat and Range: Rainforest, wet eucalypt forest. TNQ only, *C. rhomboidalis*, Magnetic I. to Sarina; *C. rubrigularis*, Big Tableland, to Mt Halifax (near Townsville).

C. rhomboidalis , QM

Carlia rubrigularis, QM, Bruce Cowell

QM

Carlia rostralis

Identification: SVL 70 mm. Four fingers, 5 toes. Lower eyelid movable with small transparent window. Ear opening vertical, pointed scales on front edge. Body brown, black flecks along back; black stripe from tip of snout to behind forelimb (to hindlimb in male), bordered above by white stripe. Midbody scale rows 30–38; back scales with rounded hind edge and moderately raised lines.

Habitat and Range: Grassland, woodland. TNQ, Laura to near Townsville; also Gulf of Carpentaria.

Similar Species: *C. longipes* (see p. 212).

QM, Bruce Cowell

Carlia schmeltzii

Identification: SVL 69 mm. Four fingers, 5 toes. Lower eyelid movable with small transparent window. Ear opening vertical, 2 short, rounded scales on front edge. Body brown, flanks grey-brown. Breeding male, lower flanks red, throat scales edged with black. Midbody scale rows 31–38; back scales 6-sided with 2 or 3 strongly raised lines.

Habitat and Range: Open forest, woodland. TNQ, Cooktown to Sarina; also Weipa to south-east Qld.

QM

Carlia scirtetis

Identification: SVL 64 mm. Four fingers, 5 toes. Lower eyelid movable with small transparent window. Ear opening vertical, surrounded by pointed scales. Body brownish black, lighter flecks on back may form 3 ill-defined lines. Pale blue spots on limbs. Midbody scale rows 40–45; back scales with rounded hind edge and 3 or 4 moderately raised lines.

Habitat and Range: Granite boulders. TNQ only, Black Mtn NP.

Carlia storri
Carlia vivax

Identification: SVL 47 mm. Four fingers, five toes. Lower eyelid movable with transparent window. *C. storri*, ear opening round, surrounded by pointed scales; lower eyelid has small window. Breeding male, brown, legs and tail orange; female, greenish-brown, pale lines from behind eyes to tail, along mid-back, and between fore and hindlimbs. *C. vivax*, ear opening vertical, 1 large rounded scale on front edge; lower eyelid has large window. Breeding male brown, sides pink, throat blue; females light brown, with 2 white stripes on either side of body. Midbody scale rows 23–34; back scales 6-sided with 2 strongly raised lines.

Habit and Range: Open forest, woodland, beach foredunes. *C. storri*, TNQ, Cooktown to Townsville; also northern and eastern Cape York, Qld. *C. vivax*, TNQ, Cooktown to Sarina, including continental islands; Australia, eastern Qld and north-eastern NSW.

Carlia storri, QM, Bruce Cowell

C. vivax, QM, Steve Wilson

Coeranoscincus frontalis

Identification: SVL 250 mm. Limbless. Lower eyelid movable, scaly. No ear opening. Body grey to brown above, cream below; head white in juveniles. Midbody scale rows 28–32; back scales smooth.

Habitat and Range: Rainforest. TNQ only, Mt Sorrow (near Cape Tribulation) to Mt Elliot.

QM, Steve Wilson

Cryptoblepharus litoralis, QM

C. plagiocephalus, QM, Bruce Cowell

Cryptoblepharus litoralis
Cryptoblepharus plagiocephalus

Identification: SVL to 55 mm. Eye covered by transparent, immovable scale. Ear opening present. Body greyish-brown, ragged-edged pale stripes from above eyes to tail. Midbody scale rows 22–30; back scales smooth. *C. litoralis*, feet with shiny black lower surfaces; *C. plagiocephalus*, feet with brownish lower surfaces.

Habitat and Range: *C. litoralis*, beaches, on rocks and trees; TNQ, Cooktown to near Mackay; Australia, Torres Strait to Gladstone, Qld. *C. plagiocephalus*, woodland, open forest; TNQ, Palmerville (near Cooktown) to Bowen; Australia, WA, NT, Qld and western SA.

QM, Bruce Cowell

Cryptoblepharus virgatus

Identification: SVL 40 mm. Eye covered by transparent immovable scale. Ear opening present. Body dark; prominent, straight edged, black and cream stripes from above eyes to base of tail. Midbody scale rows 20–28; back scales smooth.

Habitat and Range: Dry forest, woodland, mangroves, urban areas. TNQ, Cooktown to Sarina. Coastal eastern and southern Australia.

Striped Skinks (*Ctenotus* spp.)

Ctenotus monticola

Identification: SVL 65 mm. Lower eyelid movable, scaly. Ear opening present, 2–4 enlarged scales on front edge. Back brown, thin pale-edged, black centre stripe; dark-edged white stripes from eyes to tail; sides blackish with row of pale blotches; white line from snout to tail on flanks. Midbody scale rows 24–28; back scales smooth.

Habitat and Range: Woodland with granite outcrops. TNQ only, near Mareeba.

QM, Steve Wilson

Ctenotus robustus
Ctenotus spaldingi
Ctenotus nullum

Identification: SVL to 110 mm. Lower eyelid movable, scaly. Ear opening present, 3–7 enlarged scales on front edge. Back olive to brown; broad, pale-edged, black stripe along centre (bold to obscure); dark-edged, white stripes from eyes to tail; sides dark brown to black with row of small, pale spots; obscure pale line on flanks with brown mottling below. *C. spaldingi*, 3 supraocular scales; *C. nullum* and *C. robustus*, 4 supraocular scales. *C. nullum*, prefrontals separated or in narrow contact; *C. robustus*, prefrontals in broad contact. Midbody scale rows 26–32; back scales smooth.

Habitat and Range: Dry forest, woodland. *C. robustus*, TNQ, Cooktown to Sarina; coastal northern, eastern and southern Australia. *C. spaldingi*, TNQ, Cooktown to Chillagoe; Australia, northern NT and northern Qld. *C. nullum*, TNQ only, near Cooktown (Laura, Black Mtn NP, Shipton's Flat).

Ctenotus robustus, QM. Jeff Wright

Ctenotus spaldingi, Steve Wilson

Ctenotus nullum, QM. Seve Wilson

Ctenotus taeniolatus

Identification: SVL 65 mm. Lower eyelid movable, scaly. Ear opening present, 2–5 small scales on front edge. Body with pale and dark stripes. Midbody scale rows 26–34; back scales smooth.

Habitat and Range: Open forest, woodland, parks and gardens. TNQ, Cairns to Mackay. Australia, south to northern Vic.

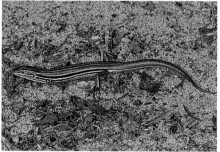

QM

QM

Ctenotus terrareginae

Identification: SVL 91 mm. Lower eyelid movable, scaly. Ear opening present, 3–4 pointed scales on front edge. Back dark brown, black vertebral stripe on neck; narrow white stripe from eye to tail tip, edged above with black. Bold, narrow, white stripe along middle of flanks; upper flanks with broad black stripe; lower flanks with dark brown zone containing white blotches towards front. Midbody scale rows 26–28; back scales smooth.

Habitat and Range: Open forest. TNQ only, Hinchinbrook I., Kirrama Ra., Paluma.

QM, Gary Cranitch

Pink-tongued Skink
Cyclodomorphus gerrardii

Identification: SVL 200 mm. Lower eyelid movable, scaly. Ear opening present, enlarged scales on front edge. Body grey to brown, black bands from neck to tip of tail; tip of snout black. Some adults unbanded, juveniles strongly banded. Midbody scale rows 30–34; back scales smooth.

Habitat and Range: Rainforest, tall open forest, woodland, parks and gardens. TNQ, Cairns to Ingham, near Proserpine, Clarke Ra. Australia, coastal areas south to Sydney.

QM, Jeff Wright

Major Skink
Egernia frerei

Identification: SVL 180 mm. Lower eyelid movable, scaly. Ear opening present, enlarged scales on front edge. Body brown; back with longitudinal rows of black streaks; sides blackish with numerous pale flecks. Midbody scale rows 32–36; back scales with several, low, raised lines.

Habitat and Range: Rainforest, open forest, woodland. TNQ, Cooktown to Mackay. Eastern Australia, Torres Strait to north-eastern NSW.

Hosmer's Skink
Egernia hosmeri

Identification: SVL 80 mm. Lower eyelid movable, scaly. Ear opening present, enlarged scales on front edge. Body fawn to rich brown with scattered, pale and dark blotches. Midbody scale rows 24–28; back scales with 3–4 spiny, raised lines.

Habitat and Range: Rocky, dry ranges, open forest. TNQ, Kaban (near Ravenshoe), Stannary Hills (near Herberton). Australia, eastern NT, north Qld, (excluding Cape York).

QM, Bruce Cowell

Yakka Skink
Egernia rugosa

Identification: SVL 200 mm. Lower eyelid movable, scaly. Ear opening present, enlarged scales on front edge. Body brown; broad, dark, back stripe. Midbody scale rows 26–30; back scales with low, raised lines.

Habitat and Range: Dry open forest, woodland. TNQ, near Cooktown, Herbert R. Gorge (near Ingham). Australia, patchy distribution from eastern Cape York to south-eastern Qld.

QM, Bruce Cowell

Eulamprus amplus

Identification: SVL 110 mm. Lower eyelid movable, scaly. Ear opening present. Body olive-brown with narrow, yellowish bands; prominent black patch above forelimb. Midbody scale rows 40–52; back scales smooth.

Habitat and Range: Rainforest. TNQ only, Mt Abbot to Mt Jukes (near Mackay).

QM

Eulamprus frerei, QM. Jeff Wright

E. sokosoma, QM. Steve Wilson

E. tenuis, QM

Bar-sided Skinks
Eulamprus brachysoma
Eulamprus frerei
Eulamprus sokosoma
Eulamprus tenuis

Identification: SVL to 86 mm. Lower eyelid movable, scaly. Ear opening present. Body greyish to dark brown; dark, ragged-edged streak from head to tail base. Midbody scale rows 28–38; back scales smooth. Species difficult to distinguish. *E. frerei,* upper secondary temporal overlapped by lower secondary temporal. *E. tenuis,* dark vertebral streak on neck. *E. brachysoma,* medium brown with 28–32 midbody scale rows. *E. sokosoma,* light brown with 32–38 midbody scale rows.

Habitat and Range: Open forest, vine thickets, rainforest. *E. brachysoma,* TNQ, Cooktown to Mackay; Australia, eastern Qld. *E. frerei,* TNQ only, summit of Mt Bartle Frere. *E. sokosoma,* TNQ, near Townsville; Australia, patchy distribution south to Carnarvon Ra., Qld. *E. tenuis,* TNQ, Mareeba to Mackay; Australia, north-eastern Qld to south-eastern NSW.

QM

Eulamprus luteilateralis

Identification: SVL 90 mm. Lower eyelid movable, scaly. Ear opening present. Body brown with scattered darker scales; flanks orange with scattered white spots; prominent black patch above forelimb. Midbody scale rows 36–42; back scales smooth.

Habitat and Range: Upland rainforest. TNQ only, Clarke Ra.

Eulamprus tigrinus

Identification: SVL 80 mm. Lower eyelid movable, scaly. Ear opening present. Body coppery-brown; back and sides with irregular, broken, black bars, no black blotching on head. Midbody scale rows 28–32; back scales smooth.

Habitat and Range: Rainforest. TNQ only, Shipton's Flat to Kirrama Ra.

Similar Species: *E. brachysoma*, usually with continuous, black, side stripe; black blotching on top of head (see p. 220).

Michael Anthony

Eastern Water Skink
Eulamprus quoyii

Identification: SVL 100 mm. Lower eyelid movable, scaly. Ear opening present. Body olive-brown; distinct gold stripes down sides of back from eyes to tail base; sides with broad black zone and pale flecks. Midbody scale rows 36–44; back scales smooth.

Habitat and Range: Open forest, rainforest, urban areas, usually near water. TNQ, Cooktown to Sarina. Australia, also south to southern NSW; along Murray-Darling R. system, SA and Vic.

QM, Jeff Wright

Glaphyromorphus cracens

Identification: SVL 50 mm. Limbs short. Lower eyelid movable, scaly. Ear opening present. Body fawn to brown, flecked with black; broad black side stripes from tip of snout to tail base. Midbody scale rows 20–22; back scales smooth.

Habitat and Range: Woodland, vine thickets. TNQ only, Chillagoe to west of Townsville.

QM, Steve Wilson

Glaphyromorphus fuscicaudis, Steve Wilson

G. nigricaudis, Michael Anthony

Glaphyromorphus fuscicaudis
Glaphyromorphus nigricaudis

Identification: SVL 90 mm. Lower eyelid movable, scaly. Ear opening present. Body brown, with black flecks that form wavy bands at front. Midbody scale rows 26–30; back scales smooth. *G. fuscicaudis*, 60 or more scales along back between parietals and back edge of hindlimb. *G. nigricaudis*, less than 60 scales.

Habitat and Range: Open forest, heath, rainforest. *G. fuscicaudis*, TNQ only, Big Tableland to Bluewater Ra. *G. nigricaudis*, TNQ, Cooktown to Dunk I; Australia, also northern and eastern Cape York, Arnhem Land, NT.

Michael Anthony

Glaphyromorphus mjobergi

Identification: SVL 90 mm. Limbs short. Lower eyelid movable, scaly. Ear opening present. Body rich brown; back plain, or each scale bearing a black streak; sides chequered with darker blotches. Midbody scale rows 22; back scales smooth.

Habitat and Range: Upland rainforest. TNQ only, Carbine Tableland to Vine Ck (near Ravenshoe).

Steve Wilson

Glaphyromorphus pumilus

Identification: SVL 50 mm. Limbs short. Lower eyelid movable, scaly. Ear opening present. Body fawn to brown; dark brown fleck on each scale; two rows of larger flecks along centre of back; broad, black side stripes from snout to tail. Midbody scale rows 20; back scales smooth.

Habitat and Range: Woodland, dry open forest. TNQ, near Cooktown and Cairns. Australia, eastern Cape York.

Glaphyromorphus punctulatus

Identification: SVL 55 mm. Limbs short. Lower eyelid movable, scaly. Ear opening present. Body brown; dark brown flecks on back and flanks. Midbody scale rows 18-20; back scales smooth.

Habitat and Range: Open forest, rainforest edges. TNQ, Ravenshoe to Broken R. (near Mackay), including continental islands. also south to Mt Walsh, south-eastern Qld.

QM, Bruce Cowell

Prickly Forest Skink
Gnypetoscincus queenslandiae

Identification: SVL 80 mm. Lower eyelid movable, scaly. Ear opening present. Body dark brown with irregular pale bands. Midbody scale rows 32–36; back scales prickly.

Habitat and Range: Rainforest. TNQ only, Big Tableland to Kirrama Ra.

QM, Jeff Wright

Sun Skinks (*Lampropholis* spp.)

Lampropholis adonis

Identification: SVL 51 mm. Lower eyelid movable with transparent window. Ear opening present. Body mid to dark brown, black flecks on back; flanks dark or with rows of dark streaks; belly grey; tail often with reddish flush below. Midbody scale rows 25–33; back scales smooth with 3–4 weak lines.

Habitat and Range: Rainforest. TNQ, Mt Dryander (near Proserpine) to Eungella. Australia, also Carnarvon Ra., Maryborough to Gympie, Qld.

QM, Jeff Wright

QM, Bruce Cowell

Lampropholis coggeri

Identification: SVL 41mm. Lower eyelid movable with transparent window. Ear opening present. Body reddish-brown to olive-brown with pale spots and black dashes; sides dark, flecked with pale spots. Midbody scale rows 26-31; back scales smooth. Dark sides grade evenly into lighter lower flanks.

Habitat and Range: Rainforest. TNQ only, Big Tableland to Mt Elliot.

Similar Species: *L. robertsi,* dark sides sharply demarcated from lighter lower flanks (see p. 225).

Michael Anthony

Lampropholis delicata

Identification: SVL 40 mm. Lower eyelid movable with transparent window. Ear opening present. Body greyish-brown to bronze; sides usually darker than back; narrow, white line often on flanks. Midbody scale rows 24–30; back scales smooth.

Habitat and Range: Open forest, woodland, heath, parks and gardens. TNQ, Mount Molloy to Mackay. Eastern and southern Australia, south to Port Lincoln, SA, eastern Tas.

QM

Lampropholis mirabilis

Identification: SVL 50 mm. Lower eyelid movable with transparent window. Ear opening present. Body brownish with scattered light and dark blotches and spots; flanks with obscure vertical bars. Midbody scale rows 29–33; back scales smooth.

Habitat and Range: Rainforest, vine thickets, dense riverine forest. TNQ only, Townsville area (Magnetic I., Mt Cleveland, Mt Elliot).

Lampropholis robertsi

Identification: SVL 49 mm. Lower eyelid movable with transparent window. Ear opening present. Body reddish-brown to golden-brown; sides black to chocolate-brown. Midbody scale rows 25–30; back scales usually smooth.

Habitat and Range: Upland rainforest. TNQ only, Mt Boolbun South (near Cooktown) to Mt Fisher (near Ravenshoe).

Similar Species: *L. coggeri* (see p. 224).

Steve Wilson

Lerista colliveri

Identification: SVL 84 mm. Forelimb a minute stub; hindlimb small, 1 toe. Lower eyelid movable with transparent window. Ear opening minute, overlapped by surrounding scales. Body tan with more or less continuous, dark lines. Midbody scale rows 18; back scales smooth.

Habitat and Range: Open forest, vine thickets. TNQ, near Townsville (Hervey Ra. to Fanning R.). Australia, also west to Hughenden, Qld.

QM, Glenn Shea

Lerista zonulata

Identification: SVL 45 mm. Limbs small. Four fingers, 4 toes. Eye covered by transparent, immovable scale. Ear opening minute, overlapped by surrounding scales. Body bronze, 4 rows of black dots on back; broad, black stripe along flanks. Midbody scale rows 20–22; back scales smooth.

Habitat and Range: Dry open forest, woodland. TNQ, Windsor Tableland to Cape Upstart. Australia, north-eastern Qld, west to Hughenden.

QM, D Knowles

Lygisaurus laevis, Steve Wilson

L. tanneri, QM. Jeff Wright

Lygisaurus zuma, Steve Wilson

Litter Skinks (*Lygisaurus* spp.)

Lygisaurus aeratus
Lygisaurus laevis
Lygisaurus tanneri
Lygisaurus zuma

Identification: SVL 39 mm. Four fingers, 5 toes. Lower eyelid movable with transparent window. Ear opening present. Body brownish, speckling on back and flanks. Breeding male, red throat, tail and hindlimbs. Midbody scale rows 19–27; back scales smooth. *L. aeratus* and *L. zuma*, large window in lower eyelid. *L. aeratus*, pointed scales around ear. *L. zuma*, flat, low scales around ear. *L. laevis* and *L. tanneri*, small window in lower eyelid. *L. laevis*, pointed scales around ear. *L. tanneri*, flat, low scales around ear.

Habitat and Range: Grassland, open forest, rainforest. *L. aeratus*, TNQ, Cooktown to Rollingstone; also north to Coen. *L. laevis*, TNQ only, near Cooktown to Bramston Beach. *L. tanneri*, TNQ, near Cooktown, also north to McIvor R. (Cape York). *L. zuma*, TNQ only, Paluma to Mackay.

Lygisaurus foliorum

Identification: SVL 39 mm. Four fingers, 5 toes. Eye covered by transparent, immovable scale. Ear opening present, sharp or low flat scales around edges. Body greybrown; sides of throat speckled. Breeding male, pinkish-orange throat, tail and hindlimbs. Midbody scale rows 21–25; back scales smooth.

Habitat and Range: Open forest, woodland. TNQ, Tinaroo. Australia, north-eastern Qld to north-eastern NSW.

QM

Dwarf Skinks
Menetia sadlieri
Menetia timlowi

Identification: SVL 29 mm. Four fingers, 5 toes. Eye covered by transparent, immovable scale. Ear opening present. Body brown with darker sides. Midbody scale rows 18–20; back scales smooth. *M. sadlieri*, 2 pretemporal scales; *M. timlowi*, 1 pretemporal scale.

Habitat and Range: Woodland. *M. sadlieri*, TNQ only, Magnetic I.; *M. timlowi*, TNQ, near Mt Garnet; Australia, north-eastern to southern Qld.

Menetia timlowi, QM, Steve Wilson

Fire-tailed Skink
Morethia taeniopleura

Identification: SVL 40 mm. Eye covered by transparent, immovable scale. Ear opening present. Body grey-brown; pale stripe from snout, above eye to hind limb; sides glossy black, white stripe on lower flanks; tail russet to bright red. Midbody scale rows 26–34; back scales smooth.

Habitat and Range: Woodland. TNQ, Cooktown to Mt Aberdeen (near Bowen). Australia, eastern Qld.

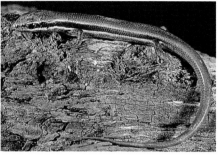
QM

Shade Skinks (*Saproscincus* spp.)

Saproscincus basiliscus

Identification: SVL 50 mm. Lower eyelid movable with transparent window. Ear opening present. Body pale brown to reddish-brown; black stripe from nostril to base of tail; pale spot at thigh/tail junction. Midbody scale rows 22–29; back scales smooth; 50–59 scales between parietals and back edge of hindlimb.

Habitat and Range: Rainforest. TNQ only, Roaring Meg Falls (near Cape Tribulation) to Mt Elliot.

Similar species: *S. lewisi*, SVL to 42 mm, 46–50 scales between parietals and back edge of hindlimb (see p. 228).

QM, Jeff Wright

QM, Steve Wilson

Saproscincus czechurai

Identification: SVL 40 mm. Lower eyelid movable with transparent window. Ear opening present. Body reddish-brown with scattered, dark and pale flecks; pale spot at thigh/tail junction. Midbody scale rows 22–24; back scales smooth.

Habitat and Range: Upland rainforest. TNQ only, Big Tableland to Cardwell Ra.

Similar Species: *S. tetradactylus* (see below).

Saproscincus hannahae, QM, Bruce Cowell

Saproscincus lewisi, QM, Jeff Wright

Saproscincus hannahae
Saproscincus lewisi

Identification: SVL 42 mm. Lower eyelid movable with transparent window. Ear opening present. Body fawn to mid-brown, scattered dark spots on back; brown band between eye and forelimb; sides speckled; pale spot at thigh/tail junction. Midbody scale rows 20–24; back scales smooth.

Habitat and Range: Rainforest. *S. hannahae*, TNQ only, Mt Dryander (near Proserpine) to Sarina. *S. lewisi*, TNQ, Helenvale to Cape Tribulation; Australia, also north to Mt Webb.

Similar Species: *S. basiliscus* (see p. 227).

Steve Wilson

Saproscincus tetradactylus

Identification: SVL 30 mm. Four fingers, 5 toes. Lower eyelid movable with transparent window. Ear opening present. Body dark brown; broken black stripe from behind eye to base of tail; pale spot at thigh/tail junction. Midbody scale rows 22–26; back scales smooth.

Habitat and Range: Rainforest. TNQ only, Mossman Gorge to Paluma.

Similar Species: *S. czechurai*, 5 fingers (see above).

Bartle-Frere Skink
Techmarscincus jigurru

Identification: SVL 70 mm. Lower eyelid movable with transparent window. Ear-opening present. Body rich brown with darker and lighter flecks; flanks blackish, with pale series of blotches. Midbody scale rows 30; back scales smooth.

Habitat and Range: Rainforest. TNQ only, summit of Mt Bartle Frere.

QM, Jeff Wright

Eastern Blue-tongued Lizard
Tiliqua scincoides

Identification: SVL 300 mm. Limbs short. Lower eyelid movable, scaly. Ear opening present, 2–3 enlarged scales on front edge. Body greyish-brown, irregular dark bands on back and tail. Midbody scale rows 34–40; back scales smooth.

Habitat and Range: Heath, open forest, woodland. TNQ, Cooktown to Cardwell, near Bowen and Proserpine. Northern and eastern Australia.

QM, Bruce Cowell

Dragons

Dragons have long limbs and tails, and rough, 'matt' skins. Many species have enlarged, spiny scales on the back and neck. Sixty-six species are known in Australia.

Nobbi
Amphibolurus nobbi

Identification: SVL 75 mm. Tail long, slender; twice as long as SVL. Body grey to brown, series of dark blotches across back; yellowish stripe down either side of back, another along mid-line of each flank; pink flush often on tail. Row of enlarged scales down centre of back, no black patch in front of forelimb.

Habitat and Range: Tall open forest, woodland. TNQ, Ravenshoe to near Proserpine. Australia, eastern Qld, northern and western NSW, eastern SA.

Similar Species: *Diporiphora* spp., no row of enlarged scales down back, often black patch in front of forelimb (see p. 230).

QM

QM

Frilled Lizard
Chlamydosaurus kingii

Identification: SVL 220 mm. Tail long, slender; twice as long as SVL. Large frill around head. Body grey, brown to orange or almost black.

Habitat and Range: Open forest, woodland. TNQ, Cooktown area, Herberton, Mareeba, Mount Molloy, Proserpine area. Northern and eastern Australia to Brisbane, Qld.

D. australis, QM

D. bilineata, QM

Tommy Round-head
Diporiphora australis
Northern Two-lined Dragon
Diporiphora bilineata

Identification: SVL 50 mm. Tail long, slender; 2.3 times longer than SVL. Body pale grey to reddish-brown; back has pale grey vertebral stripe and dark bars; pale stripe down either side. *D. australis* has gular fold (throat crease lined with minute scales); *D. bilineata* lacks gular fold.

Habitat and Range: Dry forest and woodland, coastal dunes. *D. australis*, TNQ, Maytown (near Cooktown) to Collinsville; Australia, northern and eastern Qld to Brisbane. *D. bilineata*, TNQ, Cooktown to Chillagoe; Australia, northern NT, northern Qld.

Similar Species: Nobbi (see p. 229).

QM, Jeff Wright

Boyd's Forest Dragon
Hypsilurus boydii

Identification: SVL 150 mm. Tail long, slender; twice as long as SVL. Neck with fleshy fold, topped with large, white spines. Large spines along centre of back. Body rich brown, sides blackish.

Habitat and Range: Rainforest. TNQ only, Big Tableland to Paluma.

Eastern Water Dragon
Physignathus lesueurii

Identification: SVL 200 mm. Tail long and slender; 2–2.5 times longer than SVL. Enlarged spines on neck and centre of back. Body grey-brown, blackish bands across back, black stripe behind eye; lower surfaces yellowish to red.

Habitat and Range: Waterways in closed and moist, open forest. TNQ, north arm of Endeavour R. to Sarina. Australia, coastal areas south to Vic.

QM

Goannas

Goannas have long necks and slender heads. Their skin is covered in small, bead-like scales. They have powerful feet with long, curved claws. A goanna's tongue is forked, unlike that of other lizards. Twenty-four species are known in Australia.

Sand Goanna
Varanus gouldii

Yellow-spotted Monitor
Varanus panoptes

Identification: SVL 670 mm. Tail flattened sideways, long, slender; 1.5 times longer than SVL. Body yellowish to dark brown with bands of pale and dark spots; dark stripe behind eye. *V. gouldii*, tail tip without dark bands, belly with scattered dark flecks. *V. panoptes*, tail tip with dark bands, rows of dark spots across belly.

Habitat and Range: Dry forest, woodland. *V. gouldii*, TNQ, Cooktown to Townsville; Australia-wide, except extreme south-east. *V. panoptes*, TNQ, Cairns to Carlisle I.; northern and western Australia.

V. gouldii, QM

V. panoptes, QM

QM, Bruce Cowell

Spotted Tree Monitor
Varanus scalaris

Identification: SVL 250 mm. Tail cylindrical, long, slender; 1.5 times longer than SVL. Body grey to black with large, dark-centred, cream spots. Scales above eyes gradually merge with those in centre of head.

Habitat and Range: Rainforest, open forest. TNQ, Home Rule (near Cooktown) to near Proserpine. Northern and eastern Australia.

Similar Species: Black-tailed Monitor scales above eyes very small, forming sharp boundary with larger scales in centre of head (see p. 233).

QM

Rusty Monitor
Varanus semiremex

Identification: SVL 260 mm. Tail cylindrical at base, flattened sideways towards tip, long, slender; 1.6 times longer than SVL. Body greyish-brown with scattered black flecks.

Habitat and Range: Mangroves, coastal swamps. TNQ, Cardwell, Townsville area; Cape Hillsborough area. Australia, patchy distribution from Cape York to Gladstone, Qld.

QM, Gary Cranitch

Storr's Monitor
Varanus storri

Identification: SVL 160 mm. Tail cylindrical with distinct spines; 1.4 times longer than SVL. Body pale to reddish-brown with darker, 'netted' pattern.

Habitat and Range: Open forest, in rocky areas. TNQ, Archer Point (near Cooktown), Lappa Junction (near Chillagoe), Fanning R. Caves (near Townsville). Patchy distribution across northern Australia.

Black-tailed Monitor
Varanus tristis

Identification: SVL 280 mm. Tail cylindrical, long, slender; up to 2.3 times longer than SVL. Body grey, brown or black with small, dark-centred cream spots; head, neck and tail often black.

Habitat and Range: Open forest, woodland. TNQ, Cooktown to Shute Harbour, including continental islands. Australia-wide, except south and south-east.

Similar Species: Spotted Tree Monitor (see p. 232).

QM

Lace Monitor
Varanus varius

Identification: SVL 550 mm. Tail long, slender, narrow; 1.5 times longer than SVL. Body grey to black with creamy, yellow bands and rows of spots; black bands across chin.

Habitat and Range: Woodland, open and closed forest. TNQ, Shipton's Flat to Eungella and Mackay. Coastal Australia, Cape Melville (Cape York), Qld, to south-east SA.

QM

Brown Tree Snake, QM, Jeff Wright

SNAKES

Forty-one species of snakes are known from Tropical North Queensland. In the following species accounts, the front-fanged (elapid) species are presented first and include all medically significant and potentially dangerous terrestrial species. Accounts of the elapids are followed by those of the back-fanged and solid-toothed species (colubrid), pythons (boids) and blind snakes (typhlopids).

The TNQ and Australian distributions for each species are based on scientific papers and specimens in the Queensland Museum collection. While these present a good picture of where the species occur, it is important to recognise that they may not always be complete. A handful of Australian species also occur in New Guinea and eastern Indonesia, but details of these have not been included. Reports of new occurrences (based on specimens, not just sightings) are always welcomed by the Museum.

Identification

The photographs here provide enough information for identification in many cases, but it is not wise to rely on these alone. Colour can be deceptive when identifying a snake. Both Red-bellied Black and Small-eyed Snakes have black backs and red bellies; and Eastern Brown Snakes and Coastal Taipans can be brown, with cream bellies flecked with orange or salmon pink. Most snake species vary in colour and pattern and, although the photographs here show typical colours, information in the accounts should be checked. Where two species look alike, the accounts tell how to distinguish them. If there is doubt, or if someone has been bitten, contact the Queensland Museum. Identification advice can be obtained from either the Inquiry Centre (07 3840 7640) or the Vertebrate Section (07 3840 7708, 3840 7709). Written requests for information should be directed to the Queensland Museum Inquiry Centre, PO Box 3300, South Brisbane, Queensland 4101. Advice regarding the treatment of snakebite should be obtained from the Poisons Information Centre (131126).

If a snake is dead, or if a shed skin is available, the scales are useful for identification. The number of rows of scales around the middle of the body (mid-body scales) are counted, starting and finishing at (but not including) the large row of scales on the belly. Because rows of mid-

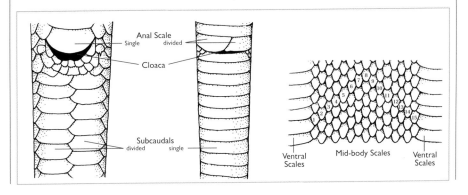

body scales overlap, they should be counted along a diagonal or in a 'zig zag'. The scale in front of the cloaca (anal scale) should be checked to see if it is single or divided and the scales under the tail (subcaudals) should be examined. Ventral (belly) scales can be checked, if doubt remains about an identification.

Potential Danger

The world's most venomous species of land snakes occur in Queensland. Twenty-seven of the land-dwelling species found in TNQ are venomous. Less than half of these are potentially dangerous. The distinction between 'venomous' and 'potentially dangerous' is clear. Crowned Snakes eat only tiny lizards and their venom is not dangerous to humans. By contrast, the Eastern Brown and Coastal Taipan prey on large animals, which they immobilise with highly toxic venom. Bites by these species are potentially dangerous to humans and can be fatal.

A 'full' bite by any of eight species (Coastal Taipan, Mulga, Death Adder, Northern Death Adder, Eastern Brown, Rough-scaled, Small-eyed and Red-bellied Black Snakes) in TNQ could prove fatal, if appropriate first aid and medical attention were not administered rapidly. Juveniles of these species are also potentially dangerous. The Papuan Whip, Black Whip and Yellow-faced Whip Snakes and the Pale-headed Snake are capable of inflicting bites that may have serious local and, occasionally, systemic effects.

In Australia, despite the presence of highly venomous species, the frequency of serious cases of snake bite is low and death from snake bite is rare. (Some 3000 cases of snakebite are reported each year. About 10 per cent are 'serious'.) The incidence of deaths from snake bite in Australia has declined steadily since the late 1940s (on average 3.5 per year) to less than 1 death per year (1988–90). This results from a better understanding of the effects of venoms on the human body and from effective first aid and medical treatment.

Snake venoms are a complex mix. They contain toxins with different effects.

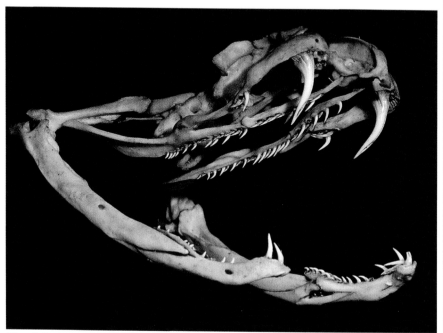

Taipan skull, QM

Death Adder, QM, Bruce Cowell

Neurotoxins affect the peripheral nervous system, causing drowsiness, paralysis and difficulty in breathing. Myotoxins destroy muscle tissues, resulting in weakness and kidney malfunction. Haemotoxins affect the blood by increasing clotting (coagulant) or bleeding (anticoagulant effects) or destroying blood cells (haemolysis). The severity of symptoms depends on the species of snake, its size and the size and health of the victim. There may be pain, swelling or bruising around the bite (local effects), or more widespread effects on entire body systems (systemic effects).

In Case of Snakebite

Any case of snake bite must be assessed carefully. Unless the snake is definitely non-venomous, or one of the species with only mild venom, first aid should be applied and medical help sought at the nearest casualty section of a public hospital. If a child has been bitten, first aid should be applied and medical advice must be sought. Any bite by a snake may require tetanus protection. Where a bite has occurred, identification of the snake is best undertaken by a Museum expert.

Properly-applied first aid will delay the onset of serious symptoms that may follow snake bite. The following procedure was devised by Dr (now Professor) Struan Sutherland and his colleagues at the Commonwealth Serum Laboratories in Melbourne. It is recommended for bites by all potentially dangerous Australian snakes.

1. Apply a broad firm bandage to cover the bitten area. In the case of a limb, as much as possible of the limb should be bound (as tightly as for a sprained ankle).

2. Immobilise the affected limb with a splint; leave this in place until medical care at a public hospital is reached.

3. Discourage the victim from moving around more than necessary.

4. If the snake can be killed safely, do so and bring it with the victim for identification.

5. Do not wash the bite site.
   It is always best to avoid being bitten.

Most snakes give an aggressor every chance to retreat. Several potentially dangerous species adopt characteristic defensive postures. Black Snakes flatten their necks and hiss and feint frantically. The Eastern Brown Snake 'stands up' in a distinctive 'S' position and strikes repeatedly. However, some species give little or no warning before biting and the move from a defensive posture to a warning or full bite can take place rapidly, with little provocation. For example, just being too close to a Coastal Taipan can result in a bite.

Snakes that are only mildly venomous, or which lack venom, also use warning behaviour. The Bandy Bandy's bold black and white colour signifies 'go away'. When provoked, a Bandy Bandy will reinforce this message by throwing itself into vertical loops, thrashing about and repeatedly re-arranging its posture. The Brown Tree Snake will 'stand up', hiss and feint, sometimes with mouth agape. Blind Snakes are non-venomous, but can emit a repulsive stench from special glands. The inherent message about how to avoid being bitten by snakes is clear — always leave them well alone.

**JA Covacevich, PJ Couper
and AP Amey**

Front-fanged Snakes

Front-fanged snakes (elapids) are the venomous species that dominate the Australian snake fauna. Their fangs (hollow teeth connected via ducts to venom glands near their eyes) are set at the front of their upper jaws. Although the group includes some of the world's most venomous species of snakes, the majority of elapids are inoffensive and virtually harmless.

QM, Bruce Cowell

Death Adder
Acanthophis antarcticus

Identification: Length to 60 cm. Head arrow-shaped. Tail sharply tapered to spine-like scale. Reddish or brown above; greyish or cream below; often banded with black flecks or darker brown. Mid-body scales 21–23; anal single; subcaudals, front single, back divided; ventrals 110–124.

Habitat and Range: Open forest. TNQ, Cairns to Eungella, including continental islands. Northern and eastern Australia.

Notes: Preys on frogs, Cane Toads (snake dies), small reptiles, birds, mammals. Live-bearer, up to 42 young.

Potentially dangerous. Venom strongly neurotoxic, weakly haemolytic and anti-coagulant.

QM, Bruce Cowell

Northern Death Adder
Acanthophis praelongus

Identification: Length to 40 cm. Head arrow-shaped. Tail sharply tapered to spine-like scale. Reddish or brown above, often banded with black flecks or darker brown; greyish or cream below. Mid-body scales 17–21; anal single; subcaudals, front single, back divided; ventrals 126–152.

Habitat and Range: Open forest. TNQ, Cooktown to Townsville. Australia, northern WA, NT, northern Qld.

Notes: Preys on frogs, Cane Toads (snake dies), small reptiles, birds, mammals. Live-bearer, number of young not known, probably about 8.

Potentially dangerous. Venom strongly neurotoxic, weakly haemolytic and anti-coagulant.

Northern Crowned Snake
Cacophis churchilli

Identification: Length to 30 cm. Metallic brown above; narrow, yellow band on back of head; greyish below. Mid-body scales 15; anal and subcaudals divided; ventrals 160–175.

Habitat and Range: Rainforest, moist open forest. Confined to Wet Tropics between Cape Tribulation and Dunk I., Qld.

Notes: Inoffensive, reluctant biter. Venom of low toxicity. Preys on skinks. Egg-layer, clutch size to 5.

Michael Anthony

White-crowned Snake
Cacophis harriettae

Identification: Length to 50 cm. Gun-metal grey above; cream 'stripe' round snout and neck area. Mid-body scales 15; anal and subcaudals divided; ventrals 180–200.

Habitat and Range: Open forest. TNQ, Proserpine to Mackay, including continental islands; also to north-eastern NSW.

Notes: Inoffensive, reluctant biter. Venom of low toxicity. Preys on skinks. Egg-layer, clutch size to 10.

Bruce Cowell

Krefft's Crowned Snake
Cacophis krefftii

Identification: Length to 35 cm. Dark brown, almost black above; narrow cream band runs across nape and towards snout; belly cream, scales edged with dark grey. Mid-body scales 15; anal and subcaudals divided; ventrals 140–160.

Habitat and Range: Rainforest and moist open forest. TNQ, Eungella area; also south-eastern Qld to mid-eastern NSW.

Notes: Inoffensive, reluctant biter. Venom of low toxicity. Preys on small skinks. Egg-layer, clutch size to 5.

QM

Steve Wilson

Carpentaria Whip Snake
Cryptophis boschmai

Identification: Length to 45 cm. Brown above; whitish below. Mid-body scales 15; anal and subcaudals single; ventrals 145–190.

Habitat and Range: Open forest. TNQ, Cooktown to Mackay; Australia, coastal northern and eastern Qld.

Notes: Inoffensive, reluctant biter. Venom of low toxicity. Live-bearer, up to 11 young.

Michael Anthony

Small-eyed Snake
Cryptophis nigrescens

Identification: Length to 1 m. Shiny black or grey-black above; cream to pink, sometimes red below. Mid-body scales 15; anal and subcaudals single; ventrals 165–210.

Habitat and Range: Open forest, rainforest, pasture and agricultural land. TNQ, Cooktown to Townsville, Mackay to Sarina. Coastal Australia, Cape York, Qld, to Vic.

Notes: Preys on skinks, geckos. Live-bearer, up to 8 young.

Potentially dangerous. Ready biter. Venom myotoxic.

Black-striped Snake
Cryptophis nigrostriatus

Identification: Length to 60 cm. Dark brown to reddish-brown above, always with full-length, darker stripe on mid-line; whitish below. Mid-body scales 15; anal and subcaudals single; ventrals 160–190.

Habitat and Range: Open forest. TNQ, Cooktown to Townsville, near Proserpine; Australia, coastal areas, Cape York to Gladstone, Qld.

Notes: Inoffensive, reluctant biter. Venom of low toxicity. Preys on skinks. Live-bearer, up to 9 young.

Michael Anthony

Yellow-faced Whip Snake
Demansia psammophis

Identification: Length to 1 m. Very slender, long tail; large prominent eyes. Bluish-grey, usually with rust-coloured 'stripes' along front third of back; eye surrounded by distinct 'comma' of black and yellow; narrow, dark lines across front of snout, between nostrils; belly usually green-grey. Mid-body scales 15; anal and subcaudals divided; ventrals 165–230.

Habitat and range: Open forest. TNQ, Cooktown to Mt Elliot, Proserpine to Sarina. Australia-wide, except northern NT and WA.

Notes: Preys on skinks, frogs, lizard eggs. Egg-layer, clutch size to 9.

Potential danger low, but in some circumstances (e.g. where multiple bites are concerned or where victim is a child), bites should be treated with caution. Venom weakly neurotoxic.

QM

Collared Whip Snake
Demansia torquata

Identification: Length to 70 cm. Very slender. Grey to brown above; head darker than body, marked by narrow, dark line across front of snout and between nostrils; pale rim around eye and dark streak curving back beneath it to form distinct 'comma'; grey-green below. Mid-body scales 15; anal and subcaudals divided; ventrals 185–220.

Habitat and Range: Open forest. TNQ, Cooktown to Airlie Beach, including continental islands. Australia, eastern NT, Qld except extreme south-east.

Notes: Venom weakly toxic. Preys on skinks, geckos. Egg-layer, clutch size to 8.

QM, Bruce Cowell

Black Whip Snake, QM, Bruce Cowell

Black Whip Snake
Demansia vestigiata
Papuan Whip Snake
Demansia papuensis

Identification: Eye large; body and tail long, slender; mid-body scales 15; anal and subcaudals divided. *D. vestigiata*, length 1.5 m; rich brown above, spotted black and flecked white; small, dark blotches on top of head; belly green-grey; ventrals 165–197. *D. papuensis*, length 2 m; black or dark brown above; belly pale grey to greenish; ventrals 192–228.

Habitat and Range: Open forest. *D. vestigiata*, TNQ, Cooktown to Sarina; Australia, northern WA, NT, Qld to Ipswich. *D. papuensis*, TNQ, Cooktown to Bowen; Australia, northern WA, NT, Qld to near Clermont.

Notes: *D. vestigiata*, preys on frogs and skinks. *D. papuensis*, prey unknown, probably frogs and skinks. Egg-layers; *D. vestigiata*, clutch size to 13; *D. papuensis*, clutch size to 20.

Potentially dangerous. *D. vestigiata*, bites not reported; putative effects similar to those from *D. papuensis* bites. *D. papuensis*, venom primarily neurotoxic; large specimens capable of serious (but probably not fatal) envenomation.

QM, Bruce Cowell

Barnard's Snake
Furina barnardi

Identification: Length to 50 cm. Brown above, light tan 'collar', dark brown snout; belly whitish. Mid-body scales 15; anal and subcaudals divided; ventrals about 185.

Habitat and Range: Open forest. TNQ, near Townsville; also south to Duaringa. Qld.

Notes: Probably not dangerous. Venom unknown. Preys on skinks. Egg-layer, clutch size to 10. Among the least known of Australian elapids.

Red-naped Snake
Furina diadema

Identification: Length to 40 cm. Brown above, with dark, 'netted' pattern from black edges of scales; head and nape area glossy black with orange to red band; belly cream. Mid-body scales 15, anal and subcaudals divided; ventrals 160–210.

Habitat and Range: Open forest. TNQ, Townsville, Proserpine to Mackay including continental islands. Australia, southern Qld, NSW, eastern SA.

Notes: Inoffensive, extremely reluctant biter. Venom weakly toxic. Preys on skinks. Egg-layer, clutch size to 5.

QM, Bruce Cowell

Orange-naped Snake
Furina ornata

Identification: Length to 40 cm. Light or dark orange or red-brown above; head almost black with reddish band that can be obscure in adults; belly cream. Mid-body scales 15; anal and subcaudals divided; ventrals 160–240.

Habitat and Range: Open forest. TNQ, Cooktown to Ayr. Australia, northern WA, NT, Qld.

Notes: Inoffensive, reluctant biter. Venom weakly toxic. Preys on skinks. Egg-layer, clutch size to 6.

Michael Anthony

Brown-headed Snake
Furina tristis

Identification: Length to 87 cm. Shiny dark brown above, lighter brown head, broad beige or cream 'collar'; belly cream. Mid-body scales 17; anal and subcaudals divided; ventrals 160–190.

Habitat and Range: Open forest. TNQ, Cooktown to Cape Tribulation; also Torres Strait, eastern Cape York, Qld.

Notes: Preys on skinks. Egg-layer, clutch size to 6.

Potentially dangerous. Easily provoked. Venom unknown, so large specimens should be treated with caution.

QM

QM

Marsh Snake
Hemiaspis signata

Identification: Length to 50 cm. Olive to grey above; two narrow, pale lines on each side of face, running through upper lip and from eye onto neck; belly grey to black. Mid-body scales 17; anal divided; subcaudals single; ventrals 150–170.

Habitat and Range: Rainforest and moist open forest. TNQ, Helenvale to Dunk I., Ayr, Eungella. Coastal Australia, Helenvale Qld, to near Eden, NSW.

Notes: Preys on frogs, skinks. Live-bearer, up to 20 young.

Not potentially dangerous, but venom is unknown and bites by large specimens should be treated with caution.

QM

Pale-headed snake
Hoplocephalus bitorquatus

Identification: Length to 80 cm. Head broad and distinct from narrow neck. Grey above; paler band across rear of head, bordered behind by black band and, in front, by row of black blotches; lips barred with black; belly grey. Mid-body scales 19 or 21; anal and subcaudals single; ventrals 190–225.

Habitat and Range: Open forest. TNQ, uncommon, known only from Mareeba, Herberton and Charters Towers. Australia, patchy distribution, Mareeba, Qld, to mid-eastern NSW.

Notes: Preys on frogs, lizards. Live-bearer, up to 11 young.

Potentially dangerous. Ready biter. Venom poorly known, primarily neurotoxic. One serious case of envenomation by large specimen has been reported.

Coastal Taipan
Oxyuranus scutellatus

Identification: Length to 2.6 m. Head large, distinct from neck. Glossy pale to dark brown above; belly cream, sometimes with orange or pink spots or blotches. Mid-body scales 21 or 23; anal single; subcaudals divided; ventrals 220–250.

Habitat and Range: Open forest, pasture, monsoon forest, grassy beach dunes. TNQ, Cooktown to Sarina. Australia, north-western WA, northern NT, coastal Qld from Cape York to Beaudesert.

Notes: Preys on mammals (rats, mice, bandicoots, marsupial 'cats'). Egg-layer, clutch size to 22.

Potentially the most dangerous snake in the world. Nervous, ready biter. Venom highly neurotoxic, also myotoxic and coagulant.

QM

QM, G Cranitch

Mulga Snake
Pseudechis australis

Identification: Length to 3 m. Head large, not distinct from neck. Pale brown above, cream below. Mid-body scales 17; anal divided; subcaudals, front single, back divided; ventrals 185–225.

Habitat and Range: Open forest. TNQ, Cooktown, near Mossman, Herberton, Gloucester I., near Paluma, Ayr, Charters Towers, Mackay. Drier areas Australia-wide, except southern coastal regions and Tas.

Notes: Preys on frogs, reptiles (dragons, skinks, goannas), mammals (rats and mice). Egg-layer, clutch size to 19.

Potentially dangerous. Ready biter. Venom strongly haemotoxic.

QM, Alan Easton

QM

Red-bellied Black Snake
Pseudechis porphyriacus

Identification: Length to 2 m. Glossy, coal black above; belly cream below, red extends to sides. Mid-body scales 17; anal divided; subcaudals, front single, back divided; ventrals 170–215.

Habitat and Range: Rainforest, moist open forest, pasture. TNQ, Big Tableland to Mt Elliot, Prosperpine, Eungella. Australia, also Gladstone, Qld, to NSW, Vic., south-eastern SA.

Notes: Preys on fish, frogs, Cane Toad (snake dies); skinks, snakes, small mammals. Live-bearer, up to 12 young. **Potentially dangerous. Venom strongly haemotoxic.**

QM

Eastern Brown Snake
Pseudonaja textilis

Identification: Length to 2.2 m. Colour and pattern highly variable. Often pale brown above; cream below, with pink or orange spots or blotches. Mid-body scales 17; anal and subcaudals divided; ventrals 185–235.

Habitat and Range: Open forest, pasture, agricultural land. TNQ, Cooktown to Sarina. Australia, Qld, NSW, much of Vic., isolated population in NT.

Notes: Preys on frogs, reptiles, birds, mammals. Egg-layer, clutch size to 28. **Potentially dangerous. Ready biter. Venom highly neurotoxic.**

Steve Wilson

North-eastern Burrowing Snake
Simoselaps warro

Identification: Length to 30 cm. Cream, orange or dark orange above with two dark, almost black marks on head and neck; belly cream, sometimes with dark line down middle of tail. Mid-body scales 15; anal and subcaudals divided; ventrals 135–165.

Habitat and Range: Open forest. TNQ, near Herberton, Mareeba, Mt Garnet, Townsville to Charters Towers; also south to Gladstone, Qld.

Notes: Reluctant biter. Venom unknown, probably weakly toxic. Preys on skinks. Egg-layer, clutch size to 5.

Curl Snake
Suta suta

Identification: Length to 60 cm. Brown above; head and nape with dark brown, nearly black 'hood'; belly cream. Mid-body scales 19; anal and subcaudals single; ventrals 150–170.

Habitat and Range: Open forest. TNQ, Mareeba, Chillagoe, Mingela. Australia, eastern WA, NT, drier parts of Qld, NSW, SA.

Notes: Preys on frogs, reptiles, reptile eggs, mammals. Live-bearer, to 7 young.

Potentially dangerous. Venom poorly known. Several cases of envenomation with moderate to severe symptoms have been reported.

QM, Bruce Cowell

Rough-scaled Snake
Tropidechis carinatus

Identification: Length to 1 m. Scales of back and sides with raised lines (keels). Head distinct from neck. Olive to greyish above, usually with black flecks forming a series of irregular bands or blotches; greenish-grey below. Mid-body scales 23; anal single; subcaudals single; ventrals 160–185.

Habitat and Range: Rainforest, moist open forest, pasture. TNQ, Thornton Peak to Bluewater Ra. Australia, also south-eastern Qld to mid-eastern NSW

Notes: Preys on frogs, reptiles, birds, mammals. Live-bearer, up to 19 young.

Similar Species: Freshwater Snake (see page 250). Rough-scaled Snake and Fresh-water Snake are only Australian land snakes with ridged back and side scales.

Potentially dangerous. Ready biter. Venom highly neurotoxic.

QM, Bruce Cowell

Bruce Cowell

Bandy Bandy
Vermicella annulata

Identification: Length to 75 cm. Head not distinct from body. Strongly banded black and white, above and below. Mid-body scales 15; anal and subcaudals divided; ventrals 180–320.

Habitat and Range: Open forest. TNQ, near Atherton, Mingela, and Mackay. Australia, Qld, most of NSW, SA, NT, central and mid-coastal WA.

Notes: Reluctant biter. Venom believed to be only weakly toxic. One case of envemonation reported to have resulted in considerable discomfort. Preys on blind snakes. Egg-layer, clutch size to 13.

Back-fanged and Solid-toothed Snakes

Outside Australia, colubrids dominate the snake fauna. Australia has only 10 species of which six occur in TNQ. Australian colubrids either have no fangs, or fangs towards the back of their mouths.

QM

Brown Tree Snake
Boiga irregularis

Identification: Length to 2 m. Body and tail slender. Head large, distinct from narrow neck; eyes large, protruding. Brown above, ragged-edged darker crossbands on back and sides; belly cream to orange. Mid-body scales 19–23; anal single; subcaudals divided; ventrals 225–265.

Habitat and Range: Rainforest, open forest, farmed areas; often found coiled up in buildings, tree hollows or caves, or on rocks. TNQ, Cooktown to Sarina. Northern and eastern Australia.

Notes: Not potentially dangerous, but ready biter. Weakly venomous with small fangs set at rear of mouth. Bites from large specimens should be treated with caution. Preys on birds (especially those in cages), mammals (mice, rats, small marsupials). Egg-layer, clutch size to 6.

Northern Tree Snake
Dendrelaphis calligastra

Identification: Length to 1.2 m. Green, brown or greyish above; belly cream or yellow below; dark streak through eye. Mid-body scales 13; anal divided; subcaudals divided; ventrals 180–230.

Habitat and Range: Rainforest, open forest, urban and farmed areas. TNQ, Cooktown to Paluma; also eastern Cape York.

Notes: Inoffensive. Lacks venom. Preys on frogs, reptiles. Egg-layer, clutch size to 7.

Michael Anthony

Green Tree Snake
Dendrelaphis punctulata

Identification: Length to 2 m. Extremely slender body, whip-like tail; small ridge along outer edges of belly scales. Colour variable; back and sides olive, green, black or, rarely, blue; usually yellow on throat and belly; pale blue flecks often seen on flanks. Mid-body scales 13 (rarely 15); anal and subcaudals divided; ventrals 180–230.

Habitat and Range: Rainforest edges, open forest, pasture, urban areas. TNQ, Cooktown to Sarina. Northern and eastern Australia.

Notes: Inoffensive, lacks venom. Preys on fish, frogs, small reptiles, occasionally mice. Egg-layer, clutch size to 8.

QM, Bruce Cowell

Macleay's Water snake
Enhydris polylepis

Identification: Length to 80 cm. Olive-brown to almost black above with lighter, sometimes speckled sides; pale below, dark line down middle of tail. Mid-body scales 21–23; anal and subcaudals divided; ventrals 140–160.

Habitat and Range: Aquatic; clearer freshwater streams. TNQ, Cooktown to Townsville; also Cape York, Qld, northern NT.

Notes: Ready biter, not potentially dangerous. Venom weakly toxic. Preys on fish, frogs. Live-bearer, up to 12 young.

QM

QM

Slaty-grey Snake
Stegonotus cucullatus

Identification: Length to 1.5 m. Leaden-grey above; belly whitish or pale-grey. Mid-body scales 17 (occasionally 19); anal single; subcaudals divided; ventrals 170–225.

Habitat and Range: Open forest, rainforest. TNQ, Cooktown to Hervey Ra.; also Cape York, Qld.

Notes: Inoffensive. Lacks venom. Preys on reptiles (geckos, skinks, dragons), their eggs, small mammals (rats, mice). Egg-layer, clutch size to 12.

QM, Jeff Wright

Freshwater Snake
Tropidonophis mairii

Identification: Length to 75 cm. Each scale on back and sides has raised, longitudinal lines, forming prominent parallel keels down length of body and tail. Brown to olive with indistinct, ragged-edged, darker crossbands; dark spaces between scales on upper lip; lower flanks often flushed with pink; belly cream. Mid-body scales 15 (rarely 17); anal and subcaudals divided; ventrals 130–165.

Habitat and Range: Rainforest edges, open forest. TNQ, Cooktown to Sarina. Coastal northern and eastern Australia, Derby, WA, to northern NSW.

Notes: Not potentially dangerous. Ready biter, but lacks venom. Preys on skinks, frogs, Cane Toads, tadpoles. Can eat young toads, but larger toads prove fatal. Egg-layer, clutch size to 12.

Similar Species: Rough-scaled Snake, (see p. 247).

Pythons

Pythons are non-venomous and have large, backwardly-curved, solid teeth. A python kills its prey by constriction, suffocating it in ever-tightening coils. Most pythons can detect prey through heat-sensory 'pits' on their lower lips. These pits detect minute temperature changes and, along with the numerous rows of body scales (35 or more vs 24 or less), distinguish pythons from other snakes. Pythons occur in temperate to tropical areas in Australia, Asia and Africa. Australia has 14 species. Five occur in TNQ.

Spotted Python
Antaresia maculosa

Identification: Length to 1 m. Light brown with dark brown, irregular blotches, sometimes forming broken bands; very shiny above; belly greyish or cream. Mid-body scales 34–45; anal single; some subcaudals single, most divided; ventrals 245–290.

Habitat and Range: Open forest. TNQ, Cooktown to Mackay, including continental islands. Eastern Qld.

Notes: Not potentially dangerous, reluctant biter. Preys on reptiles, birds, small mammals. Egg-layer, clutch size to 13.

QM

Blacked-headed Python
Aspidites melanocephalus

Identification: Length to 2.5 m. Differs from other pythons in lacking heat-sensitive 'pits' on lower jaw. Body banded brown and cream. Head, neck and throat shiny black. Mid-body scales 50–65; anal single; subcaudals, front single, back divided; ventrals 315–359; head scales large and regular.

Habitat and Range: Dry open forest. TNQ, near Cooktown, Mount Carbine, Mount Molloy, Townsville, Charters Towers. Drier parts of tropical Australia.

Notes: Not potentially dangerous, but ready biter. Preys on reptiles (including snakes), birds, mammals. Egg-layer, clutch size to 11.

QM

QM, Bruce Cowell

Water Python
Liasis mackloti

Identification: Length to 3 m. Very shiny, any shade of brown, olive or grey to almost black above; belly yellow to cream. Mid-body scales 40–55; anal single; subcaudals divided; ventrals 270–300; head scales large and regular.

Habitat and Range: Open forest, often near water. TNQ, Cooktown to Ayr, Proserpine. Coastal northern Australia between Brome, WA, and Proserpine, Qld.

Notes: Not potentially dangerous, but ready biter. Preys on mammals (especially rats), birds and reptiles. Egg-layer, clutch size to 16.

QM, Bruce Cowell

Amethystine Python
Morelia amethistina

Identification: Length to 5 m. Australia's largest snake. Iridescent greenish, grey or brown, usually with dark lines and streaks above; belly pale grey, greenish-grey. Mid-body scales 41–57; anal single; subcaudals mostly divided; ventrals 289–346; head scales large and regular.

Habitat and Range: Rainforest, open forest. TNQ, Cooktown to Townsville, including continental islands; also Qld north of Cooktown.

Notes: Not potentially dangerous, but ready biter. Preys on mammals (rats, bandicoots, wallabies), birds (especially domestic chickens). Egg-layer, clutch size to 12.

QM, Jeff Wright

Carpet Snake
Morelia spilota

Identification: Length to 3 m. Dark green above, with bright cream to yellow lines and blotches. Mid-body scales 40–65; anal single, subcaudals divided; ventrals 240–310; head scales very small, bead-like and irregular.

Habitat and Range: Rainforest, open forest, pasture, agricultural land, suburban areas. TNQ, Cooktown to Sarina. Mainland eastern Australia, south-western WA, northern NT.

Notes: Not potentially dangerous, but ready biter. Preys on mammals (rats, possums, flying foxes, small dogs, cats), less frequently birds, occasionally frogs and Cane Toads (snake dies). Egg-layer, clutch size to 47.

Blind Snakes

Blind snakes are small (to 40 cm), smooth, worm-like burrowers. Their eyes are reduced to diffuse dark spots, which are probably capable of discerning little more than light and dark. A blind snake's tail is bluntly-rounded and usually ends in a short spur. Body scales are small, glossy and close-fitting. Belly scales are small and undifferentiated from remaining body scales. Blind snakes are egg-layers. They feed on termites and the eggs, larvae and pupae of ants. Blind snakes are often uncovered in the galleries and chambers of their prey or in soil cracks beneath rocks and stones. At night, particularly following rain, they emerge to forage on the surface. All species are non-venomous. Their sole defences are secretive habits and the ability some species have to exude an unpleasant odour if harassed. Australia has 34 species of blind snakes. Four occur in TNQ.

Blind Snakes
Ramphotyphlops spp.

Identification:

R. braminus: mid-body scales 20; nasal cleft divides nasal scale, visible from above.

R. broomi: mid-body scales 20; nasal cleft divides nasal scale, not or scarcely visible from above.

R. polygrammicus: mid-body scales 22; rostral scale (from above) circular.

R. robertsi: mid-body scales 22; rostral scale (from above) elongated.

Habitat and Range:

R. braminus, suburban areas. TNQ, Townsville. Australia, patchy distribution, Darwin, NT, tip of Cape York, Townsville, Qld.

R. broomi, open forest. TNQ, Cooktown to Mount Garnet; also south-west to Greenvale, Qld.

R. polygrammicus, rainforest. TNQ, Black Mtn NP to Dunk I.; also Torres Strait. Cape York, Qld.

R. robertsi, moist open forest. TNQ only, Shipton's Flat.

Notes: Blind Snakes are incapable of biting humans.

Ramphotyphlops broomi, QM

Ramphotyphlops robertsi, QM. Lewis Roberts

Papuan Frogmouth, QM, Bruce Cowell

BIRDS

Tropical North Queensland is home to more than half the bird species in Australia. While many species are shared with other parts of Australia, TNQ does have an impressive number of endemic birds (those that occur naturally only within the area). In a book of this nature, it is not possible to cover all the birds in the region. However, those most commonly encountered are included, as well as some of the more interesting species. There are several comprehensive field guides on Australian birds and at least two excellent books that deal exclusively with the birds of the Wet Tropics. In the following species accounts, the birds are listed according to taxonomic order (scientific classification).

There are many excellent sites for birdwatching throughout TNQ, however, care must be taken in coastal regions where estuarine crocodiles might be encountered. Areas where at least two types of habitat meet, known as 'ecotones', usually have a good diversity of bird species. Near Cooktown, waterbirds can be seen on the sandbanks of the Endeavour River and at Keatings Lagoon. Mount Cook National Park has many species of 'bush' birds. Further south, in the lowland rainforest adjacent to the road around Shipton's Flat, the break in the forest offers an opportunity to glimpse some interesting northern species.

Birds that favour dry woodland can be seen around Mount Carbine. An early morning boat trip on the Daintree River, with a guide who caters for birdwatchers, is also worthwhile. Moving towards the upland rainforest, nearby Mt Lewis has many great sites along the road and a few open areas that give unimpeded views of rainforest species. To the south are open forests and dry woodlands. The area around Big Mitchell Creek, north of Mareeba, is the place to see dry country species, including the White-browed Robin.

The two famous Tableland lakes, Barrine and Eacham, are wonderful birdwatching sites, particularly along the graded national park tracks. Little Kingfishers are occasionally seen on the track around Lake Eacham. The Crater National Park, south of Atherton, is one of the best birdwatching areas on the Tableland. Here, Bridled Honeyeaters come to the picnic tables and the Chowchilla is often seen along the tracks. On the Atherton Tableland, patches of remnant rainforest along the roads are quite productive and the short walking track in front of Millaa Millaa Falls is also surprisingly good.

In Cairns, the Botanic Gardens, Mount Whitfield Conservation Park, Centenary Lakes, Cairns Esplanade and the Mangrove Boardwalk are famous, not only for the numbers of birds, but also as places to meet birdwatchers from around the world.

Eubenangee Swamp is a large wetland south of Cairns with a river walk where some endemic species can be easily observed. Nearby, the area around Josephine Falls is favoured habitat for the three *Meliphaga* honeyeaters. Try and separate each species by the calls. Just south of Innisfail, at Lacey Creek State Forest, the Southern Cassowary and Buff-breasted Paradise-Kingfisher are often encountered. This spectacular migratory kingfisher will only be found reliably between November and February. A boat trip to Dunk Island makes a pleasant diversion with likely sightings of the Orange-footed Scrubfowl, Rose-crowned Fruit-Dove and Yellow-breasted Sunbird.

The township of Paluma and nearby Mount Spec are the southernmost point for several interesting rainforest species. Townsville Town Common has good numbers of Brolgas and the public hide is excellent for viewing waterbirds, as well as Yellow Honeyeaters and White-gaped Honeyeaters. Just south of Townsville, Bowling Green Bay National Park at Mount Elliot is another place to see White-browed Robins.

Conway National Park, near Proserpine, and Cape Hillsborough National Park, near Mackay, are two large conservation areas with much birdlife and wonderful seascapes. Inland from Mackay, are Finch Hatton Gorge and nearby Eungella National Park, home of the rare Eungella Honeyeater, one of the most recently discovered Australian birds.

Ian Venables

Cassowaries

QM, Bruce Cowell

Southern Cassowary
Casuarius casuarius

Identification: Large. Length 1.5–2 m. Body black; bare blue and red skin on neck and head; bony helmet on head; heavy legs. Juvenile, brown body with rufous head. Flightless.

Habitat and Range: Rainforest, nearby gardens and roads. Cape York to Ingham, Qld; New Guinea.

Notes: Endangered. Can be dangerous when cornered or with chicks.

Megapodes

Bruce Cowell

Australian Brush Turkey
Alectura lathami

Other Names: Brush Turkey, Scrub Turkey, Wild Turkey.

Identification: Length 60–70 cm. Body black, some dark grey scallops on underside; head and neck skin red, yellow wattle around neck. Male, larger hanging wattle than female. Chick mustard brown.

Habitat and Range: Closed forest, dense vegetation, suburbs. Cape York, Qld, to Woolongong, NSW.

Notes: Eggs incubated in large mounds of vegetable matter built by male.

Orange-footed Scrubfowl
Megapodius reinwardt

Other Names: Jungle Fowl, Scrub Hen.

Identification: Length 40–47 cm. Body dark grey, wings dark brown; small crest on head; heavy orange legs. Chick dark brown.

Habitat and Range: Coastal lowland forest, vine scrub, mangroves. Kimberley region, WA, northern NT, Cape York, including many off-shore islands, to Shoalwater Bay, Qld; New Guinea, Vanuatu, Indonesia, Philippines.

Notes: Eggs incubated in large mounds of vegetable matter built by male.

QM, Bruce Cowell

Ducks and Geese

Magpie Goose
Anseranas semipalmata

Other Names: Black and White Goose, Pied Goose, Wild Goose.

Identification: Length 70–90 cm. Head, long neck, wings and tail black; body white; legs orange. Chick, dark brown back, white underside, rufous head.

Habitat and Range: Open shallow wetlands, wet grasslands, floodplains. Coastal northern Australia, Kimberley region, WA, to north-eastern NSW.

QM, Bruce Cowell

Wandering Whistling-duck
Dendrocygna arcuata

Other Names: Water Whistler, Whistling Tree-Duck.

Identification: Length 55–61 cm. Top of head, back of neck, back, wings and tail, dark brown; rufous scallops on back; white plumes projecting from lower edge of wing; underside rufous-orange; bill dark grey.

Habitat and Range: Dams, lakes, floodplains, lagoons, river edges, wetlands. Northern Australia to northern NSW; New Guinea, Indonesia, Phillipines.

Similar Species: Plumed Whistling-duck (*D. eytoni*), paler; bill pink and black, longer upright cream plumes.

QM, Bruce Cowell

QM, Bruce Cowell

Radjah Shelduck
Tadorna radjah

Other Names: Burdekin Duck, White-headed Shelduck.

Identification: Length 48–60 cm. Mainly white; back, outer wings and band across chest (broken band in juvenile) brown; legs and bill pink.

Habitat and Range: Shallow water (salt and fresh), mud and sand banks, fallen timber in water. Northern and eastern Australia to near Rockhampton, Qld; New Guinea.

QM, Bruce Cowell

Green Pygmy-goose
Nettapus pulchellus

Other Names: Goose Teal, Green Goose, Green Teal.

Identification: Length 30–36 cm. Male, head, neck and back glossy, dark green; cheek patch white; underside white with fine black edges to feathers forming scallops. Female similar, but front of neck white with fine black bars.

Habitat and Range: Lakes, dams, streams; among floating and other vegetation. Northern and eastern Australia, occasionally to Brisbane, Qld; New Guinea.

Bruce Cowell

Pacific Black Duck
Anas superciliosa

Other Names: Black Duck, Brown Duck, Grey Duck.

Identification: Length 47–63 cm. Face buff with brown-black crown, dark line through eye and chinstrap; body dark brown to black with buff edges to feathers; green patch on wing not always visible.

Habitat and Range: Almost any freshwater habitat. Australia-wide; New Guinea, NZ, near Pacific islands, Indonesia.

Grebes

Australasian Grebe
Tachybaptus novaehollandiae

Other Names: Dabchick, Little Grebe.

Identification: Length 23–26 cm. Non-breeding, crown dark; body brown, off-white under rump, lower face and foreneck off-white. Breeding, head black; rufous stripe on neck; yellow chin mark.

Habitat and Range: Freshwater ponds, lagoons, lakes, slow streams, dams. Australia-wide; NZ, New Guinea, some Pacific islands, Indonesia.

Bruce Cowell

Cormorants and Darters

Little Black Cormorant
Phalacocorax sulcirostris

Other Names: Little Black Shag.

Identification: Length 55–65 cm. Black with black bill and facial skin.

Habitat and Range: Fresh and saltwater lakes, reservoirs, swamps. Australia-wide, except arid regions; New Guinea, NZ, near Pacific islands, Indonesia.

Similar Species: Little Pied Cormorant (*P. melanoleucos*), similar size, white underside, yellow bill; Great Cormorant (*P. carbo*), larger with pale buff throat; Pied Cormorant (*P. varius*), white underside, orange patches at base of bill. All Australia-wide, except arid regions.

QM

Bruce Cowell

Darter
Anhinga melanogaster

Other Names: Needle-beaked Shag, Snake-bird.

Identification: Length 86–94 cm. Long neck, needle-like bill. Male, mostly black, rufous wash on foreneck, white dart behind bill to neck. Female, dark brown, foreneck whitish, white dart behind bill.

Habitat and Range: Large bodies of water, occasionally seawater. Australia-wide, except arid centre; New Guinea, southern Asia, Africa.

Herons and Egrets

QM, Bruce Cowell

White-faced Heron
Egretta novaehollandiae

Other Names: Blue Crane, Grey Heron.

Identification: Length 66–70 cm. Body bluish-grey, faint brownish sheen on breast; face and upper throat white; legs yellow.

Habitat and Range: Fresh and saltwater wetlands, grassland. Australia-wide; New Guinea; some Pacific islands, Indonesia.

RE Viljoen

Little Egret
Egretta garzetta

Other Names: Lesser Egret, Spotless Egret.

Identification: Length 55–65 cm. White; bill and legs black; small yellow facial patch between bill and eye.

Habitat and Range: Mudflats, marshlands, fresh and saltwater. Australia-wide, except arid regions; New Guinea, Asia, Europe, Africa.

Similar Species: Eastern Reef Egret (see page 261). Great Egret (*E. alba*), larger, head and neck 1.5 times body length; yellow or green between eyes and bill, gape extends past eye. Intermediate Egret (*E. intermedia*), head and neck about equal to body length; gape extends to just past eye; bill yellow or reddish. Cattle Egret (*E. ibis*), rounded head, chin plumage extends under bill forming jowl.

Eastern Reef Egret
Egretta sacra

Other Names: Blue Reef Heron, White Reef Heron, Sacred Heron.

Identification: Length 60–70 cm. Two colour forms, body all white or dark grey. Bill, greyish-brown or yellowish; legs dull yellowish and grey. Immature of dark form dark brown.

Habitat and Range: Marine habitats of mainland and islands. Esperance, WA, across north to Mallacoota, Vic.; NZ, New Guinea, some Pacific islands, east Asia.

RE Viljoen

Great-billed Heron
Ardea sumatrana

Other Names: Dusky Grey Heron, Sumatran Heron.

Identification: Length 115 cm. Tall, brown-grey with a little yellow on face. Immature, more rusty in colour. Flies with neck retracted.

Habitat and Range: Mangrove streams, inlets, mudflats, sometimes upstream from mangroves. Kimberley region, WA, to near Rockhampton, Qld; widespread south-east Asia, New Guinea.

Gary Fisher

Black Bittern
Ixobrychus flavicollis

Other Names: Yellow-necked Bittern.

Identification: Length 54–66 cm. Mainly black with bluish sheen; throat, neck and breast dull yellow with long streaks of black and white; long, sharp, yellowish bill. Juvenile paler.

Habitat and Range: Tree-lined streams and swamps, mangroves. Coastal, south-western WA; across north to northern Vic.; south-east Asia, New Guinea, Solomon Is.

QM

Ibises and Spoonbills

Bruce Cowell

Australian White Ibis
Threskiornis molucca

Other Names: Black-necked Ibis, Sacred Ibis, Sickle-bill.

Identification: Length 65–75 cm. Body white, often dirty, with black wing tips; head and upper neck has bare black skin; long, black, down-curved bill.

Habitat and Range: Wetlands, mudflats, lakes, fresh and saltwater grassland, rubbish tips, garbage tins, lawns. Australia-wide, except much of arid south-west.

Bruce Cowell

Royal Spoonbill
Platalea regia

Other Names: Black-billed Spoonbill.

Identification: Length 74–81 cm. White; large, black, spoon-shaped bill; legs black.

Habitat and Range: Wetlands, mostly freshwater. Australia-wide, except arid areas; NZ, New Guinea, Indonesia.

Similar Species: Yellow-billed Spoonbill (*P. flavipes*), pale, yellow-cream bill.

Storks

RE Viljoen

Black-necked Stork
Ephippiorhynchus asiaticus

Other Names: Jabiru, Policeman bird.

Identification: Length 110–137 cm. Bill long (30 cm), thick, black. Tall; body black and white; long glossy black neck with green sheen; long red legs. Female, yellow eyes. Immature, upperside mid-brown; underside paler; legs dark grey-brown.

Habitat and Range: Wetlands, mudflats, floodplains, dams, grasslands, streams. Coastal, Exmouth Gulf, WA, across north to near Sydney, NSW; New Guinea, south-east Asia, India.

Eagles, Hawks and Falcons

Osprey
Pandion haliaetus

Other Names: Fish-hawk, White-headed Osprey.

Identification: Length 50–65 cm. Wingspan 145–170 cm. Head, neck and underside white, upperside and mask through eye dark brown; pale brown band across breast. In flight, mainly white underneath, dark trailing edge on fingered wings, distinct angle on leading edge at wrist.

Habitat and Range: Coastal and nearby waters. Australia-wide; worldwide.

QM, Bruce Cowell

Black Kite
Milvus migrans

Other Names: Allied Kite, Fork-tailed Kite.

Identification: Length 45–55 cm. Wingspan 120–140 cm. Body dark brown, wing tips almost black; face pale grey; tail long, tip V-shaped. Wings held slightly down when soaring or gliding; tips fingered, held slightly back. Often in low flying flocks.

Habitat and Range: Tidal wetlands, treed watercourses, grasslands, around stockyards, abattoirs, rubbish tips. Australia-wide, except WA desert areas; New Guinea, Asia, southern Europe, Africa.

Bruce Cowell

Whistling Kite
Haliastur sphenurus

Other Names: Carrion Hawk, Eagle Hawk, Whistling Eagle.

Identification: Length 50–60 cm. Wingspan 120–145 cm. Head and underside mid-brown, breast with rufous wash; upperside dark brown. In flight, wings held forward; fingered wing-tips black; black rectangular patch on trailing edge from body to half-way along wings. Tail long.

Habitat and Range: Open areas near streams, swamps, lakes, bays, beaches. Australia-wide, except some arid areas, parts of Tas.; New Guinea, some Pacific islands.

Bruce Cowell

Bruce Cowell

Brahminy Kite
Haliastur indus

Other Names: Red-backed Sea-eagle, White-headed Sea-eagle.

Identification: Length 45–60 cm. Wing-span 110–125 cm. Body reddish-brown; head, neck and breast white. Immature, brown, head and breast streaked buff. In flight, wings held almost flat, fingered wing-tips. Immature has white patch at base of dark wing tips and white line along wing centre.

Habitat and Range: Beaches, mudflats, rivers and nearby forests. Coastal northern Australia, Shark Bay, WA, to near Newcastle, NSW; New Guinea, nearby islands, south-east Asia, India.

RE Viljoen

White-bellied Sea-eagle
Haliaeetus leucogaster

Other Names: White-breasted Sea-Eagle or Fish-hawk.

Identification: Length 75–85 cm. Wing-span 180–220 cm. Head, neck and under-side white; back mid-grey. Immature, dark brown with pale brown head and belly. Glides with wings raised, fingered wing-tips. Short, wedge-shaped tail.

Habitat and Range: Along coast, reservoirs, rivers, lakes. Coastal Australia, ranges far inland in east; New Guinea, nearby islands, south-east Asia, India.

Similar Species: Wedge-tailed Eagle (*Aquila audax*), darker and has longer, wedged-shaped tail.

Nankeen Kestrel
Falco cenchroides

Other Names: Hoverer, Mosquito Hawk, Windhover.

Identification: Length 30–35 cm. Wingspan 60–80 cm. Male, crown, nape and tail grey; black band on tail tip; back pale rufous, wing with black tips; underside white. Female, head pale rufous. In flight, wings pointed, mostly white with some black spots, bands under wings and tail; rufous wash on breast.

Habitat and Range: Open areas, grassland, clearings, forms. Australia-wide; New Guinea, Indonesia.

Similar Species: Two other common species hover — Black-shouldered Kite (*Elanus axcillaris*), mainly white with black and grey; light form of Brown Falcon (*F. berigora*), trousers rufous (not white), no black band across tail tip.

QM

Cranes

Brolga
Grus rubicunda

Other Names: Australian Crane, Native Companion.

Identification: Length 105–134 cm. Tall, pale grey; bright red band around back of head; bill horn-coloured; legs dark grey. Adult birds have dewlap. Immature, brownish-grey, lacks red on head.

Habitat and Range: Floodplains, grassland, shallow wetlands, swamps, pasture. Northern and eastern Australia; New Guinea.

Similar Species: Sarus Crane (*G. antigone*), red on head extends down one-third of neck, red legs.

QM, Bruce Cowell

Rails, Crakes and Coots

QM, Bruce Cowell

Buff-banded Rail
Gallirallus philippensis

Other Names: Banded Landrail, Painted Rail.

Identification: Length 28–35 cm. Top of head and back brown; eyebrow whitish; reddish-brown patch through eye and along neck; underside has fine black and white bars, ochre patch on breast; throat pale grey.

Habitat and Range: Grass and thick vegetation around swamps, streams, pasture, gardens. Australia-wide, except dry interior; NZ, many Pacific islands, New Guinea, south-east Asia.

Bruce Cowell

Purple Swamphen
Porphyrio porphyrio

Other Names: Bald Coot, Eastern Swamphen, Pukeko.

Identification: Length 44–48 cm. Head, back and wings black; neck and breast deep blue; bill and forehead shield red; legs red with dark knees.

Habitat and Range: Lakes, swamps, rivers, parks. Eastern and northern Australia and south-western WA; NZ, some Pacific islands, New Guinea, south-east Asia, southern Europe, Africa.

Similar Species: Dusky Moorhen (*Gallinula tenebrosa*), yellow tip on red bill. Eurasian Coot (*Fulica atra*), white bill and frontal shield.

Waders

Bar-tailed Godwit
Limosa lapponica

Other Names: Barred-rumped Godwit.

Identification: Length 37–46 cm. Long, slightly upturned bill, black with pink base. Non-breeding, upperside pale grey-brown finely streaked with dark brown; breast pale grey-brown; belly white; tail white with fine brown bars; legs long, dark grey. Can have rufous underside near breeding season.

Habitat and Range: Coastal beaches, mudflats, edges of lakes and swamps; mainly September–April. Most of Australia; New Guinea, NZ, Pacific islands, coastal areas in Asia, Europe, Alaska, north-west Canada, Africa.

Notes: Migratory, breeds in Siberia and Alaska.

Similar Species: Black-tailed Godwit (*L. limosa*), more uniformly brown, tail tip black.

QM

Whimbrel
Numenius phaeopus

Other Names: Jack Curlew.

Identification: Length 38–45 cm. Back dark brown, speckled pale brown; head dark brown, thin buff eyebrows and stripe on top of head; underside whitish with dark brown streaks; bill long, down-curved; long grey legs.

Habitat and Range: Coastal beaches and mudflats; September–April. Coastal Australia; almost worldwide.

Notes: Migratory, breeds in Arctic regions.

Similar Species: Eastern Curlew (*N. madagascariensis*), larger, longer bill; streaked head.

RE Viljoen

RE Viljoen

Common Greenshank
Tringa nebularia

Other Names: Greater Greenshank, Greenshank.

Identification: Length 30–35 cm. Upperside mid grey-brown; underside white with a few dark spots; bill dark grey, medium length, slightly upturned; legs long, dull yellow-green.

Habitat and Range: Fresh or saltwater mudflats, shallow pools. Coastal Australia and suitable inland areas; worldwide, except Americas.

Similar Species: Marsh Sandpiper (*T. stagnatilis*), smaller, thinner, more delicate bill.

RE Viljoen

Sharp-tailed Sandpiper
Calidris acuminata

Other Names: Sharpie.

Identification: Length 17–23 cm. Head streaked with dark brown over rufous; eyebrows white; upperside dark brown with pale edges to feathers; underside white. Bill dark brown, almost straight, as long as head; legs dull green to yellowish. Upperside has rufous wash near breeding season.

Habitat and Range: Coastal mudflats, wetlands, edges of swamps, pools and lakes. Australia-wide, except some arid areas; NZ, New Guinea, breeds in Antarctic region, migratory.

Environmental Protection Agency

Comb-crested Jacana
Irediparra gallinacea

Other Names: Jesus-bird, Lilly-trotter, Lotusbird.

Identification: Length 20–27 cm. Back and wings brown; black at back of neck extended as band across breast; throat white with orange tinge; belly white; pink to red crested comb on head; legs green with enormous toes.

Habitat and Range: Water lilies on wetlands and ponds. Kimberley region, WA, across north to Sydney, NSW; New Guinea, south-east Asia.

Notes: Walks on floating vegetation.

Stone Curlews

Bush Stone-curlew
Burhinus grallarius

Other Names: Bush Thick-knee, Southern Stone-curlew, Willaroo.

Identification: Length 54–59 cm. Upperside mottled black, brown and grey; underside white with black streaks and ochre wash. Front of face and eyebrow white; white wing flash.

Habitat and Range: Open forest and woodland, parks, wide roadsides. Australia-wide, except dry centre and south; New Guinea.

Notes: Call, drawn out wailing 'weeer, eearr'.

QM

Plovers

Masked Lapwing
Vanellus miles

Other Names: Spur-winged Plover or Wattled Plover.

Identification: Length 30–37 cm. Crown black; upperside pale grey brown; neck and underside white; bill, face and wattle flaps around face) yellow. Northern form has longer wattles than southern form which has back of neck and sides of breast black.

Habitat and Range: Pasture, grassland, parks. Australia-wide, except arid interior and much of WA; NZ, New Guinea.

QM, Bruce Cowell

Gulls and Terns

Silver Gull
Larus novaehollandiae

Other Names: Red-billed Gull, Seagull.

Identification: Length 36–44 cm. White; wings and back pale grey; bill and legs red. Immature, brown-patterned wings; bill and legs reddish-black.

Habitat and Range: Shorelines, garbage tips, rivers, dams and lakes. Australia-wide; New Guinea, NZ, some Pacific islands.

Bruce Cowell

QM, Bruce Cowell

Crested Tern
Sterna bergii

Other Names: Diver, Greater Crested Tern, Torres Strait Tern.

Identification: Length 37–43 cm. Crown black, tending to crest at rear; wings and back mid-grey; white elsewhere; bill pale yellow; legs black.

Habitat and Range: Coastal waters and islands. Coastal Australia; New Guinea, NZ, some Pacific islands, southern Asia, Africa.

Similar Species: Lesser Crested Tern (*S. bengalensis*), less common; bill pale orange.

Pigeons and Doves

QM, Bruce Cowell

Spotted Turtle-dove
Streptopelia chinensis

Other Names: Chinese Dove, Indian Turtle Dove, Laceneck Dove.

Identification: Length 28–33 cm. Head pale grey; rear of neck black with white spots; back, wings and tail brown; breast greyish-pink; belly dull white.

Habitat and Range: Gardens and parks. Eastern Australia, Cooktown, Qld, to Eyre Peninsular, SA, Tas., south-west WA; south-east Asia, India.

Notes: Introduced. Call 'coo-coo-crew'.

QM, Bruce Cowell

Emerald Dove
Chalcophaps indica

Other Names: Emerald Pigeon, Green Dove, Green-winged Pigeon.

Identification: Length 23–28 cm. Body mid-brown, wings green, tail black.

Habitat and Range: Closed forest. Northern and eastern Australia, Kimberley region, WA, to northern NT and eastern Qld, south to Batemans Bay, NSW; New Guinea, south-east Asia, India.

Peaceful Dove
Geopelia striata

Other Names: Barred Dove, Doodle-doo, Zebra Dove.

Identification: Length 19–24 cm. Head, back and tail greyish-brown; back, wings, neck and breast barred black; lower breast pinkish-grey.

Habitat and Range: Open forest, woodland, farms, parks, gardens. Australia-wide, except south-west and centre; New Guinea, south-east Asia.

QM, Bruce Cowell

Bar-shouldered Dove
Geopelia humeralis

Other Names: Pandanus Pigeon, River Pigeon, Scrub Dove.

Identification: Length 26–30 cm. Head, back, wings and tail brown; throat and upper breast blue-grey; lower neck and shoulder orange-brown, barred black; belly white.

Habitat and Range: Shrubs near water, forest edges, mangroves, thick vegetation around pasture, gardens; coastal and near coastal areas. North-western WA, across north to Sydney, NSW; New Guinea.

Notes: Call 'wook, woo, woo'.

Bruce Cowell

Rose-crowned Fruit-dove
Ptilinopus regina

Other Names: Red-crowned Pigeon, Pink Cap.

Identification: Length 20–25 cm. Crown rose; back, wings and tail green; face, neck and upper breast pale grey; belly orange-yellow with pink wash; tail tipped yellow. Immature, green with yellow belly.

Habitat and Range: Closed forest, mangroves, trees on islands. Kimberley region, WA, across north to Hunter R., NSW.

Similar Species: Superb Fruit-dove (*P. superbus*), male, bluish-black breast band and white belly; female, white belly, no black band.

Notes: Call an accelerating and descending, '00-00-00-00-00 …'

RE Viljoen

QM, Bruce Cowell

Pied Imperial Pigeon
Ducula bicolor

Other Names: Nutmeg Pigeon, Spice Pigeon, Torres Strait Pigeon.

Identification: Length 38–44 cm. Body white, flight feathers of wing and tail black.

Habitat and Range: Rainforest and nearby open forest, mangroves, treed off-shore islands. Northern Australia, Kimberley region, WA, to south of Sarina, Qld; New Guinea, south-east Asia.

Notes: Migratory, arrives September from New Guinea and Indonesia, departs February-April.

Cockatoos and Parrots

QM, Gary Cranitch

Sulphur-crested Cockatoo
Cacatua galerita

Other Names: White Cockatoo.

Identification: Length 44–55 cm. White with pale yellow crest, bill dark grey.

Habitat and Range: Rainforest, open forest, woodland, farmland, parks and gardens. Northern and eastern Australia, Kimberley region, WA, to Adelaide, SA. Introduced to NZ.

Notes: Call a raucous screech. Nests in steeply sloping hollow limbs or tree trunks, 20 m or more above ground.

Rainbow Lorikeet
Trichoglossus haematodus

Other Names: Blue-bellied Lorikeet, Blue Mountain Lory, Bluey.

Identification: Length 25–32 cm. Head blue; back, wings and tail green; breast red and orange; belly blue; bill red.

Habitat and Range: Most habitats. Northern and eastern Australia, Kimberley region, WA, to Adelaide, SA; New Guinea, Indonesia, some Pacific islands.

Bruce Cowell

Double-eyed Fig-parrot
Cyclopsitta diophthalma macleayana

Other Names: Blue-faced Lorikeet, Dwarf Parrot, Lorilet.

Identification: Length 13–16 cm. Plump, green with red forehead, red dash under eye; blue below red dash.

Habitat and Range: Rainforest, paperbark forest, vine scrub, some gardens. Cooktown to Mackay, Qld.

Notes: Two other subspecies in Australia — *C.d. marshalli* (Cape York), more red and less blue on head. *C. d. coxeni* (south-eastern Qld and north-eastern NSW), blue forehead and pale red under eye.

Robin Hill

Pale-headed Rosella
Platycercus adscitus

Other Names: Blue-cheeked Parrot, Moreton Bay Rosella.

Identification: Length 28–32 cm. Head pale yellow becoming much brighter down black-speckled back; cheeks white; underside pale blue; wings rich purple-blue; tail dark blue with green wash; red under upper tail.

Habitat and Range: Open forest, woodland, ranging far inland. Cape York, Qld, to Richmond R., NSW.

Notes: A partially blue-cheeked subspecies occurs from Cape York to about Mount Mulligan, Qld.

Bruce Cowell

Cuckoos

Robin Hill

Brush Cuckoo
Cacomantis variolosus

Other Names: Square-tailed Cuckoo.

Identification: Length 22–26 cm. Head, neck and throat grey; back, wings and tail brown; underside greyish-buff. Immature, upperside dark brown with buff streaks and spots; underside whitish with brown bars.

Habitat and Range: Forest, paperbark swamps. Northern and eastern Australia, Kimberley region, WA, to Portland, Vic.; New Guinea, Indonesia, Solomon Is.

Similar Species: Fantailed Cuckoo (*C. flabelliformis*), upperside dark grey; underside pale rufous; call a descending trill often given twice.

Notes: Parasitises nests of smaller fairy-wrens, honeyeaters, fantails and similar sized species. Call a series of descending loud whistles.

Male, RE. Viljoen

Common Koel
Eudynamys scolopacea

Other Names: Black Cuckoo, Coo-ee Bird, Rainbird.

Identification: Length 39–46 cm. Male, glossy black with pale grey bill, eyes red. Female, head black, black dashes below eyes; upperside dark brown speckled with white; underside pale ochre, finely barred brown. Immature, similar to female, but head rufous-brown.

Habitat and Range: Rainforest edges, open forest, woodland, farms, parks and gardens. Northern and eastern Australia, Kimberley region, WA, to Sydney, NSW.

Notes: Migrates to New Guinea and Indonesia. Parasitises nests of mainly larger honeyeaters, orioles, Figbird and Magpie-lark. Call — male, loud 'koo-er-roo' or 'who-who-a-roo-a-roo-a...', female, harsh 'chung-chung-chung'.

Channel-billed Cuckoo
Scythrops novaehollandiae

Other Names: Fig Hawk, Flood or Storm-bird.

Identification: Length 58–67 cm. Pale grey, dark grey wings, barred tail. Thick, straw-coloured, down-curved bill. Red skin around eye.

Habitat and Range: Open forest, woodland, farms, gardens. Kimberley region, WA, across north to Batemans Bay, NSW. Ranges well inland. Migrates from New Guinea and Indonesia in warmer months, returns March–April.

Notes: Parsitises mainly nests of Australian Magpie, Pied Currawong and crows.

QM

Coucals

Pheasant Coucal
Centropus phasianinus

Other Names: Cane or Swamp Pheasant.

Identification: Length 50–80 cm. Breeding, back brown; wings and long tail with paler streaks and bars; head and underside black. Non-breeding, head and underside similar to back, brown with paler streaks.

Habitat and Range: Thick, long grass. North West Cape, WA, across north to south of Sydney, NSW; New Guinea.

Notes: Often runs on ground, flies clumsily.

QM

Owls

Rufous Owl
Ninox rufa

Identification: Length 44–55 cm. Upperside dark rust-brown with fine, pale barring; underside greyish-orange with rufous barring; eyes yellow; tail has dark and light grey barring.

Habitat and Range: Forest, often near streams. Northern Australia, Kimberley region, WA, to Rockhampton, Qld; New Guinea.

Notes: Call a slow 'woo-hoo'.

J Whittle

D and A Magarry

Lesser Sooty Owl
Tyto multipunctata

Identification: Length 31–38 cm. Female larger. Face disc-shaped, white to pale grey with dark shadows around dark eyes; head, back and wings sooty grey, spotted with white and grey; underside barred and flecked with sooty grey.

Habitat and Range: Tall rainforest and wet eucalypt forest in mountain areas. Cooktown to Mt Spec and Paluma, Qld.

Similar Species: Barn Owl (*T. albas*), upperside pale rufous-grey, underside white. Grass Owl (*T. capensis*), upperside mid grey-brown. Masked Owl (*T. novaehollandiae*), black line around face disc.

Notes: Call a descending screech.

Frogmouths

QM, Bruce Cowell

Papuan Frogmouth
Podargus papuensis

Other Names: Large Frogmouth.

Identification: Length 45–60 cm. Upperside dark rufous and grey with fine pale grey and black streaks; wings have buff spots; underside pale grey with rufous wash and white mottling; eyes orange.

Habitat and Range: Edges of rainforest and trees along streams. Cape York to Paluma, Qld; New Guinea, nearby islands.

Similar Species: Tawny Frogmouth (*P. strigoides*), smaller (32–50 cm), prominent vertical streaks on underside.

Nightjars

Large-tailed Nightjar
Caprimulgus macrurus

Other Names: Axebird, Carpenterbird, White-tailed Nightjar.

Identification: Length 25–29 cm. Mottled grey-brown and black; moustache stripes, small spots on wings and outer tail tips white.

Habitat and Range: Leaf-littered ground in open forest and rainforest edges. Coastal, near Derby, WA, across north to near Maryborough, Qld; India, southern China, Philippines, Indonesia, New Guinea.

Notes: Nocturnal. Calls mostly dusk, dawn; sounds like an axe chopping hollow log.

QM

Swifts

White-rumped Swiftlet
Collocalia spodiopygius

Other Names: Grey or Grey-rumped Swiftlet.

Identification: Length 11–12 cm. Narrow curved, swept-back wings; shallow forked tail. Dark grey; small, off-white to grey patch on rump.

Habitat and Range: Aerial over most habitats. Claudie R. to Mackay, Qld; Indonesia, New Guinea, western Pacific islands.

Notes: Nests in caves, rocky hollows.

Nature Focus, Fred Bohner

Kingfishers

Little Kingfisher
Alcedo pusilla

Identification: Length 11 cm. Upperside deep blue, white dots in front of eyes; small white slashes on sides of neck; underside white; bill black.

Habitat and Range: Wooded pools and lakes, forested streams, mangroves. Coastal, Arnhemland, NT, Gulf of Capentaria to near Mackay, Qld; Indonesia, New Guinea, Solomon Is.

Notes: World's smallest kingfisher.

Robin Hill

RE Viljoen

Buff-breasted Paradise-kingfisher
Tanysiptera sylvia

Other Names: Long-tailed Kingfisher, White-tailed Kingfisher.

Identification: Length 29–35 cm (including tail). Crown, wings and upper outer tail, blue; back and line through eye, black; patch on back, rump and long tail, white; underside orange; bill red. Juvenile, upperside brown with blue wash; underside buff with black streaks: bill grey; tail short.

Habitat and Range: Lowland rainforest with little undergrowth. Cape York to Mackay, Qld, in summer months. Winters in New Guinea and nearby islands.

Notes: Nests in termite mounds on ground (see p. 87).

QM, Bruce Cowell

Blue-winged Kookaburra
Dacelo leachii

Other Names: Barking Jackass, Howling Jackass, Leach's Kingfisher.

Identification: Length 38–46 cm. Head white with fine black streaks; eye white; back greyish-brown; wings bright, pale blue; underside whitish with faint scallops.

Habitat and Range: Open forest, woodland. Northern Australia, Geraldton, WA, to Boonah, Qld; New Guinea.

Notes: Call sounds like barking dog.

Similar Species: Laughing Kookaburra (*D. novaeguineae*), black line through eyes and over top of head. Call a raucous laugh.

Forest Kingfisher
Todiramphus macleayii

Other Names: Blue, Bush or Macleay Kingfisher.

Identification: Length 18–23 cm. Head dark blue, black line through eye, two white spots on forehead; upperside deep blue with turquoise back; underside white; wings show white dash in flight.

Habitat and Range: Open forest, woodland, mangroves. Northern NT, Cape York, Qld, to Manning R., NSW; New Guinea, Timor, nearby islands.

Similar Species: Sacred Kingfisher (*T. sancta*), upperside blue-green; underside white washed with orange.

Notes: Partly migratory in southern range.

QM

Bee-eaters

Rainbow Bee-eater
Merops ornatus

Other Names: Gold Digger, Pin-tail, Rainbowbird.

Identification: Length 22–28 cm. Head pale green with orange and yellow throat; lower back and underside of tail blue; black line through eye; upper breast and tail black. Two long spines extend from tail, shorter in female, none in immature. In flight, orange under pointed wings.

Habitat and Range: Light forest, woodland, grassed areas especially where there is sandy soil or loam areas for tunnel nesting. Australia-wide, except arid areas and Tas.; New Guinea, south-east Asia.

RE Viljoen

Rollers

QM, Bruce Cowell

Dollarbird
Eurystomus orientalis

Other Names: Eastern Broad-billed Roller.

Identification: Length 26–30 cm. Plump; head dark brown, wings and back greenish-blue; tail tip black; bill and legs red. Immature, dark brown bill. In flight, pale blue (appears white) spot on wing.

Habitat and Range: Open forest, woodland, along streams, farms, suburbs. Northern and eastern Australia. Summer migrant from south-east Asia and New Guinea.

Pittas

QM, Bruce Cowell

Noisy Pitta
Pitta versicolor

Other Names: Buff-breasted Pitta, Dragoonbird, Painted Thrush.

Identification: Length 17–21 cm. Head black with brown headband; back, wings and tail green; pale blue patch on wing; underside dull yellow; black between legs; red under tail.

Habitat and Range: Rainforest and nearby open forest, mangroves, heavily vegetated gardens, parks and golf courses. Cape York, Qld, to Hunter River, NSW.

Fairy-wrens

Female, Nature Focus, Len Robinson

Lovely Fairy-wren
Malurus amabilis

Other Name: Lovely Wren.

Identification: Length 12–14 cm. Male, crown, ear patch and mid-back vivid blue; throat and breast black; inner wing red; cocked tail pale grey-blue. Female, crown and back pale blue, greyer towards tail; forehead and underside white. Non-breeding males may resemble females.

Habitat and Range: Rainforest edges, open forest, swamps, mangroves, bushy road verges. Cape York to Innisfail, Qld.

Red-backed Fairy-wren
Malurus melanocephalus

Other Names: Black-headed Wren, Orange-backed Wren.

Identification: Length 10–13 cm. Male, black with bright orange to red saddle; wings brown. Female, upperside brown; underside white with ochre wash at rear. Non-breeding male may resemble female, but with a few black feathers around head.

Habitat and Range: Tall grass at edges of forest, swamps, and streams, also farms, gardens. Kimberley region, WA, across north to Hunter R., NSW, ranges far inland.

RE Viljoen

Scrubwrens

Yellow-throated Scrubwren
Sericornis citreogularis

Other Names: Black-nest Bird, Devilbird.

Identification: Length 12–15 cm. Upperside brown; black face mask with yellow above and below and on throat; underside whitish with pale brown wash.

Habitat and Range: Dense, dark, forest floors, nearby vines and undergrowth. Near Cooktown to Mt Spec, Qld, and Gympie, Qld, to Illawarra, NSW.

Similar Species: White-browed Scrubwren (*S. frontalis*) pale eye, white above and below black face mask.

RE. Viljoen

Gerygones

Large-billed Gerygone
Gerygone magnirostris

Other Names: Large-billed Flyeater, Large-billed Warbler.

Identification: Length 11 cm. Upperside and tail mid-brown; underside white with pale brown wash on flanks; eye red with white, divided eye-ring.

Habitat and Range: Rainforest, along streams, paperbark swamps, mangroves. Coastal, Kimberley region, WA, to Sarina, Qld; New Guinea.

Nature Focus, EE Zillmann

Nature Focus, A D Trounson

Fairy Gerygone
Gerygone palpebrosa

Other Names: Hornet-nest Bird, Fairy Warbler.

Identification: Length 10–11.5 cm. Upperside greyish-olive; white spot between eye and bill, underside pale yellow. North of Innisfail (Qld), male has black throat, white moustache; further south black throat becomes smaller and paler. Female and immature, white throats.

Habitat and Range: Rainforest edges, vine scrub, mangroves. Cape York to Gympie, Qld; New Guinea and nearby islands.

Thornbills

Nature Focus, Dick Whitford

Mountain Thornbill
Acanthiza katherina

Identification: Length 10 cm. Upperside greenish-grey; rump dull rufous; tail black; underside white with yellowish wash to rear; fine dark scalloping on forehead; eye white with fine streaks below.

Habitat and Range: Mountain rainforest. Cedar Bay NP to Mt Spec, Qld.

Similar Species: Brown Thornbill (*A. pusilla*), eye red, rufous scallops on forehead, dark streaked throat and breast.

Honeyeaters

RE Viljoen

Helmeted Friarbird
Philemon buceroides

Other Names: Sandstone Friarbird.

Identification: Length 30–37 cm. Crown, nape and throat pale brown, often tuft at back of head; bill dark grey with low, long knob above; dark grey facial skin arching around red eye; upperside mid-brown; underside pale beige. Immature, no knob on bill, pale scalloping on upper back.

Habitat and Range: Open forest, mangroves, parks and gardens. Northern NT, Cape York to Rockhampton, Qld; New Guinea, Indonesia.

Blue-faced Honeyeater
Entomyzon cyanotis

Other Names: Bananabird, Blue-eye.

Identification: Length 25–32 cm. Head black; blue patch around eye; white band around nape; upperside bright olive; black bib on throat; underside white; eyes white. Immature, green to grey facial patch, dark grey bib.

Habitat and Range: Open forest, woodland. Kimberley region, WA, across north to SA, ranging inland; New Guinea.

RE Viljoen

Noisy Miner
Manorina melanocephala

Other Names: Mickey, Soldierbird.

Identification: Length 24–28 cm. Forehead white; crown and cheeks black; upperside and breast grey-brown; belly white; bill ,bare patch behind eye, legs and wash on wings yellow.

Habitat and Range: Dry open forest, woodland. Common in urban areas. Musgrave (Cape York), Qld, to Adelaide, SA, ranging well inland.

Bruce Cowell

Macleay's Honeyeater
Xanthotis macleayana

Other Names: Buff-striped Honeyeater, Yellow-streaked Honeyeater.

Identification: Length 18–21 cm. Cap brown-black; upperside brown with white streaks, shoulders rufous; throat and upper breast brown-grey, underside mid-grey-brown with white streaks. Pale orange patch of bare skin around eye. Moderately long, down-curved bill.

Habitat and Range: Rainforest edges, moist forest particularly near water; heavily vegetated gardens. Lowlands and highlands. Cooktown to Paluma, Qld.

RE Viljoen

RE Viljoen

Yellow-spotted Honeyeater
Meliphaga notata

Other Names: Lesser Lewin Honeyeater.

Identification: Length 17–19 cm. Head and upperside dull olive-green with pale yellow spot behind eye; underside grey with olive wash. Call a strong 'yee-you'.

Habitat and Range: Lowland rainforest, streamside vegetation along coast. Cape York to Townsville, Qld; New Guinea.

Similar Species: Graceful Honeyeater (*M. gracilis*), length 14–16 cm; slightly paler; call a single, soft 'plik' or a repeated 'wik, wik, wik' (about seven times). Lewin's Honeyeater (*M. lewinii*), length 18–22 cm; crescent-shaped yellow spot behind eye; call a fast, repeated 'tute tute, tute …' .

RE Viljoen

Yellow Honeyeater
Lichenostomus flavus

Identification: Length 16–18 cm. Plump, greenish-yellow with slightly dusky face mask and moustache.

Habitat and Range: Lowland open forest, woodland, parks, gardens. Gulf of Carpentaria and Cape York to Broad Sound (near Rockhampton), Qld.

Bridled Honeyeater
Lichenostomus frenatus

Other Names: Mountain Honeyeater.

Identification: Length 18–22 cm. Crown and upperside dark brown; underside mid-grey-brown; face black with white line from bill to eye; white tuft above eye; yellow ear dash; bill black with yellow base.

Habitat and Range: Highland rainforest, open forest, woodland, streams. Cooktown to Paluma, Qld.

Similar Species: Eungella Honeyeater (*L. hindwoodi*), only found in Eungella area west of Mackay, Qld. Uncommon.

Bruce Cowell

Varied Honeyeater
Lichenostomus versicolor

Identification: Length 18-21 cm. Head, back and tail brown; black line from bill through eye to sides of neck; underside yellow with fine brown streaks.

Habitat and Range: Mangroves, nearby parks and gardens. Cape York to Townsville, Qld; New Guinea and nearby islands.

Similar Species: Mangrove Honeyeater (*L. fasciogularis*), upperside grey-brown; underside pale grey-brown with brown streaks; breast and throat brown with fine white scallops; Townsville, Qld, to Macleay R., NSW.

Robin Hill

White-gaped Honeyeater
Lichenostomus unicolor

Other Names: Erect-tailed Honeyeater, River Honeyeater.

Identification: Length 18–21 cm. Upperside mid-grey-brown; underside paler grey-brown; whitish gape line on bill to under eye.

Habitat and Range: Woodland, mangroves, parks and gardens. Kimberley region, WA, northern NT, lower Cape York from Lakefield to Burdekin R., Qld. Common in Townsville gardens.

Fledgling, AUSCAPE, Frank Woerle

Brown-backed Honeyeater
Ramsayornis modestus

Other Names: Unadorned Honeyeater.

Identification: Length 11–13 cm. Upperside mid-brown; thin white line from behind bill to under eye; underside white with indistinct brown bars across sides of breast; bill dull pink. Immature, yellow line from bill to under eye; breast bars replaced by fine brown streaks.

Habitat and Range: Near swamps and wetlands, mangroves, urban areas. Torres Strait to Townsville, Qld; New Guinea, where it is thought many Australian birds migrate during winter.

QM, Bruce Cowell

RE Viljoen

Dusky Honeyeater
Myzomela obscura

Identification: Length 12–15 cm. Upper-side and throat dark brown; rusty wash on face and neck; belly light brown.

Habitat and Range: Rainforest, open forest, streamside vegetation, woodland, mangroves. Northern NT, Gulf of Carpentaria, Cape York to just north of Brisbane, Qld; New Guinea, Indonesia.

Similar Species: Scarlet Honeyeater (*M. sanguinolenta*), female, slightly smaller, paler, usually has red wash on throat and lower face.

Australian Robins

Robin Hill

Lemon-bellied Flycatcher
Microeca flavigaster

Other Names: Lemon-breasted Flycatcher.

Identification: Length 11–14 cm. Upper-side mid-brown; wings darker; throat white; breast and belly lemon-yellow with grey wash at sides; white line from bill to eye and thin eye ring.

Habitat and Range: Dry vine scrub, open forest, woodland. Kimberley region, WA, northern NT, Cape York to Broad Sound (near Rockhampton), Qld; New Guinea.

Similar Species: Jacky Winter (*M. fascinans*), wide, white eye-brow extending well past eye; no yellow on underside.

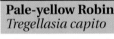

Robin Hill

Pale-yellow Robin
Tregellasia capito

Other Names: Large-headed Robin.

Identification: Length 12–14 cm. Head grey-brown, upperside olive-green; throat white; underside pale-yellow; pale pink-orange from bill to eye ring of same colour (white in southern race). Juvenile, brown, white streaks on head.

Habitat and Range: Rainforest, streamside vegetation particularly where there are prickly vines. Cooktown to Paluma, Qld, and Gympie, Qld, to Hastings R., NSW.

Mangrove Robin
Eopsaltria pulverulenta

Other Names: Ashy Robin, White-tailed Robin.

Identification: Length 14–17 cm. Head and back ash-grey with darker tail; black from bill to eye; underside white with light grey wash on breast; upper sides of tail white. Immature brown, mottled rufous with white streaks.

Habitat and Range: Mangroves, often among roots. Coastal, Exmouth Gulf, WA, to Burdekin R., Qld; New Guinea.

Nature Focus, Babs and Bert Wells

White-browed Robin
Poecilodryas superciliosa

Other Names: Buff-sided Robin, White-winged Fly-robin.

Identification: Length 14–18 cm. Upperside brown; face and wings black; wide white eyebrows and flashes on wings; underside white, washed light grey below breast.

Habitat and Range: Along streams in rainforest, open forest and dry forest. Coastal northern Australia to north of Rockhampton, Qld.

Robin Hill

Grey-headed Robin
Heteromylas albispecularis

Other Names: Ashy-fronted Robin.

Identification: Length 16–18 cm. Head and breast grey; neck and back brown; throat and belly white; white wing dash; rump and sides tan; bill black with whitish tip; legs pink.

Habitat and Range: Highland rainforest, nearby clearings, parks and gardens. Cooktown to Paluma, Qld.

RE Viljoen

Logrunners

Nature Focus, Len Robinson

Chowchilla
Orthonyx spaldingi

Other Names: Auctioneer-bird, Northern Logrunner, Spaldings Spinetail.

Identification: Length 26–28 cm. Upperside dark brown; underside white; eye ring white. Male, white throat; female, orange throat.

Habitat and Range: Leaf-strewn floor of mountain rainforest. Cooktown to Mt Spec, Qld.

Whipbirds

R.E. Viljoen

Eastern Whipbird
Psophodes olivaceus

Other Names: Stockwhip Bird, Whipbird.

Identification: Length 25–31 cm. Crested head, throat and breast black; upperside dark olive-green; patches on sides of throat, belly, tips of tail feathers, white. Immature and juvenile, lack white throat patches.

Habitat and Range: Rainforest, dense eucalypt forest, thick scrubs. Coastal, Cooktown to Paluma, Qld and near Rockhampton, Qld, to Vic.

Whistlers and Shrike-thrushes

J Whittle

Grey Whistler
Pachycephala simplex

Other Names: Brown Whistler.

Identification: Length 14–20 cm. Head grey; upperside brown-grey; indistinct white eyebrow; underside white with brown wash on breast.

Habitat and Range: Rainforest, dense streamside forest, paperbark forest, monsoon forest. Arnhemland, NT, Cape York to near Ingham, Qld; New Guinea, eastern Indonesia.

Golden Whistler
Pachycephala pectoralis

Other Names: Ringcoachie, Thunderbird, White-throated Thickhead.

Identification: Length 16.5–18.5 cm. Male, head and breast band black; throat white; back and wings olive-green; collar, breast and belly yellow. Female, upperside brownish-grey; underside brownish-grey to off-white with lemon under base of tail. Immature similar to female, but with rufous edges on wing feathers.

Habitat and Ranges: Rainforest, open forest, woodland, sometimes mangroves. Cooktown, Qld, to inland of Eyre Peninsula, SA, south-western WA; New Guinea, many Pacific islands, Indonesia.

Similar Species: Mangrove Golden Whistler (*P. melanura*), male slightly smaller, brighter, broader yellow collar; female in Qld, yellow belly, grey-brown throat.

RE Viljoen

Little Shrike-thrush
Colluricincla megarhyncha

Other Names: Little or Rufous Thrush, Rufous Shrike-thrush.

Identification: Length 17–19 cm. Upperside olive-brown; underside rufous; throat white; bill pinkish-brown.

Habitat and Range: Rainforest, streamside vegetation, mangroves. Kimberley region, WA, throughout coastal Qld, south to Taree, NSW.

Robin Hill

Bower's Shrike-thrush
Colluricincla boweri

Other Names: Stripe-breasted Thrush.

Identification: Length 19–21 cm. Head, back and inner wings mid-grey; outer wings and tail brown with rufous edges to feathers; underside rufous with throat and breast paler and streaked grey.

Habitat and Range: Upland rainforest and nearby areas. Cooktown to Paluma, Qld.

Nature Focus, J Purnell

Monarchs and Flycatchers

RE Viljoen

Spectacled Monarch
Monarcha trivirgatus

Other Names: Black-fronted Flycatcher, White-bellied Flycatcher.

Identification: Length 14–16 cm. Head and upperside grey; face to behind eye black; wing tips black; throat and breast rufous-orange; belly and outer tail tip white.

Habitat and Range: Lowland rainforest, moist open forest, streamside vegetation. Coastal areas, Cape York, Qld, to Port Stephens, NSW; migrates from southern areas in cooler months; New Guinea.

Similar Species: Black-faced Monarch (*M. melanopsis*), face to front of eye black; breast and belly rufous-orange.

Robin Hill

Pied Monarch
Arses kaupi

Other Names: Pied Flycatcher, Black-breasted Flycatcher.

Identification: Length 14–16 cm. Head back, tail and breast band, blue-black; outer wings brown-black; nape (can be frilled), lower back, throat and belly white. Female, breast band broader, duller; even more so in immature.

Habitat and Range: Rainforest, streamside forest, mangroves, nearby forest. Coastal Qld, Mount Amos (near Helenvale) to Hinchinbrook I.

Leaden Flycatcher
Myiagra rubecula

Other Names: Blue Flycatcher, Frogbird.

Identification: Length 14–16 cm. Male, upperside lead-grey with bluish-grey on head and breast; underside white. Female, upperside dull grey; wings grey-brown; throat and breast pale rufous; belly white.

Habitat and Range: Open forest, dry woodland. Kimberley region, WA, across north to Melbourne, Vic.; New Guinea.

Similar Species: Satin Flycatcher (*M. cyano-leuca*), male, blue-black on upperside and breast; female, grey wings.

Female, RE Viljoen

Magpie-lark
Gralliana cyanoleuca

Other names: Little Magpie, Mudlark, Peewee.

Identification: Length 26–30 cm. Crown, back and breast black; sides of neck and belly white; white line on wings. Adults have white eye and bill; male, black above and below bill; female, white, above and below bill. Immature, brown iris; bill grey with black above and white below.

Habitat and Range: Open areas with trees. Australia-wide, except western interior; New Guinea, Timor.

Female, RE Viljoen

Fantails

Grey Fantail
Rhipidura fuliginosa

Other Names: Cranky Fan, Dusky Fantail, Snapper.

Identification: Length 14–17 cm. Upperside and breast band dark grey; underside white with cream wash on belly; eyebrow, ear-line and tail tips white. Fans tail.

Habitat and Range: Highland rainforest; many winter in lowland open forest. Australia-wide, except western interior; New Guinea, some Pacific islands.

Similar Species: Northern Fantail (*R. rufiventris*), broad mid-grey band across breast with white striations; very small white eyebrows; rarely seen; less active.

Bruce Cowell

Willie Wagtail
Rhipidura leucophrys

Other Names: Australian Nightingale, Frogbird, Morningbird.

Identification: Length 19–22 cm. Head, throat, back, wings and tail black; Underside and fine eyebrow white.

Habitat and Range: Open areas. Australia-wide; New Guinea, Indonesia, nearby islands.

RE Viljoen

Cuckoo Shrikes

Immature, QM

Black-faced Cuckoo-shrike
Coracina novaehollandiae

Other Names: Bifcus, Blue or Grey Jay, Shufflewing.

Identification: Length 30–36 cm. Face and throat black; whitish under tail; grey elsewhere. Immature, black mask through and a little beyond eye.

Habitat and Range: Open forest, woodland, urban areas. Australia-wide; New Guinea, Indonesia, Solomon Is.

Nature Focus, Hubert Blatterer

Barred Cuckoo-shrike
Coracina lineata

Other Names: Swainson's Cuckoo-shrike, Yellow-eyed Cuckoo-shrike.

Identification: Length 24–29 cm. Upperside, throat and upper breast mid blue-grey; wingtips, tip of tail and between bill and eyes black; lower breast and belly white, barred mid-grey; yellow eye. Juvenile white, speckled with grey. Immature, upperside grey; underside white, lightly barred pale grey.

Habitat and Range: Rainforest and eucalypt forest along streams. Coastal, Cape York, Qld, to Hastings R., NSW; New Guinea, Solomon Is.

Orioles and Figbirds

QM, Bruce Cowell

Yellow Oriole
Oriolus flavocomctus

Identification: Length 25–30 cm. Upperside yellow-green streaked black; underside greenish-yellow streaked black; bill fleshy-orange; eyes red.

Habitat and Range: Rainforests, streamside vegetation, woodland, mangroves. Kimberley region, WA, northern NT, Cape York to Ingham, Qld.

Similar Species: Olive-backed Oriole (*O. sagittatus*), underside white with teardrop-shaped black striations.

Figbird
Sphecotheres viridis

Other Names: Bananabird, Mulberrybird, Southern or Yellow Figbird.

Identification: Length 27–30 cm. Male, head black; pink to red patch of skin around eye; upperside olive-green. In north, underside, yellow; mid-range, breast yellow, belly white; in south, throat and breast grey, belly white. Tail black, outer feathers white. Female, head and upperside olive-brown; underside white with brown streaks; grey skin around eye; bill black.

Habitat and Range: Rainforest edges, fruiting trees in open forest, woodland, parks and gardens. Kimberley region, WA, northern NT, Cape York, Qld, to Jervis Bay, NSW; New Guinea, Indonesia.

QM, Bruce Cowell

Woodswallows, Butcherbirds and Australian Magpies

White-breasted Woodswallow
Artamus leucorynchus

Other Names: Swallow-shrike.

Identification: Length 16–18 cm. Head, throat, wings, back and tail slate-grey; underside white.

Habitat and Range: Open areas. Australia-wide, except southern coast, south-west and western interior; New Guinea, Indonesia, Philippines and adjacent islands including New Caledonia and Fiji.

Notes: Often perched in clusters.

Bruce Cowell

Nature Focus. John Mc Cann

Black Butcherbird
Cracticus quoyi

Other Names: Rufous Butcherbird, Rufous Crow-shrike.

Identification: Length 33–44 cm. Most birds all black with black-tipped, grey bill. Rufous form and some juveniles, dark brown with pale rufous streaks on upperside; pale rufous underside.

Habitat and Range: Coastal scrubs, mangroves and parks. Northern NT, Cape York to Ingham, Qld; New Guinea.

QM

Pied Butcherbird
Cracticus nigrogularis

Other Names: Black-throated Butcherbird, Crow-shrike, Organbird.

Identification: Length 32–36 cm. Head, throat, upper breast, back, wings and tail black; nape, lower breast, belly, stripes on wings, rump and outer tail tips white. Bill pale grey with black tip, hooked. Black mostly replaced by brown in juvenile.

Similar species: Grey Butcherbird (*C. torquatus*), back grey; throat and upper breast white.

Habitat and Range: Dry forest edges, woodland, grassland, farms. Widespread mainland Australia.

Bruce Cowell

Australian Magpie
Gymnorhina tibicen

Other Names: Flutebird, Organbird, Piper.

Identification: Length 34–44 cm. Body black, except white nape, wingbar, rump and upper tail; bill grey with black tip. Female, grey wash on white nape. Immature, greyer all over.

Habitat and Range: Open areas with some trees, farms, parks and gardens. Australia-wide, except western interior; New Guinea.

Birds of Paradise

Victoria's Riflebird
Ptiloris victoriae

Identification: Length 23–25 cm. Long, down-curved bill, short tail. Male, black; throat shield, crown and upper tail iridescent blue-green; belly dark olive-green. Female, upperside grey-brown, eyebrow and throat white; belly pale rufous with fine brown chevrons.

Habitat and Range: Rainforest and nearby open forest. Cooktown to Mount Spec, Qld.

Female, R Hill

Crows

Torressian Crow
Corvus orru

Other Names: Kelly.

Identification: Length 48–53 cm. Glossy black; bill black; adults have white eyes.

Habitat and Range: Rainforest edges, open forest, woodland, open areas, urban areas. Most of northern Australia; New Guinea, Indonesia.

QM, Bruce Cowell

Bowerbirds

Spotted Catbird
Ailuroedus melanotis

Identification: Length 26–31 cm. Head dark brown with fine buff spots; upperside green with some white spots; underside pale yellow-green with pointed white spots; bill bone; eyes red.

Habitat and Range: Rainforest. North-eastern Cape York, Cooktown to Paluma, Qld.

Notes: Call can sound like meowing of a cat or like a baby crying.

R Hill

Robin Hill

Bower, QM

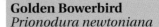

Golden Bowerbird
Prionodura newtoniana

Other Names: Golden or Queensland Gardner, Newton's Bowerbird.

Identification: Length 23–25 cm. Male, head, wings and upper tail mid-brown; back of head, nape and underside bright yellow. Female, upperside mid-brown; underside mid-grey.

Habitat and Range: Highland rainforest. Cooktown to Townsville, Qld.

Notes: Bower very large, consists of two columns of sticks built around small trees, joined at base; decorated with lichens and pale flowers.

Great Bowerbird
Chlamydera nuchalis

Other Names: Queensland Bowerbird.

Identification: Length 32–38 cm. Head, neck and underside brownish-grey; upperside dark grey-brown with heavy grey scalloping, pink crest on back of neck, hidden, except when displaying.

Habitat and Range: Dry woodland, drier urban areas. Northern Australia from Kimberley region, WA, to Townsville, Qld.

Similar Species: Spotted Bowerbird (*C. maculata*) underside yellow-brown; upperside spotted.

Notes: Bower large, about 50 cm high, up to 1 m long; consists of a stage and two walls of sticks; decorated with white stones, bones and shells and some green, red and shiny objects.

R Hill

Finches

Crimson Finch
Neochmia phaeton

Other Names: Blood Finch.

Identification: Length 12–14 cm. Male, bill, face, throat, breast and tail crimson; crown and nape grey-brown with red patches; back and wings brown; belly black. Female, grey-brown with crimson face and wash on wings and tail.

Habitat and Range: Grassland, tall grass near woodlands, swamps, cultivation, roadsides, edges of canefields, gardens near water. Kimberley region, WA, to Gulf of Carpentaria, western Cape York, Cairns to Sarina, Qld; New Guinea.

Robin Hill

Red-browed Finch
Neochmia temporalis

Other Names: Redbill, Red-browed Firetail.

Identification: Length 11–12 cm. Head, breast and flanks grey; back and wings olive-green; bill, eyebrows and rump red. Immature, head and underside grey; back olive-green; rump red; bill dark grey.

Habitat and Range: Grasses and shrubs at edge of rainforest. Eastern Australia, Cape York, Qld, to Adelaide, SA.

RE Viljoen

Chestnut-breasted Mannikin
Lonchura castaneothorax

Other Names: Barleybird, Bullfinch (erroneus), Chestnut Finch.

Identification: Length 10–12 cm. Head grey; back and wings brown; face, throat, band across breast, under tail and bars on flanks black; lower breast and belly white; upper breast chestnut; bill pale grey. Juvenile, head grey, back brown, underside cream, faint chestnut wash on breast.

Habitat and Range: Grassland, grassy roadsides and wetlands. Kimberley region, WA, northern NT, Cape York, Qld, to southern NSW; New Guinea.

RE Viljoen

Sunbirds

Male, QM, Bruce Cowell

Yellow-bellied Sunbird
Nectarinia jugularis

Other Names: Allied Sunbird, Sunbird.

Identification: Length 10–12 cm. Upperside olive-green; underside and thin eyebrow bright yellow; bill long and down-curved. Male, throat and upper breast iridescent dark blue. Female, underside yellow.

Habitat and Range: Rainforest edges, streams, mangroves, cultivation, gardens. Cape York to south of Gladstone, Qld; New Guinea, Solomon Is., south-east Asia.

Flowerpeckers

Male, RE Viljoen

Mistletoebird
Dicaeum hirundinaceum

Other names: Australian Flower Pecker, Australian Flower Swallow.

Identification: Length 9.5–11 cm. Male, upperside glossy blue-black; throat, breast and under tail scarlet; underside whitish with black line below red breast. Female, upperside mid-grey; underside whitish; under-tail red.

Habitat and Range: Vegetation with mistletoe and nearby vegetation, gardens with native and exotic berries. Australia-wide, except Tas.; Indonesia.

Swallows

Bruce Cowell

Welcome Swallow
Hirundo neoxena

Other Names: Australian or House Swallow.

Identification: Length 15 cm. Forehead, face, throat and upper breast brown-orange; upperside glossy blue-black; underside dull grey. Tail deeply forked, black with row of white spots near body.

Habitat and Range: Aerial, most habitats. Australia-wide, except north-west and far north, but occurs on Cape York, Qld; NZ.

Silvereyes

Silvereye
Zosterops lateralis

Other Names: Eastern Silvereye, Grey-breasted Silvereye, Whiteye.

Identification: Length 10–12.5 cm. Head and rump pale olive; throat and vent greenish-yellow; back and breast grey; wings grey-green; belly white.

Habitat and Range: Most vegetated habitats. Eastern and southern Australia, except dry areas; NZ, some Pacific islands.

R.E. Viljoen

Starlings and Mynas

Metallic Starling
Aplonis metallica

Other Names: Glossy Starling, Shining Starling.

Identification: Length 18–24 cm. Glossy black with purple and green sheen; eyes red; pointed tail. Immature, underside white with heavy black streaks.

Habitat and Range: Lowland rainforest, moist open forest, mangroves, parks. Coastal Qld, Cape York to Mackay. Most migrate from New Guinea, Solomon Is. and Indonesia in warmer months.

QM, Bruce Cowell

Common Myna
Acridotheres tristis

Other names: Calcutta Myna, Common Mynah, Indian Myna.

Identification: Length 23–25 cm. Brown with black head; white patches on wings; bill, legs and bare skin around eye yellow.

Habitat and Range: Around towns, farming areas and along main roads. Mossman to Proserpine, west to Mt Garnett and Chilllagoe, Darling Downs, Lockyer Valley, Fassifern Valley to Brisbane, Qld; Kempsey, NSW, to Warnambool, Vic. Introduced, native Afghanistan to south-east Asia.

QM, Bruce Cowell

Eastern Grey Kangaroo, Bruce Cowell

KANGAROOS, WALLABIES AND THEIR RELATIVES

When the world thinks of the kangaroo, it thinks of Australia. The kangaroo is on our country's coat of arms and many other national symbols.

The name 'kangaroo' is used to refer to larger animals, such as the Red and Grey Kangaroos and the Wallaroo. Medium-sized kangaroos are generally known as wallabies, while the smaller species have more colourful names, such as pademelon and bettong.

Of the 48 species of macropods (kangaroos, wallabies and their relatives), currently listed for Australia, 32 species are found in Queensland and, of these, 19 are found in Tropical North Queensland. While the status of most of these animals is considered to be common, the tree-kangaroos and two species of rock-wallabies are listed as rare.

The Northern Bettong and the Proserpine Rock-wallaby are considered endangered. Both species require specific habitats and the impact of humans and feral animals has had an adverse effect on them. However, Species Recovery Plans and re-introduction programs with captive-bred animals are underway.

Habitat requirements vary dramatically within the macropod group, ranging from wet tropical rainforests to dry open grasslands. The smallest species in TNQ, the Musky Rat-kangaroo, is as at home on the floor of tropical rainforests and vine forests, as are the tree kangaroos that live high in the canopy. Red-legged Pademelons also use these tropical forests, but have adapted to dry vine scrubs and thickets. However, most species are to be found in tall, open forests and dry open woodlands.

All macropods (with the exception of the Musky Rat-kangaroo) are nocturnal and are best observed during their feeding periods in the early morning and late afternoon. The Musky Rat-kangaroo is diurnal and can be seen throughout the day in the tropical rainforests.

Rock-wallabies, as their name implies, are found in rocky habitats within open forests and woodlands. They need cliffs, hillsides and rock piles to provide shelter and may be seen sunning themselves on rocky outcrops.

The best way to observe tree-kangaroos is with the aid of a spotlight. In some parts of the Atherton Tablelands, Lumholtz's Tree-kangaroo can be seen in the early morning foraging for food. These creatures are well adapted to life in the trees, possessing long forearms with long curved claws and short, broad hindfeet. They are able to hop in a similar fashion to other kangaroos, but are also able to walk bipedally.

The macropods of the open forest can be seen on roadside verges, forest edges and grasslands. Their habit of roadside feeding causes problems with motor vehicles, often with fatal results.

The smaller macropod species are probably the most fascinating to watch. Look out for the Rufous Bettong with material for its nest in the curl of its tail, and the strikingly coloured Spectacled Hare-wallaby. Many of the larger wallabies are highly social. The Whiptail Wallaby can be found in groups of up to 50 (usually females and young).

The nomadic Red Kangaroo (*Macropus rufus*), the largest of the grazing kangaroos in Australia, inhabits the open forests and open grassy plains west of the Great Dividing Range. Although it is not normally found in TNQ, when drought conditions prevail inland, this species will migrate to the coastal plain.

Peter Johnson

QM, Bruce Cowell

Musky Rat-kangaroo
Hypsiprymnodon moschatus

Identification: Body length 23 cm; tail length 14 cm; weight, male to 529 g, female to 511 g. Body rich brown, interspersed with dark brown; muzzle dark brown to black, hairless; head grey-brown. Body fur thick, soft, shorter on head. Forepaws dark brown, lightly furred, with climbing pads. Belly fur light grey-brown, sometimes white patch on underside. Tail dark brown, covered with small scales. Hind feet dark brown, lightly furred, with well developed climbing pads. Big toe on inside of each hind foot.

Habitat and Range: Tropical rainforest. Endemic to TNQ; Patchy distribution to 1000 m. Cooktown to Ingham.

Similar Species: Northern Brown Bandicoot (see p. 334); Long-nosed Bandicoot (see p. 335)

Notes: Active during day; forages in leaf litter for fruit, insects, fungi. Solitary, but fallen fruit attracts aggregations of animals. Females give birth to 2 young, sometimes 3 if food is plentiful. Gait is quadrupedal 'canter'. Scats cylindrical, less than 5 mm wide; dark brown or black.

QM, Bruce Cowell

Rufous Bettong
Aepyprymnus rufescens

Other Names: Rufous Rat-kangaroo, Kangaroo Rat.

Identification: Body length 39 cm; tail length 34 cm; weight 3–3.5 kg. Upper body has grizzled appearance, light reddish-brown interspersed with silver-white. Belly white. Long claws on forepaws for digging.

Habitat and Range: Grassy understoreys of open forest, to low, dry open woodland; grazes paddocks and roadside verges. Cooktown, Qld, to NSW–Vic. border.

Similar Species: Northern Bettong (see p. 303)

Notes: Solitary. Eats herbs and grasses; digs roots, tubers and fungi. Material for nest carried in curled tail. Scats cylindrical or round, 10–20 mm long.

Northern Bettong
Bettongia tropica

Other Name: Brush-tailed Bettong

Identification: Body length 36 cm; tail length 31 cm; weight to 1.2 kg. Body grey, darker above, lighter below; muzzle pink and hairless. Tail grey with short black crest on upper side towards end.

Habitat and Range: Endemic to TNQ. Population at Lake Tinaroo inhabits grassy, open forest. Lamb Ra. population, grassy, open forest and woodland on western slopes of range, 400–1000 m elevation. Animal's presence several kilometres into rainforest may be due to roads.

Similar Species: Rufous Bettong (see p. 303).

Notes: Endangered. Nocturnal, solitary. Eats underground fruiting bodies of mycorrhiza fungi, underground roots of Cockatoo Grass (*Allopteropsis semialata*) and a species of lily (*Hypoxis*). Grass nest. Hops with low springy step.

QM, Bruce Cowell

Bennett's Tree-kangaroo
Dendrolagus bennettianus

Other Names: Tree-climber, Tree Wallaby, Jarabeena.

Identification: Body length, male 72–75 cm, female 69–70 cm; tail length, male 820–840 cm, female 730–800 cm; weight, male 11–13 kg; female 8–10 kg. Upper body dark brown, greyish tinge to forehead and nose. Shoulders, neck and back of head rusty-brown. Chest and belly light fawn. Fore-paws and hind feet black. Hind feet broad with large soft pads. Forearms heavily muscled. Tail has black patch at base.

Habitat and Range: Lowland vine forest and mountain rainforest. Endemic to TNQ. Mt Amos (near Helenvale) to Daintree R., west to Windsor Tablelands.

Similar Species: Lumholtz's Tree-kangaroo (see p. 304)

Notes: Rare. Shy, nocturnal. Feeds on leaves, and fruit when available. Spends most of time in canopy, but agile on ground. Scats cylindrical 10–20 mm wide.

Jean-Paul Ferrero, AUSCAPE

QM, Bruce Cowell

Lumholtz's Tree-kangaroo
Dendrolagus lumholtzi

Other Names: Climber, Tree-climber, Boongary.

Identification: Body length, male 59 cm, female 55 cm; tail length 69 cm; weight, male 9 kg, female 7 kg. Face, head, back of ears, neck shoulders and upper back blackish-brown; lower back lighter. Yellowish-grey band across forehead, down cheeks and under throat. Distinct crest from nose and top of head to shoulders. Underside, inside of leg, outside of lower leg, yellowish-grey. Upper surface of fore-paws and hind feet blackish-brown. Ears short and rounded. Forepaws with long, curved claws. Hind feet short, broad with soft, spongy pads. Tail blackish-brown on underside and towards end; lighter on upper surface. Rufous-brown patch at base of tail, sometimes with bare area where animal sits. Juveniles and sub-adults with tuft on tail that is lost with age. Breeding males, seasonal orange flush on belly and inside of legs.

Habitat and Range: Rainforest and to lesser extent, fringing open forests. Endemic to TNQ; Daintree R. to Ingham. Highest population densities above 800 m; sparse below 300 m.

Similar Species: Bennett's Tree-kangaroo (see p. 303)

Notes: Rare. Nocturnal; solitary, although small feeding groups occasionally seen. Food includes leaves, fruit, flowers; also corn and other vegetables. Uses fern clumps and vine entanglements in tall trees as day roosts. Scats cylindrical, 10–20 cm wide.

Agile Wallaby
Macropus agilis

Other Names: Sandy Wallaby, Grass Wallaby.

Identification: Body length, male 80 cm, female 65 cm; tail length, male 77 cm, female, 64 cm; weight, male 16–27 kg, female, 9–15 kg. Body yellowish-brown to orange-buff; white face stripe; outer edge of ear dark brown to black; white hip stripe. Face sharply pointed; muzzle partly hairy.

Habitat and Range: Dry open forest with low brush understorey, particularly areas bordering wetlands, streams and grassland; also dry vine scrub, roadside verges, grazing paddocks, sugar cane crops. Northern Australia, Kimberley region, WA, to Rockhampton, Qld; South Stradbroke I, Peel I., Southern Qld.

Similar Species: Black-striped Wallaby (see p. 307).

Notes: Nocturnal. Gregarious, lives in small groups (up to 10) and can form larger feeding groups. Scats oval with occasional square pieces, 10–12 mm wide.

Bruce Cowell

Eastern Grey Kangaroo
Macropus giganteus

Other Name: Forester.

Identification: Body length, male 54–121 cm; female 51–101 cm; tail length, male 43–109 cm, female 44–84 cm; weight, male 4–66 kg, female 3.5–32 kg. Upper body brown with light underside. Some animals silvery due to silver-tipped hairs on face and belly. Tail darker than body, sometimes almost black. Muzzle hairy.

Habitat and Range: Open forest and woodland with grassy understorey; also paperbark woodland. Coen, to southern Qld; most of NSW, Vic., south-eastern SA, north-eastern Tas.

Notes: Nocturnal. Gregarious, lives in groups of up to 10, but sedentary. Scats oval or square, 10–20 mm long.

Bruce Cowell

QM, Bruce Cowell

Whiptail Wallaby
Macropus parryi

Other Names: Pretty-faced Wallaby, Grey-faced Wallaby, Grey or Blue Flyer.

Identification: Body length, male 84 cm, female, 69 cm; tail length, male 94 cm, female 78 cm; weight, male 14–21 kg, female 7–15 kg. Upper body brownish-grey; underside white. Outside of ears dark brown; yellow patch at base of ear entrance; top of head (between ears) lighter. White cheek stripe on upper lip; light grey stripe on hip. Digits of forepaws and hind feet black. Tail long, grey with dark tip.

Habitat and Range: Undulating to hilly country with dry open forest and grassy understorey. Cooktown, Qld, to NSW central coast.

Similar Species: Agile Wallaby (see p. 305)

Notes: Nocturnal. Social, some groups with 50 individuals. Scats square and oval; 10–12 mm wide.

QM, Bruce Cowell

Common Wallaroo
Macropus robustus

Other Names: Walla, Hill Kangaroo, Euro.

Identification: Body length, male 58–108 cm, female 57–83 cm; tail length, male 55–90 cm, female 53–74 cm; weight, male 7–46 kg, female 6–25 kg. Male stocky with short, powerful forearms, large chest muscles. Upper body black mixed with rusty-red. Female, upper body blue-grey with some rusty-red. Muzzle of both sexes black and hairless. Foot pads resemble surface of table tennis bat, enable animal to move over rocky and slippery habitat.

Habitat and Range: Steep escarpments, rocky hills and large rock piles; over-hanging rocks, ledges and caves provide shelter. Also dry open forest cover on hills. Australia-wide, except western Cape York, Vic., Tas. and extreme south of SA and WA.

Similar Species: Antilopine Wallaroo (*Macropus antilopinus*).

Notes: Nocturnal. Less gregarious than other large species; largest males solitary. Scats square, pellet sized, 10–20 mm wide.

Black-striped Wallaby
Macropus dorsalis

Identification: Body length, 53–82 cm; tail length 54–83 cm; weight, male to 20 kg, females to 7.5 kg. Upper body grey-brown. White cheek stripe on upper lip. Black stripe between eyes, across head and neck to half way down back. White hip stripe. Light brown across shoulders. Tail grey, darker at tip. Underside white.

Habitat and Range: Forested woodland with shrub layer, also rubber vine thicket. Chillagoe, west to Blackall, Qld, south to central NSW.

QM, Bruce Cowell

Notes: Scats oval, 10–20 mm wide.

Red-legged Pademelon
Thylogale stigmatica

Other Names: Pademelon, Northern Red-legged Pademelon.

Identification: Body length, male 49 cm, female 46 cm; tail length, male 44 cm, female 35 cm; weight, male 3.7–6.8 kg, female 2.5–4.2 kg. Upper body grey-brown (darker in rainforest; paler in more open habitat). Light grey across shoulders and upper arms (more pronounced in adult males). Cheeks, forearms, outside and inside of hind legs, rufous-brown. Lighter hip stripe. Underside dirty cream in northern forms; pale grey in southern forms. Tail grey-brown, lightly furred. Some have lighter tail tip.

QM, Bruce Cowell

Habitat and Range: Tropical rainforest; also wet eucalypt forest, deciduous vine thickets and gallery forests. Patchy distribution, Cape York, Qld, south to central coast of NSW.

Notes: Solitary, secretive, presence indicated by distinct thumping of hind feet on ground before fleeing. Eats leaves, fruit and grass on forest edge. In northern Qld, is important food source for dingoes. Scats cylindrical; 10–20 mm wide.

QM, Bruce Cowell

Swamp Wallaby
Wallabia bicolor

Other names: Black-tailed Wallaby, Stinker.

Identification: Body length, male 75 cm, female 69 cm; tail length, male 76 cm, female 69 cm; weight, male 12.3–20.5 kg, female 10.3–15.4 kg. Upper body dark red-brown to black, flecked with yellow; underside light red-brown to yellow. Face in front of eyes black with grey hairs. Light red-brown to yellow cheek striped on upper lip extending toward ear. Muzzle black and hairless. Forepaws, digits of hind feet and last two-thirds of tail usually black; sometimes white tail tip. Black patch where arms meet body in resting position. Yellow to orange patch of fur on internal base of ear.

Habitat and Range: Open forest with brush understorey; also dry vine thickets in northern Qld; brigalow scrub favoured in southern Qld. Patchy distribution east and west of Great Dividing Range from Cape York, Qld, to Vic. and SA.

Notes: Solitary, but sometimes forms feeding groups. Scats oval and square; 10–20 mm wide.

QM, Bruce Cowell

Spectacled Hare-wallaby
Lagorchestes conspicillatus

Identification: Body length, male 44 cm, female 43 cm; tail length, male 49 cm, female 46 cm; weight, male, 3–4.7 kg, female 2–4.3 kg. Upper body dark brown; underside sprinkled with white-tipped, rufous-brown hairs. Underside of tail grey-white. Rich rufous-brown ring around eye. Light grey hip stripe.

Habitat and Range: Open forest with grass understorey. From Ballow I., northern WA, across central NT to Qld border, north to Weipa and Cape York, south to Rockhampton, Qld.

Similar Species: When seen at night, Rufous Bettong (see p. 302)

Notes: Solitary and nocturnal. Scats, round, oval or square pellets, 10–20 mm.

Mareeba Rock-wallaby
Petrogale mareeba

Identification: Body length, male 48 cm, female 47 cm; tail length, male 48 cm, female 44 cm; weight, male 4.5 kg, female 3.8 kg. Upper body grey-brown, underside, forearms, hind legs and base of tail paler sandy brown-buff; Some specimens dark brown to almost black. Sometimes pale cheek and head stripe. Tail darkens towards end with slight brush at tip. Occasionally dirty-white tail tip of variable length.

Habitat and Range: Steep rocky slopes, cliffs, gorges, rocky outcrops and boulder piles in open forest. Endemic to TNQ, Mount Carbine south to Mount Garnet .

Notes: Rare. Nocturnal. Forms colonies; grazes on grasses and some fallen leaf material. Scats cylindrical, 10–20 mm wide.

QM, Bruce Cowell

Unadorned Rock-wallaby
Petrogale inornata

Identification: Body length 43–59 cm; tail length 43 cm; weight, male to 5.6 kg, female to 4.8 kg. Body grey-brown above, underside paler. Base of tail buff in colour. Pale cheek stripe. Tail darkens towards end with slight brush at tip.

Habitat and Range: Steep rock slopes, cliff, gorges and rock outcrops in open forest and dry vine thicket. Burdekin R., Bowen R., south to Fitzroy R; Whitsunday I., Qld.

Notes: Scats cylindrical, 10–20 mm wide.

BJ Nolan

P Johnson

Allied Rock-wallaby
Petrogale assimilis

Identification: Body length 45–59 cm; tail length 45–54 cm; weight, male to 5.9 kg, female to 4.8 kg. Upper body grey-brown, underparts paler. Sometimes light brown patch on rump at base of tail. Pale cheek stripe. Paws and feet darker than body. Tail darker at tip with slight brush.

Habitat and Range: Steep rocky slopes, cliffs, gorges and rocky outcrops in open forest. Townsville to Burdekin R.; Magnetic and Palm Is., Qld.

Notes: Scats cylindrical, 10–20 mm wide.

BJ Nolan

Sharman's Rock-wallaby
Petrogale sharmani

Identification: Body length 46–51 cm; tail length 46–51 cm; weight, male to 4.4 kg, female to 4.1 kg. Body grey-brown with paler underside. Pale cheek stripe. Tail dark at end with slight brush at tip.

Habitat and Range: Rare. Prefers steep rocky slopes, cliffs, outcrops in open woodland. Endemic to TNQ, restricted to west of Ingham.

Similar Species: Allied, Mareeba, Unadorned Rock-wallabies (see p. 309).

Godman's Rock-wallaby
Petrogale godmani

Identification: Body length 53 cm; tail length 56 cm; weight, male to 5.2 kg females to 4.3 kg. Upper body grey-brown; underside, forearms, hind legs and base of tail paler sandy-brown to buff. Tail dirty white.

Habitat and Range: Steep rocky slopes, rocky outcrops in open woodland. Mitchell R. (west Cape York) to Bathurst Heads (east Cape York).

Notes: Nocturnal. Grazes on grasses and some fallen leaf material. Scats cylindrical, 10–20 mm wide.

H & J Beste, Nature Focus

Proserpine Rock-wallaby
Petrogale persephone

Identification: Body length, male 58 cm, female 57 cm; tail length, male 61 cm, female 57 cm; weight, male to 8.8 kg, female to 6.2 kg. Body dark-grey; chest and belly, light grey. Dark mid-line on forehead and neck. Base of tail rufous brown. Forepaws and hind feet, black. Tail tip white.

Habitat and Range: In rock piles, rock outcrops in deciduous vine forest. Endemic to TNQ. Near town of Airlie Beach and Proserpine Dam; also acacia forests on Gloucester I.

Similar Species: Swamp Wallaby (see p. 308), Unadorned Rock-wallaby (see p. 309).

Notes: Endangered. Eats grasses, leaves and fruits. Scats cylindrical, 10–20 mm wide.

P Johnson

Greater Broad-nosed Bat, Glen Hoye

BATS

I n Australia, bats reach their greatest diversity in Tropical North Queensland, where about 40 species are found. The variety of vegetation and landforms in this area provide an abundance of roost sites, food and feeding areas. Some bat species are found throughout TNQ, while others are specialists restricted to particular locations.

Bats are divided into two groups: the Megachiroptera, such as the flying-foxes that are often seen over towns in the early evening; and the smaller Microchiroptera. Apart from size, there are a number of other differences between the groups, the most important being that the microchiropterans use echolocation to find their way around at night. The generally larger megachiropterans do not have 'radar' and use their excellent night vision to navigate and find food. The megachiropterans all have facial features that resemble dogs or foxes, hence their popular name 'flying-foxes'.

Flying-foxes are easily seen at their daytime roost sites (camps), which may contain several species. There are camps of Spectacled Flying-foxes in Central Swamp in Cairns, Tolga Scrub near Atherton and Zillie Falls near Millaa Millaa. A camp of Black Flying-foxes is in the mangroves on the banks of the Ross River, Townsville.

In most northern towns there are buildings where bats have taken up residence and their evening emergence fills the sky with silent, bird-like shapes. At night along the Cairns waterfront, several species of small bats, including the Large-footed Myotis, can be seen hawking for insects just above the water or mud flats. Occasionally, people find solitary tube-nosed bats hanging like a dead leaf on the lower branches of a tree when they are walking in the forest. The dark hollows in the trunks of strangler figs are popular roost sites for horseshoe bats. Most abandoned mines and tunnels will contain bats, such as the two species of bentwings, as well as horseshoe and leaf-nosed bats. However, old mines are usually dangerous places and should not be entered without proper equipment and due care. Large culverts under roads and stormwater drains are also used by several species as daytime roosting sites.

The recent discovery of the rabies-like Lyssavirus in bats in Australia means that people must treat sick or injured bats with caution. On no account should bats be picked up with bare hands. A thick towel should be used for handling bats and the bats taken to the nearest veterinary clinic in a cardboard box or container. Under normal circumstances, bats and humans rarely come into close contact. A person who has been bitten by a sick or injured bat should seek medical advice. Sick or injured bats and abandoned young are cared for and rehabilitated by volunteers at the Far North Queensland Wildlife Rescue, Cairns (phone: 07 4053 4467).

In the following accounts, the bats have been grouped according to what they eat and where they roost during the daytime.

Les Hall, Martin Schulz and Greg Richards

Fruit and Nectar-eating Bats

Either colonial (forming camps) or roost alone in foliage. Do not echolocate and feed on native rainforest and exotic fruits, blossoms and nectar.

QM, Jeff Wright

Black Flying-fox
Pteropus alecto

Identification: Wingspan more than 1 m, weight 500–880 g, forearm 150–190 mm. Black; belly fur often grey-tipped; reddish patch on back of head and neck, eyes sometimes surrounded by brown fur. No fur on lower legs. No tail.

Habitat and Range: Coastal; forms camps in mangroves, but also inland records from Tolga and Chillagoe. WA, NT, Qld, northern NSW; New Guinea, Indonesia.

Flight pattern: At dusk, flies towards feeding grounds, travelling at 25–35 km per hour and between 20–100 m high. Flyout direction forms patterns that change due to food availability.

Notes: Young born August–March. Camps very noisy in February–April when mating occurs. Noisy when feeding.

QM, Bruce Cowell

Spectacled Flying-fox
Pteropus conspicillatus

Identification: Wingspan more than 1 m, weight 400–900 g, forearm 150–175 mm. Blackish; belly grizzled with grey; cream to yellowish patch on back of neck from ears to shoulders. Eyes encircled by wide ring of pale yellow fur extending along muzzle. Leg fur extends to knee. No tail.

Habitat and Range: Confined to coast and ranges. Camps in rainforest or nearby swampy areas, occasionally open forest. Sometimes in small numbers in Black Flying-fox camps. Cape York to Cardwell, Qld; New Guinea.

Flight Pattern: Similar to Black Flying-fox (see above).

Notes: In breeding season (September–December), females often succumb to paralysis tick and fall to ground. Contact Far North Queensland Wildlife Rescue, (07) 4053 4467.

Little Red Flying-fox
Pteropus scapulatus

Identification: Wingspan 60–80 cm, weight 200–500 g, forearm 110–150 mm. Reddish to light brown; lighter brown to yellowish area on back of neck and shoulders; head sometimes grey. Sparse leg fur extends to knee. Tail absent. Almost transparent wings in flight; cream under wings.

Habitat and Range: Coastal to inland. Large camps Tolga Scrub, mangroves near Newel, and along inland rivers when paperbarks flower; on coastal rivers (e.g. Haughton and Upper Herbert). Widespread northern and eastern Australia.

Flight Pattern: In columns, often low to ground; gets caught on barbed-wire fences.

Notes: Camps can contain hundreds of thousands of bats clustered together (other species hang separately). On Atherton Tableland, flowering Red Mahogany (*Eucalyptus resinifera*) attracts large numbers; important pollinators of hardwood forests.

Les Hall

Eastern Tube-nosed Bat
Nyctimene robinsoni

Identification: Weight 42–56 g, forearm 65–70 mm. Back brown to brown-grey with 5 mm wide, dark brown stripe down middle; belly paler, sometimes reddish-fawn; sides of face grey. Tail short. Wings, edges of ear and tail with scattered yellow to lime-green blotches, especially on upper surface of forearms. Nostrils tubular, protrude from muzzle.

Habitat and Range: Rainforest or gallery forest along watercourses, occasionally in adjacent forest. Coastal, Cape York, Qld, to northern NSW; In TNQ, Mt Carbine, Atherton Tablelands, Clarke Ra.

Flight Pattern: Navigates visually, but able to fly at high speed through understorey vegetation. Emits high pitched whistle in flight. Occasionally caught on barbed-wire fences near thick scrub.

Notes: Roosts alone. Resembles dead leaf; blotches look like sunflecks. Finds food by smell; favourite food figs.

Les Hall

Les Hall

Common Blossom Bat
Syconycteris australis

Identification: Weight 12–18 g, forearm 38–43 mm. Back reddish-brown; belly light fawn. Looks like miniature flying-fox. No soft spur (calcaneum) on heel.

Habitat and Range: Rainforest, gallery forest along watercourses, heathland, paperbark swamps, open forest. Cape York, Qld, to Taree, NSW; New Guinea.

Flight Pattern: Flies 1–3 m above ground, along tracks, through dense vegetation and vines; may forage higher in canopy.

Similar Species: Northern Blossom Bat. Soft spur on heel and flap-like 'pyjamas' on inner sides of legs. Northern Australia.

Notes: Roosts alone in dense vegetation. Obtains nectar using long tongue also eats small fruit, particularly figs.

Carnivorous Bats

Roost in caves, overhangs, abandoned mines, boulder piles and disused buildings.

Les Hall

Ghost Bat
Macroderma gigas

Identification: Body weight 100–165 g, forearm 96–113 mm. Light grey or light fawn, paler underneath. Juveniles sooty-grey. Large ears, joined at base for half length. Eyes large. Tragus (fleshy lobe in ear) has split tip. Simple noseleaf. Lower lip grooved in middle. No tail.

Habitat and Range: Dry open forest, vine scrub, tall forest, rainforest. In rainforest, forages in clearings, along watercourses. Tropical Australia (colonies at Black Mtn NP, Mareeba, Cape Hillsborough, Qld).

Flight Pattern: Slow, deliberate, will circle and investigate campfires or unusual sounds. Often flies close to ground, sometimes caught on barbed-wire fences. Audible bird-like chirp when disturbed.

Notes: Call frequency around 40 kHz. Eats insects, small vertebrates including birds. Roosts often have several entrances. Young born August–October. Rare and threatened. Report all sightings to nearest Parks and Wildlife office.

Insectivorous Bats

1. Geneneralist roosters.

Large-footed Myotis
Myotis macropus

Les Hall

Identification: Body weight 5–11 g, forearm 36–41 mm. Greyish-brown, slightly paler on belly; sometimes rufous. Old bats gingerish, particularly around face; occasionally patches of white. Ears funnel-shaped; tail enclosed in membrane; feet long (10–14 mm).

Habitat and Range: Rainforest, to open woodland, mangroves. Eastern Australia.

Flight Pattern: Back and forth over water.

Notes: Call frequency a steep sweep from 55–30 kHz for about 5 milliseconds. Forages over freshwater and tidal reaches (e.g. along Cairns waterfront, over Lakes Barrine and Eacham, along Barron River). Rakes water surface with long feet to catch aquatic insects and small fish. Roosts, include overhangs, caves, etc., dense foliage.

2. Roost in caves, mines, tunnels, rockpiles, road culverts and occasionally in buildings.

Large Bentwing Bat
Miniopterus schreibersii

Les Hall

Identification: Body weight 10–20 g, forearm 43–50 mm. Dark chocolate to reddish-brown on back, slightly paler below. High-crowned head rises sharply from muzzle; ears short, round. Wing structure differs from other bats; end section of third finger (wing tip) 4 times length of middle section

Habitat and Range: Rainforest, dry vine scrub, open forest and mangroves. Northern, eastern and southern Australia, Cape York, west to Chillagoe and Undara, Qld; Europe, Africa, Asia, New Guinea.

Flight Pattern: Flies above canopy, but forages below on windy and full moon nights. Travels long distances in one night.

Notes: Call frequency a steep sweep from 55–43 kHz in about 7 milliseconds. Often shares roost with Little Bentwing Bat (see p. 318). Common cave bat of eastern Australia. Young born December.

Les Hall

Little Bentwing Bat
Miniopterus australis

Identification: Body weight 5–9 g, forearm, 36–42 mm. Greyish-brown, slightly paler belly, short ears, domed head. Wing similar to Large Bentwing Bat (see p. 317).

Habitat and Range: Rainforest, open forest, coastal scrub, mangroves. Cape York, Qld, to Taree, NSW; New Guinea, south-east Asia.

Flight Pattern: Swift, manoeuvrable, in, around and under forest canopy. Often flies along tracks and roads through rainforest.

Notes: Call frequency a steep sweep from 70–58 kHz in about 5 milliseconds. Forms large colonies in summer when young are born. Roosts in dense clusters, particularly in winter; can be inactive for several days.

Les Hall

Eastern Horseshoe Bat
Rhinolophus megaphyllus

Identification: Body weight 6–13 g, forearm, 44–50 mm. Greyish-brown on back; lighter on belly; old bats gingerish; orange fur not uncommon. Noseleaf has horseshoe-shaped outer edge around nostrils, central protruding flap, flat tapered upper section. Tail shorter than extended hind leg.

Habitat and Range: Mangroves, woodland, open forest; common in rainforest. Cape York, west to Georgetown, Qld, south to Vic; New Guinea.

Flight Pattern: Swift, slightly undulating often close to ground, also in and around canopy. Perches in trees when feeding and resting at night.

Notes: Call frequency constant 68 kHz. Broad, pointed ears continually twitch as it scans environment. Calls emitted from nostrils, not mouth like other echolocating bats. Roosts in rock cracks, boulder piles, stormwater and road drains, tree-hollows, anywhere dark and out of sight. Hangs by toes from ceiling of roost. Will enter houses while feeding (e.g. regularly seen around bar of Lion's Den Hotel, south of Cooktown). Often uses verandahs as night roost.

Large-eared Horseshoe Bat
Rhinolophus philippinensis

Identification: Body weight 8–16 g, fore-arm 50–58 mm. Ears long, 25 mm from base to tip. Greyish-brown with big ears; pronounced nose-leaf, often yellowish in centre.

Habitat and Range: Open forest, wood-land, vine thickets, gallery forest, rainforest. Cape York to Townsville, west to Chillagoe, Qld; New Guinea, Timor, Sulawesi, Borneo, Kei I., Philippines.

Flight Pattern: Flies 2–3 m, sometimes higher above ground along tracks and around edges of thick vegetation.

Notes: Call frequency constant 30–33 kHz. Hangs by toes from ceiling of roost; flicks ears forwards and sideways when approached. Often roosts with Eastern Horseshoe Bat (see p. 318).

Les Hall

Diadem Leaf-nosed Bat
Hipposideros diadema

Identification: Body weight 34–50 g, forearm 77–85 mm. Grey-brown on back, but can be orange to rusty-brown; creamy-white patch on shoulder; belly always lighter. Upper noseleaf with four pits, wider than lower section around nostrils; three extra leaflets below outer edge of lower section. Female, false pair of teats in pubic area.

Habitat and Range: Open forest, vine thickets, gallery forest, rainforest; also along tropical coast in boulder piles behind beaches. Coastal Qld, Cape York to Townsville, west to Chillagoe, inshore islands; south-east Asia, Solomon Is.

Flight Pattern: Ambushes large insects (e.g. grasshoppers, beetles). Flight swift, 2–3 m above ground, often follows tracks through vegetation.

Notes: Roosts alone or in colonies in humid caves, mines, buildings, drain pipes under roads. Feeding roost indicated by drop-pings and discarded insect remains.

QM

Les Hall

Dusky Leaf-nosed Bat
Hipposideros ater

Identification: Body weight 3–6 g, forearm 34–42 mm. Belly mottled grey-brown, sometimes rufous at tips; back slightly darker, occasional orange or pale grey-white individuals. Simple noseleaf, squarish, without extra leaflets or lobes. Female, pair of false teats in pubic area and mammary teat in each armpit.

Habitat and Range: Open forest, gallery forest, vine thickets, occasionally rainforest. Northern NT, Cape York to Rockhampton, inland from Carnarvon Ra. to Mount Isa, Qld; India to south-east Asia.

Flight Pattern: Fluttery, zigzag, 1–2 m, sometimes higher above ground. Forages around low bushes for moths.

Notes: Call frequency constant 154 kHz. Roosts colonially in hot, humid caves, mines, rock piles; also as solitary individual or occasionally in small aggregations. Bats hang from ceiling spaced about a wing span (10–15 cm) apart.

Les Hall

Fawn Leaf-nosed Bat
Hipposideros cervinus

Identification: Body weight 5–9 g, forearm 42–48 mm. Back brownish-grey with rusty tinge; belly slightly paler; occasional orange or pale brown phase. Noseleaf differs from other leaf-nosed bats with upper section narrower than lower section, two extra leaflets under lower section.

Habitat and Range: Rainforest, gallery forest, vine thickets, open woodland. Coastal northern Qld, Cape York to Helenvale; New Guinea, south-east Asia.

Flight Pattern: Flies slowly, at 1–2 m above ground, rarely higher. Catches small moths, beetles and other insects. Continually circles trees and buildings.

Notes: Call frequency constant 140 kHz. Small colonies also roost in rock piles; will share roost with Eastern Horseshoe Bat (see p. 318).

Semon's Leaf-nosed Bat
Hipposideros semoni

Identification: Body weight 5–12 g, fore-arm 42–50 mm. Back brownish-grey to dark grey; belly lighter. Upper section of noseleaf with four pits and small lump in middle of top edge, lower section with long (6 mm), club-shaped wart from top edge; two extra leaflets under bottom section.

Habitat and Range: Rainforest, forest, open woodland, vine thickets. Coastal northern Qld, Cape York to Townsville; New Guinea.

Flight Pattern: Swift, fairly direct, with short deviations to capture flying insects.

Notes: Call frequency constant 82–84 kHz. Roosts alone, usually in small limestone and sandstone caves, but will share roosts with other horseshoe bats. Prefers less humid areas, partly lit, near entrance.

Les Hall

Common Sheathtail Bat
Taphozous georgianus

Identification: Body weight 15–30 g, forearm 60–73 mm. Back fur grey to drab brown with creamy-brown bases; belly lighter brown. Long narrow wings. Tail emerges from upper centre of tail membrane and becomes free.

Habitat and Range: All types of vegetation adjacent to suitable roost sites. Will feed over rainforest, but prefers open forest. NT, WA, northern and central Qld, west to Mount Isa.

Flight Pattern: Fast and high flying; has been recorded feeding on insects 100 m above the ground. Audible call.

Similar Species: Coastal Sheathtail Bat, (see p. 322).

Notes: Call frequency a shallow sweep, mainly at 16–18 kHz for about 10 milliseconds. Forages over gorges and escarpments. Roosts alone or in small numbers in limestone caves, granite boulder piles, cracks and caves in sandstone, abandoned concrete buildings.

Les Hall

Les Hall

Eastern Cave Bat
Vespadelus troughtoni

Identification: Body weight 4–7 g, forearm 33–37 mm. Yellow-brown back and head; black wing and tail membranes; lighter below. Short ears (under 15 mm) meet when folded across crown of head.

Habitat and Range: Various habitats, including eucalypt woodland, open forest, gorges and rock escarpments, agricultural land, inshore islands; from sea level to highest parts of Atherton Tablelands. Avoids rainforest, but frequents gallery forest along watercourses and rainforest edges. Distribution patchy, Cape York, Qld, to southern NSW.

Flight Pattern: Manoeuvrable with many twists and turns, below forest canopy or in open (e.g. around rock faces).

Similar Species: Eastern Forest Bat, (*V. pumilus*); Northern Broad-nosed Bat (*Scotorepens sanborni*).

Notes: Call frequency a steep sweep from 62–46 kHz in about 8 milliseconds. Colonies small. Young born late spring.

3. Roost in caves, rock cracks or overhangs, along the mainland coast or on islands.

Les Hall

Coastal Sheathtail Bat
Taphozous australis

Identification: Weight 19–24 g, forearm 61–67 mm. Fur brownish-grey with whitish-cream bases; some individuals grey or brown. Tail emerges from upper centre of tail membrane and becomes free. Male, distinct throat pouch, naked area of skin in female.

Habitat and Range: Forages over mangroves, bays and inlets and forest country near coast. Coastal areas, Cape York to Mackay, Qld; New Guinea.

Flight Pattern: Swift and high flying, flappy wingbeat. Feeds above vegetation; has been seen 2 km offshore feeding over sea.

Notes: Call frequency shallow sweep, mainly at 25 kHz for about 10 milliseconds. Small numbers cling, spider-like, to ceiling or walls of roosts. Audible bird-like chirp when alarmed. Young born December.

4. Roost in tree hollows (branches, trunks, dead trees, under loose bark), caves, fenceposts and hedges. Some roost under roofs and in the walls of buildings.

Beccari's Freetail Bat
Mormopterus beccarii

Identification: Body weight 12–19 g, forearm 34–41 mm. Back fur short, light grey; belly paler, sometimes brown or with white patches. Lips thick, wrinkled; nose pointed; ears can be lowered over face. Short, hairy toes. Distinct musty smell.

Habitat and Range: Various habitats, including, towns, open forest, rainforest, low open coastal and inland woodlands. Northern Australia, except arid south-west of Qld; New Guinea.

Les Hall

Flight Pattern: Fast flying, feeds around tree tops, flies along creeks and feeds above large waterholes.

Notes: Call frequency a shallow sweep at 23 kHz for about 8 milliseconds, increased steepness when prey targeted. Guano makes excellent, but strong plant fertiliser.

Little Northern Freetail Bat
Mormopterus loriae

Identification: Body weight 6–10 g, forearm 28–36 mm. Fur light to mid-brown with paler base. Neck pouch in males, rudimentary in females. Similar to larger Beccari's Freetail Bat (see above), but lips not as deeply wrinkled, ears not as thick, face and wings dark.

Habitat and Range: Coastal, rainforest, monsoon, gallery and open forest, woodland, cane farms. Cooktown, Qld to Sydney, NSW; New Guinea.

Les Hall

Flight Pattern: Fast, manoeuvrable, feeds over swamps, forest canopy and along watercourses.

Similar Species: Northern Freetail Bat (*Chaerephon jobensis*), White-striped Freetail Bat (*Tadarida australis*).

Notes: Call frequency a shallow sweep mainly at 34 kHz for about 8 milliseconds. Roosts in colonies. Many buildings in coastal Qld towns contain large colonies. Several similar undescribed species occur in north-eastern Qld; difficult to identify.

Les Hall

Yellow-bellied Sheathtail Bat
Saccolaimus flaviventris

Identification: Body weight 30–60 g, forearm 74–82 mm. Head and back shiny jet-black; pure white to pale yellow belly, shoulders and behind ears. Male, large throat pouch; female, naked area and ridge of skin under jaw. Tail emerges free from half-way along top of tail membrane.

Habitat and Range: Various habitats, including dry eucalypt forest, open woodland, farmland and mangroves. Most of mainland Australia, except south-western WA and arid parts of SA.

Flight Pattern: Swift, forages high above canopy. Flight fairly direct; bats chase each other in rapid zig-zag pattern.

Similar Species: Bare-rumped Sheathtail Bat (*S. saccolaimus*).

Notes: Call frequency a shallow sweep from 19–24 kHz. Audible, bird-like chirping calls. Roosts in tree hollows and dead trunks; found when trees are cut down; also roosts in animal burrows, cracks in clay banks, under rock slabs. Colony size one or two, occasionally 20–30.

Les Hall

Eastern Long-eared Bat
Nyctophilus bifax

Identification: Body weight 7–13 g, forearm 37–46 mm. Fur long, fluffy, light to dark brown; belly paler. Ears have prominent folding creases; small noseleaf. Short broad wings. Ears 16–22 mm.

Habitat and Range: Dense rainforest to open woodland. Northern Australia south to Coff's Harbour, NSW; New Guinea.

Flight Pattern: Slow, fluttery, but highly manoeuvrable flight, close to ground; often along watercourses. Will land on ground to capture insects.

Similar Species: Gould's Long-eared Bat (see p. 325).

Notes: Call frequency a steep sweep from 95–50 kHz in around 3 milliseconds. Various roosts, including tree hollows, among foliage, epiphyles. Will enter houses at night while chasing prey.

Gould's Long-eared Bat
Nyctophilus gouldi

Les Hall

Identification: Body weight 5–10 g, forearm 32–46 mm. Back fur slate-grey to grey-brown; belly lighter. Ears long (25–32 mm). Noseleaf a simple ridge above nostrils, fleshy, low ridge behind noseleaf.

Habitat and Range: Poorly known in north Qld. Moist, tall open forest at higher elevations adjacent to rainforest; high rainfall areas with dense vegetation. Mt Carbine, Qld, to south-eastern Australia, NSW, Vic., Tas.

Flight Pattern: Slow, highly manoeuvrable. Forages for insects below forest canopy.

Similar Species: Eastern Long-eared Bat, (see p. 324).

Notes: Call frequency a steep sweep from 70–38 kHz in about 5 milliseconds. Like all long-eared bats has large eyes for hunting moths, spiders. Will snatch prey, such as spiders and ants, from foliage and branches.

Gould's Wattled Bat
Chalinolobus gouldii

Les Hall

Identification: Body weight 7–17 g, forearm 36–46 mm. Head and shoulders black; lower back and belly mid-brown. Small flap of loose skin (wattle) where ear ends at corner of mouth. Similar to Large Bentwing Bat (see p. 317), but wings without long end of third finger.

Habitat and Range: Various habitats, woodland, open forest, urban areas. Uncommon in rainforest, more common in drier forests, particularly cattle properties with cleared land. Australia-wide, except tip of Cape York, Qld.

Flight Pattern: Flies swiftly at various heights above ground; will land to hunt.

Notes: Call frequency a steep sweep from 45/40–29 kHz in about 7 milliseconds. Hawks for insects under street lights. Roosts in small colonies, sometimes with other bats and even Feathertail Gliders (see p. 336).

Les Hall

Hoary Wattled Bat
Chalinolobus nigrogriseus

Identification: Body weight 4–10 g, forearm 31–38 mm. Back fur dark grey to black; belly paler, tipped with white or grey.

Habitat and Range: Various habitats, including vegetation along standing water, watercourses, open forest, coastal scrub, flood plains, grassland, woodland; uncommon in rainforest. Northern Australia to Grafton, NSW; New Guinea.

Flight Pattern: Swift, with lots of twists and turns as it chases insects. Flies close to surface of still water.

Similar species: Chocolate Wattled Bat (*C. morio*), ranges behind Mackay and Townsville, Qld. Little Pied Bat (*C. picatus*), lower rainfall areas around Townsville and west of Mackay–Proserpine.

Notes: Call frequency a steep sweep from 50–39 kHz in about 6 milliseconds. One of first bats to leave roost at dusk. Roost entrances very small.

Les Hall

Little Broad-nosed Bat
Scotorepens greyii

Identification: Body weight 4–11 g, forearm 27–35 mm. Back chestnut-brown to grey-brown, belly lighter; base of hairs lighter than tip; ginger forms known. Last tail joint free of tail membrane.

Habitat and Range: Mangroves, low woodland, open forest, gallery forest. Avoids large tracts of rainforest. Northern Australia, except tip of Cape York.

Flight Pattern: Swift, erratic, many deviations made to capture prey, such as mosquitos and moths. Often feeds over water and along watercourses.

Similar Species: Northern Broad-nosed Bat (*S. sanborni*); Greater Broad-nosed Bat (*Scoteanax rueppellii*) much larger, forearm 50–56 mm (see p. 312).

Notes: Call frequency a steep sweep from 52–38 kHz in around 7 milliseconds. Caught by Butcherbirds and Pied Currawongs as it leaves roost just before dark. Tree colonies usually small, but in houses may be more than 500.

5. Roost in dense foliage and abandoned bird-nests.

Golden-tipped Bat
Kerivoula papuensis

Identification: Body weight 5–8 g, forearm 34–40 mm. Woolly dark brown fur with distinctive gold tips; gold tips fade in older bats; only bat with short golden fur on forearms and thumbs. Distinct acrid smell.

Habitat and Range: Rainforest, tall eucalypt forest with rainforest sub-canopy and adjacent vegetation communities, occasionally eucalypt woodland and paperbark forest. Coastal eastern Australia, Cape York, Qld, to Bega, NSW; New Guinea.

Flight Pattern: Agile, manoeuvrable, flies through dense vegetation in lower forest.

Notes: Call frequency a long sweep from 140–40 kHz, low intensity. Thought to be extinct until caught at Crystal Cascades (Cairns) in 1981. Known from Cairns region, also Cape Tribulation to Mt Carbine and Atherton Tablelands. Roosts in Yellow-throated Scrubwren nests. Colonies small, up to 9 bats.

Glen Hoye

Flute-nosed Bat
Murina florium

Other name: Tube-nosed Insectivorous Bat

Identification: Body weight 6–9 g, forearm 32–37 mm. Long, soft hair on tail membrane and feet. Two colour phases: bright rufous-brown; or back and head dark smokey-grey. Tubular nostrils project sideways.

Habitat and Range: Rainforest, also adjacent open forest. Known from a few locations, Shipton's Flat to Paluma, Qld; New Guinea to Lesser Sunda Is, Indonesia.

Flight Pattern: Agile, manoeuvrable, can hover and fly through dense vegetation.

Notes: Call frequency a soft, steep sweep. Social call like tree cricket. First caught in Australia in 1981, has been called 'rarest mammal recorded alive in Australia'. Roosts in nests of Yellow-throated Scrubwrens and Fernwrens; bases of fallen palm leaves caught on branches; behind epiphytes.

Les Hall

Mahogany Glider, QM, Bruce Cowell

OTHER MAMMALS

Only in Tropical North Queensland can you step off the airport tarmac and expect to see such a diversity of mammal species within two or three hours of your hotel. For example, the Cairns area offers unrivalled mammal-watching — from live platypus in crystal creeks to dead bandicoots on canefield roadsides.

For the price of a slightly stretched neck, an astonishing assortment of possums and gliders can be seen with the aid of a torch or spotlight. With a little more commitment, a remarkable assortment of rodents, carnivorous marsupials, bats and kangaroos awaits those prepared to explore and use their binoculars. Around 35 per cent of Australia's terrestrial mammals occur in the area covered by this book and this figure represents about 45 per cent of Queensland's terrestrial mammals.

The 1990 World Heritage listing of the Cooktown–Townsville Wet Tropics brought an end to commercial logging in that zone. However, overgrazing, land clearing and its fragmentation and impoverishment continue to constitute the greatest threats to fauna and its diversity, particularly in the less visually attractive 'sugar-coast' lowlands. Threats to our native mammals, apart from habitat destruction in all forms, come mainly from human activities, such as hunting and cars, and from introduced animals (especially cats, but also foxes, dogs and presumably cane toads). Natural predation by owls, pythons, hawks and other animals is not considered a threat.

The animals in the following accounts are not all from the rainforest. Indeed, mammal watchers would be missing out if they neglected the rich assortment of seasonally dry habitats in the region. It is the unique combination and proximity of dry woodlands, wet eucalypt forests, grasslands, mangroves, rocky bluffs and rainforests that makes TNQ one of the ultimate mammal experiences for visitors and residents alike.

Steve Van Dyck

Monotremes

Bruce Cowell

Platypus
Ornithorhynchus anatinus

Identification: Body length 370 mm; tail length 130 mm; weight to 1 kg. Duck-bill, webbed feet. Male with venom-delivering spur on hind foot. No visible ears.

Habitat and Range: Freshwater (occasionally brackish) streams, some dams and lakes. Highlands to sea level, eastern Qld, south of Cooktown, eastern NSW, southern Vic., south-eastern SA, Tas.

Similar Species: Water Rat (see p. 346).

Notes: Active dawn, dusk, all day if overcast.

Threats: Set fishing nets, chemical pollution, dredging, damming of rivers.

Traces: Burrow entrance is size of hen's egg, just above water level and among tree roots. Droppings irregular nuggets (8 mm by 5 mm).

QM

Echidna
Tachyglossus aculeatus

Identification: Body length to 450 mm; weight to 7 kg. Body covered by long spines (quills). Young females and males have small, non-functional spur on inside of each ankle.

Habitat and Range: Anywhere with ground cover and ants, from rainforest to dry woodland; generally absent from inner city suburbs. Australia-wide.

Similar Species: Australia has no porcupines, hedgehogs or tenrecs to confuse with the Echidna.

Notes: Active day or night. Eats only ants, termites, dirt (accidentally).

Traces: Shed quills; droppings long (13 cm by 1.8 cm), cigar-shaped, smelly, clay-like, filled with shiny ant remains.

Carnivorous Marsupials

Northern Quoll
Dasyurus hallucatus

Identification: Body length to 300 mm; tail length to 300 mm; weight to 900 g. Grey-brown with white spots; no spots on tail. Cat-like teeth; 'big' toe clawless.

Habitat and Range: Creek lines, beaches and eucalypt woodland. WA, NT, Cape York to Gympie, Qld.

Notes: Uncommon. Mostly nocturnal; eats mammals, insects, fruit and probably carrion.

Traces: Droppings large, smelly (35 mm by 6 mm).

Similar Species: Northern Tiger Quoll (*D. m. gracilis*), body length 400 mm, tail length 372 mm, weight 1365 g; dark ginger to tan, many white spots on body and tail. Rainforest, endemic to TNQ. Probably restricted to Lamb Ra., Mt Windsor, Mt Carbine, Thornton Peak, Mt Bartle Frere and Bellenden Ker (above 900 m). At lower altitudes (down to 500 m), occasionally seen at headwaters of Johnson R. with sporadic reports on coast between Cape Tribulation and Daintree R. Endangered; almost certainly extinct elsewhere in north Qld.

Northern Quoll, QM

Northern Tiger Quoll, Michael Anthony

Brush-tailed Phascogale
Phascogale tapoatafa

Identification: Body length 200 mm; tail length 190 mm; weight 180 g. Grey with black 'bottle-brush' tail. Cat-like teeth, 'big' toe clawless. Females have poorly developed pouch.

Habitat and Range: Dry eucalypt forest to rainforest. WA, NT, Cape York, Qld to Vic.–SA border.

Similar Species: Squirrel and Sugar Gliders (see pp. 336, 337).

Notes: Uncommon. Nocturnal, mostly arboreal; eats insects, small vertebrates. Males die after mating in winter.

Traces: Droppings large and pointed (35 mm by 6 mm). Dead poultry usually throttled and badly gashed about throat.

QM

QM

Atherton Antechninus
Antechinus godmani

Identification: Body length to 155 mm; tail length to 143 mm; weight to 116 g (males almost twice as large as females). Dark gingery-brown; near-naked tail dark brown with slight crest on underside. Flatish, broad head; cat-like teeth; 'big' toe clawless; broad 'Charlie Chaplin' hind feet

Habitat and Range: Rainforest above 600 m. Endemic to TNQ, Cardwell to Lamb Ra.

Similar Species: Other antechinuses (see below), Red-cheeked Dunnart, (see pp. 333).

Notes: Rare. Mostly nocturnal (except breeding season); eats insects, worms, lizards. Males die mating in winter.

Traces: Droppings long, pointed, often tar-like (to 22 mm by 3 mm). Mating animals and lost nestlings can be located by their sharp 'tssk-tssk-tssk' calls.

Yellow-footed Antechinus
Antechinus flavipes

Identification: Body length 117 mm; tail length 97 mm; weight to 79 g. Head dark brown, eye-rings gingerish, sides, belly rump and feet orange-brown, tail tip black. (Eungella population grey-brown). Flatish, broad head; pointed snout; cat-like teeth; 'big' toe clawless; broad 'Charlie Chaplin' hind feet.

Habitat and Range: High and low altitude rainforest; moist bracken, lantana, creek verges. Less common in dry eucalypt forests. Eastern Qld, south of Cooktown; NSW, Vic., SA, WA.

Similar Species: Northern Brown Antechinus (*A. adustus*), smaller, weighs 30 g. Rainforest above 800 m. Endemic to TNQ, Mt Spurgeon to Paluma. Nocturnal, arboreal.

Notes: Active day and night. Eats mainly insects; constructs leafy nests in tree hollows and linen cupboards. Males die after mating in winter.

Traces: As for Atherton Antechinus (see above).

Yellow-footed Antechinus. QM

Northern Brown Antechinus, QM

White-footed Dunnart
Sminthopsis leucopus

Identification: Body length 95 mm; tail length 92 mm; weight 25 g. Head and body brown-grey, belly white. Pointed snout; bulging black eyes; cat-like teeth; 'big' toe clawless; tail thin. Striped 'fingerprints' on soles of hindfeet. Females have 'kangaroo-type' pouch.

Habitat and Range: Dense rainforest above 760 m. Known from four Wet Tropics localities, Lamb Ra. to Mt Spec, Qld; southern NSW, Vic., and Tas.

Traces: Droppings tar-like (15 mm by 2.5 mm).

QM

Common Dunnart
Sminthopsis murina

Identification: Body length 90 mm; tail length 80 mm; weight 22 g. Head and body brown-grey; belly white. Pointed snout; bulging black eyes; cat-like teeth; 'big' toe clawless; dotted 'fingerprints' on soles of hindfeet.

Habitat and Range: Dry open forest and woodland, often with blady or kangaroo grass. Often found under logs, fallen bark. Eastern Qld, south of Laura, west to Charleville, NSW, Vic., eastern SA.

Notes: Infrequently encountered, despite popular name. Nocturnal insect-eater.

Traces: As for White-footed Dunnart, (see above).

QM

Red-cheeked Dunnart
Sminthopsis virginiae

Identification: Body length 120 mm; tail length 120 mm; weight to 58 g. Brightly coloured with speckled grey back and orange cheeks. Pointed snout, thin tail.

Habitat and Range: Coastal woodland and grassland. NT, Cape York to Mackay, Qld.

Notes: Uncommon. Nocturnal insect-eater.

Traces: Droppings long and pointed (15 mm by 3 mm).

QM

QM, Bruce Cowell

Common Planigale
Planigale maculata

Identification: Body length 70 mm; tail length 60 mm; weight 11 g. Mouse-sized (males slightly larger than females); grey-brown. Flat head; pointed snout; cat-like teeth; 'big' toe clawless. Females have 'kangaroo-type' pouch.

Habitat and Range: Dry forest and woodland, often with blady or kangaroo grass. Often found under sheets of corrugated iron or fallen bark. WA, northern NT, Cape York, Qld to coastal northern NSW.

Similar Species: Long-tailed Planigale (*P. ingrami*), with smaller body (4 g), flatter skull; rarely found east of Great Dividing Range. House Mouse (see p. 351).

Notes: Nocturnal insect-eater.

Traces: Small, pointed droppings (5 mm by 1.5 mm).

Bandicoots

Bruce Cowell

Northern Brown Bandicoot
Isoodon macrourus

Identification: Body length 400 mm; tail length 170 mm; weight 2 kg. Harsh brown fur. Posture humped; snout long and pointed; movements jerky. Forefeet with only 3 long-nailed toes. Tail often absent (bitten off by other bandicoots).

Habitat and Range: Anywhere with gardens, lawns and suitably protective daytime cover (e.g. long grass, thick shrubs, rubbish piles). Outer suburbs from rainforest and wet and dry eucalypt forests to open paddocks, cane fields and grasslands. WA, northern NT, eastern Qld to coastal central NSW; New Guinea.

Similar Species: Long-nosed Bandicoot (see p. 335). New species closely related to Southern Brown Bandicoot (*I. obesulus*) from Davies Ck (near Cairns).

Notes: One of TNQ's most common marsupials. Nocturnal, non-climbing, omnivorous. Explosive 'balloon screech' call when disturbed.

Traces: Digs small holes (7 cm diameter) in lawns, usually in winter and spring; large excavations in gardens for roots and insect larvae. Droppings like peanut pods (25 mm by 10 mm).

Long-nosed Bandicoot
Perameles nasuta

Identification: Body length 400 mm; tail length 140 mm; weight 1.5 kg. Sandy-brown. Snout very long and pointed; posture hunched; ears pointed; fur soft. Large gap between 4th and 5th upper incisors; 3 long-clawed toes on forefeet.

Habitat and Range: From rainforest and moist gullies in north to grassy woodland in south. Cape York to NSW, Vic.

Notes: Nocturnal, non-climbing, omnivorous. Common at backyard compost heaps and gardens within more restricted, wetter range. Solitary. Shrill 'toy trumpet' squeak when disturbed.

Traces: Digs small conical holes in lawns and gardens. Droppings like irregular peanut pods (35 mm by 10 mm).

Russell Borland, Nature Focus

Koala, Possums, Gliders,

Koala
Phascolarctos cinereus

Identification: Body length 90 cm; weight 6 kg. Head and back grey; belly white. Males larger, more 'coarse-looking' (Roman-nosed, 'dirty' chest gland) than females.

Habitat and Range: Historic records from Mount Molloy (1960s). Rare, if not absent elsewhere in TNQ. Past distribution as far as Cooktown, but closest recent records from Ravenshoe; more common in south. Magnetic I. population thought to have been introduced from mainland. Qld, NSW, Vic., SA.

Notes: Nocturnal, arboreal.

Traces: Scratch marks on trunks; strong eucalyptus smell. Droppings 'avocado-shaped' (22 mm by 13 mm at widest point).

Bruce Cowell

QM

Feathertail Glider
Acrobates pygmaeus

Identification: Body length 80 mm; tail length 80 mm; weight 13 g. Back grey-brown, belly white; tail like small feather (a feature found in no other Australian mammal).

Habitat and Range: Rainforest, eucalypt forest, parks and backyard gardens. From tip of Cape York throughout eastern Qld; NSW, Vic., SA.

Similar Species: House Mouse (see p. 351).

Notes: Common, but rarely seen. Nocturnal. Lives in family groups (parents plus last one or two litters) that may number up to a dozen. While feeding on nectar, gum sap and insects, it careers around treetops and trunks more like a large insect than a marsupial. Often nests in electricity meter boxes, telephone junction covers and banana bags.

Traces: Difficult to detect in wild; droppings like House Mouse scats but pointed at both ends (5 mm by 2 mm).

QM

Sugar Glider
Petaurus breviceps

Identification: Body length 150 mm; tail length 190 mm; weight 90 g. Soft grey above with black stripe on head and body; belly usually white; thin tail often white-tipped.

Habitat and Range: Highland and lowland rainforest, woodland, eucalypt forest, mangroves. Australia-wide; New Guinea.

Similar Species: Squirrel Glider (see p. 337).

Notes: Common. Nocturnal; feeds on wattle and eucalypt saps, nectar and insects. Lives in groups of up to 10, nesting in tree hollows.

Threats: Wattle clearing, barbed-wire fences.

Traces: Dull mauve eye-shine. Loud call, 'yip-yip-yip-…'. Droppings blackish, pointed at one end, sometimes joined by hairs (12 mm by 4 mm).

Squirrel Glider
Petaurus norfolcensis

Identification: Body length 210 mm; tail length 270 mm; weight 230g. Soft grey with black stripe on head and body; belly usually white. Tail very thick, especially where it joins body.

Habitat and Range: Dry upland forest and woodland. Rare in Far North, more common south and west of Townsville. Recently recorded from Princess Hills, (west of Ingham). Also eastern NSW, Vic.

Similar Species: Sugar Glider, Mahogany Glider, (see p. 336 and below).

Notes: Nocturnal; feeds on wattle and eucalypt saps, nectar and insects. Lives in groups that nest in leaf-lined tree hollows.

Threats: Wattle clearing, barbed-wire fences.

Traces: Droppings knobbly, pointed cylinders, often with gum bands (15 mm by 5 mm).

Bruce Cowell

Mahogany Glider
Petaurus gracilis

Identification: Body length 250 mm; tail length 350 mm; weight 350 g. Soft grey or brown with black stripe on head and body; tail long, thin, black-tipped.

Habitat and Range: Coastal lowland woodland. Endemic to TNQ, very limited range; Hull R. (near Tully) to Crystal Ck (near Ingham), but may occur closer to Innisfail.

Similar Species: Squirrel Glider (see above).

Notes: Endangered, probably only 2000 animals left. Nocturnal; eats wattle and eucalypt saps, nectar, insects. Nests in tree hollows.

Threats: Habitat destruction and fragmentation; inappropriate fire regimes that allow rainforest to smother woodland. Barbed-wire fences, cats.

Traces: Gashes made in upper, pencil-thick branches of bloodwoods and large fruited Red Mahoganies, chunks from grasstree flower stalks. Droppings often with gum bands (17 mm by 5 mm).

QM, Bruce Cowell

QM

Greater Glider
Petauroides volans

Identification: Body length 340 mm; tail length 395 mm; weight 900 g. Body grey to brown, darker hands and feet. Fluffy ears; shaggy fur; long, pendulous, non-gripping tail; no stripes on body or head. Gliding membrane stretches from elbow to ankle.

Habitat and Range: Medium to tall eucalypt forest and woodland. eastern Qld, south of Mt Spurgeon, common in highlands, rare on northern coast, more common south of Townsville. Also NSW, Vic.

Similar Species: Yellow-bellied Glider (see below).

Notes: Silent, solitary, nocturnal gumleaf-eater.

Threats: Barbed-wire fences.

Traces: Landing scratches on tree trunks. Droppings size and shape of slightly flattened peas.

QM, Bruce Cowell

Yellow-bellied Glider
Petaurus australis

Identification: Body length 280 mm; tail length 420 mm; weight 550 g. Black fore and hindpaws; claws white; ears naked and black; belly buff-yellow. Gliding membrane extends from wrist to ankle.

Habitat and Range: Western slopes of tall, open, wet eucalypt forest. TNQ, Mt Windsor to Lumholtz NP; coastal central Qld south to Vic.

Similar Species: Greater Glider (see above).

Notes: Rare. Nocturnal. Noted for long glides (more than 100 m recorded), loud gurgling calls ('ooo-cree-cha-cree-cha-chigga-woo-ja') and habit of slashing tree trunks to obtain exuded gums.

Threats: Barbed-wire fences; felling of old hollow nest trees.

Traces: Weeping incisions on feed trees. Droppings like small, rough-skinned avocados, indented on side of narrow end (20 mm by 9 mm).

Long-tailed Pygmy-possum
Cercartetus caudatus

Identification: Body length 106 mm; tail length 135 mm; weight 30 g. Biscuit-brown with black 'Batman' mask across eyes.

Habitat and Range: Highland and lowland rainforest. Daintree R. to Townsville, Qld; New Guinea.

Similar Species: Prehensile-tailed Rat, (see p. 348).

Notes: Nocturnal, arboreal. Eats nectar, native fruit, insects.

Traces: Droppings small, unlikely to be noticed.

Environmental Protection Agency

Striped Possum
Dactylopsila trivirgata

Identification: Body length 263 mm; tail length 325 mm; weight 423 g. Three black stripes on white back; prominent lower jaw; elongated 4th finger.

Habitat and Range: High and lowland rainforest and lowland woodland. Cape York to Townsville, Qld; New Guinea.

Notes: Uncommon. Noisy, nocturnal, arboreal, eats insects, nectar, fruit. Pungent odour.

Traces: Growls. Rough gouges in tree trunks and branches where boring grubs have been extracted. Dull red eye-shine.

QM, Bruce Cowell

Green Ringtail Possum
Pseudochirops archeri

Identification: Body length 350 mm; tail length 330 mm; weight 1100 g. Green-grey fur with two lighter stripes down back; white reflective patch under eye and ear.

Habitat and Range: Rainforest above 300 m. Endemic to TNQ, Mt Windsor Tableland to Paluma.

Notes: Uncommon. Mainly nocturnal; eats variety of rainforest leaves and ripe figs. Sleeps during day in curled position on an exposed branch.

Traces: Dull yellow-red eye-shine.

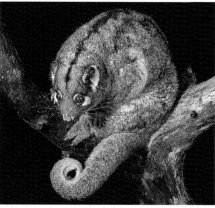

QM

QM

Lemuroid Ringtail Possum
Hemibelideus lemuroides

Identification: Body length 340 mm; tail length 340 mm; weight 950 g. Chocolate to charcoal-brown, rarely yellowish-white or reddish-ginger. Tail narrow, furred along entire length (except for last 4–5 mm). Blunt face.

Habitat and Range: Common, but restricted to upland rainforest. Endemic to TNQ. Mt Carbine Tableland to Ingham.

Similar Species: Greater Glider (see p. 338); Daintree River Ringtail (see below); Herbert River Ringtail (see p. 341). Common Brushtail (see p. 342);

Notes: Nocturnal, arboreal; eats rainforest leaves. Lives in small family groups; nests in tree hollows.

Traces: Strong musky odour; brilliant silver-lime to gold eyeshine. Droppings rounded capsules (8 mm by 5 mm).

QM, Bruce Cowell

Daintree River Ringtail Possum
Pseudochirulus cinereus

Identification: Body length 350 mm; tail length 350 mm; weight 1 kg. Caramel to dark brown, light belly, dark stripe from forehead to lower back.

Habitat and Range: Highland rainforest. Endemic to TNQ; three populations, Thornton Peak and Mt Windsor and Mt Carbine Tablelands.

Similar Species: Lemuroid Ringtail (see above).

Notes: Uncommon. Mostly nocturnal, leaf and fruit-eater. Nests in tree hollows or epiphyte clusters.

Traces: Bright red eye-shine.

Herbert River Ringtail Possum
Pseudochirulus herbertensis

QM

Identification: Body length 360 mm; tail length 365 mm; weight 1100 g. Black above, belly, arm bands and tail tip white; some almost completely black; tail tapers to nearly naked tip.

Habitat and Range: Common, but restricted to high altitude rainforest. Endemic to TNQ. Lamb Ra. to Ingham.

Similar Species: Dark individuals might be confused with Lemuroid Ringtail (see p. 340).

Notes: Nocturnal, eats leaves. Nests in tree hollows or epiphyte clusters.

Traces: Light orange eye-shine. Droppings like rounded capsules (15 mm by 5 mm).

Common Ringtail Possum
Pseudocheirus peregrinus

Environmental Protection Agency

Identification: Body length 345 mm; tail length 310 mm; weight 1 kg. Silver-grey to brown back and flanks, fawn-orange face, arms and legs; tail thin with white tip, no brush. Eyes caramel-brown.

Habitat and Range: Open forest, sea level to highlands. Non-arid areas of Qld, NSW, Vic., SA, Tas.

Similar Species: Brushtail Possum (see p. 342), Water Rat (see p. 346)

Notes: Uncommon in TNQ. Nocturnal; eats flowers and leaves.

Traces: Large basketball-sized nests. Droppings like roughly textured jellybeans (15 mm by 6 mm).

Bruce Cowell

Common Brushtail Possum
Trichosurus vulpecula

Identification: Body length 420 mm; tail length 340 mm; weight 3.5 kg. Light to steel grey with gingery shoulders and thin tail (coastal areas) or orange to charcoal (tablelands); hairy tail black to tip; paws light grey, ears large.

Habitat and Range: Highland forest. Uncommon to absent along northern sugar coast, common south of Ingham, Qld; vegetated areas Australia-wide.

Similar Species: Common Ringtail (see p. 341).

Notes: Nocturnal; feeds on eucalypt and rainforest leaves and fruit.

Traces: In breeding season, heavy breathing (a throaty 'ha-ha-ha-...') outside windows, urine stains on ceiling. Droppings like thin jellybeans with one pointed end (22 mm by 7 mm).

Native Mice

Native mice are difficult to identify. Habitat and range are good indicators. Many are similar to the introduced House Mouse (see p. 351).

QM, Jeff Wright

Lakeland Downs Mouse
Leggadina lakedownensis

Identification: Body length 68 mm; tail length 42 mm; weight 18 g. Grey-brown above, white to light grey below; extremely short tail. Female, two pairs of teats.

Habitat and Range: Woodland and grassland. WA, NT, western tip of Cape York, Cooktown to Proserpine, Qld; WA, NT

Notes: Rare, but periodically abundant. Docile when handled. Nocturnal; eats seeds, vegetation and insects. Nests in burrows.

Traces: Droppings minute (3.5 mm by 2.2 mm).

Eastern Pebble-mound Mouse
Pseudomys patrius

Identification: Body length 70 mm; tail length 76 mm; weight 14 g. Biscuit-brown above, light brown to white below. Female, two pairs of teats.

Habitat and Range: Restricted to low woodland and grassland on exposed, eroding ridges and slopes of Great Dividing Range, south of Hidden Valley (west of Paluma) to near Gympie, Qld.

Notes: Rare. Nocturnal; eats seeds, vegetation and insects.

Traces: Builds mounds (up to 2.5 m across and 10 cm high) of eroded, thumb-nail sized pebbles surrounding main entrance hole above burrows. Small droppings (6 mm by 2 mm).

QM, Jeff Wright

Delicate Mouse
Pseudomys delicatulus

Identification: Minute and fragile. Body length 65 mm; tail length 68 mm; weight 10 g. Yellowy-brown above, white below; tail very thin. Female, two pairs of teats.

Habitat and Range: Coastal sand dunes, open woodland and grassland on friable soils. Northern WA and NT, northern to south-eastern Qld.

Notes: Uncommon. Nocturnal; eats grass, seeds, insects. Nests in simple, shallow burrows.

Traces: Droppings minute (4 mm by 1.7 mm). Footprints and trackways in sand dunes.

QM, Jeff Wright

QM

Eastern Chestnut Mouse
Pseudomys gracilicaudatus

Identification: Body length 118 mm; tail length 115 mm; weight 55 g (old males heavier and larger). Speckled chestnut above, grey below; greyish-white hairs on feet; soles light grey; tail light below, dark above. Female, two pairs of teats.

Habitat and Range: Open woodland with grassy understorey. Hidden Valley (west of Paluma), Qld, to mid-eastern NSW.

Notes: Rarely encountered. Nocturnal; eats seeds, vegetation, fungi and insects.

Traces: Small droppings (6 mm by 2 mm), often with 'tail-like' hair emerging from one end.

QM, Bruce Cowell

Water Mouse
Xeromys myoides

Other Name: (Previously) False Water Rat.

Identification: Body length 100 mm; tail length 80 mm; weight 40 g. Silky, slate-grey back (sometimes spotted white), sharply defined by pure white belly; tail short, sparsely haired. Female, two pairs of teats.

Habitat and Range: Intertidal sedgeland zones adjacent to mangrove forests, also freshwater swamps and reedy lakes close to foredunes. NT, Mackay to south-east, Qld, (probably occurs in Cairns area); southern New Guinea.

Notes: One of Australia's rarest rodents. Nocturnal; eats crabs, shellfish, mud lobsters and marine flatworms. Constructs 'volcanic' mounds of peat and mud up to 60 cm high. Rarely climbs; swims, but does not pursue active aquatic lifestyle.

Threats: Disturbance to mangroves, swamps and freshwater lakes.

Traces: Large mud nests in sedgeland. Feeding scraps (crab and mud lobster shell fragments) at hollow bases of mangrove trees. Droppings large (30 mm by 5 mm), cylindrical, ends rounded, often in threes connected by hair, smelly.

Native Rats

Many species of native rats are difficult to identify by their external features and may also resemble the introduced Sewer and Ship Rats (see p. 351). Size, tail appearance and length, habitat and range are useful indicators.

Black-footed Tree-rat
Mesembriomys gouldii

Identification: Enormous, shaggy. Body length 285 mm; tail length 365 mm; weight 715 g. Grey-black above, slightly lighter below; long black tail with white brush at tip. Female, two pairs of teats.

Habitat and Range: Tropical woodland. WA, NT, Cape York to Cairns, Qld.

Similar Species: Water Rat and Giant White-tailed Rat (see p. 346–347).

Notes: Rare. Nocturnal; eats large seeds, hard fruits, flowers, insects and molluscs. Nests inside tree hollows and among palm fronds.

QM

Common Rock-rat
Zyzomys argurus

Identification: Body length 117 mm; tail length 113 mm; weight 42 g. Honey-coloured above, cream to white below, white on paws. Tail dark above, light below; thick at base; finely tufted at tip; tail likely to strip off if held. Thin snout.

Habitat and Range: Harsh, rocky outcrops. Northern to central Qld.

Notes: Seasonally common. Nocturnal; eats seeds, vegetation, fungi and insects. Does not burrow.

Traces: Droppings very small (5 mm by 2.5 mm).

QM

QM, Bruce Cowell

Water Rat
Hydromys chrysogaster

Identification: Body length 300 mm; tail length 270 mm; weight 700 g. Size of a rabbit. Brown-black back, golden belly; white tipped tail. Small ears, flattish 'square' head. Female, two pairs of teats.

Habitat and Range: River banks, estuaries, beaches, mangroves, wharves, lakes, dams, creeks and polluted watercourses. Australia-wide; New Guinea.

Similar Species: When swimming, may be mistaken for Platypus (see p. 330)

Notes: Common. Active day or night; eats mainly yabbies, mussels and fish, although poultry, frogs and snails may be taken. Builds nest at end of complex burrow along waterside.

Threats: Swamp drainage and land reclamation.

Traces: Strong fishy scent; 'runway' tracks along water's edge; feeding 'tables' scattered with shells and other leftovers; dead poultry with throats and heads roughly skinned. Droppings torpedo-shaped (25 mm long by 8 mm wide).

Grassland Melomys
Melomys burtoni

Identification: Body length 100 mm; tail length 120 mm; weight 55 g. Reddish-brown. Tail dark above and off-white below, almost hairless with small scales clearly visible. Hindfoot usually shorter than 26 mm. Female, two pairs of teats.

Habitat and Range: Grasslands, fringes bordering swamps and mangroves. Coastal, Qld to northern NSW; NT, northern WA; New Guinea.

Notes: Common. Nocturnal; solitary and aggressive with own kind; eats seeds, leaves and fruit. Agile climber; builds nest like that of a wren in long grass or thick vegetation (e.g. pandanus leaves).

Traces: Droppings similar to House Mouse (see p. 351).

QM

Fawn-footed Melomys
Melomys cervinipes

Identification: Body length 114 mm; tail length 160 mm; weight 70 g. Rat-sized. Colour variable, but adults usually brown; tail nearly naked. Hindfoot usually longer than 26 mm. Female, two pairs of teats.

Habitat and Range: Rainforest and moist lantana, bracken, grassland, creek verges. Coastal, Cooktown, Qld, to central NSW.

Notes: Common. Nocturnal; eats leaves, fruit, seeds, sugarcane. Active climber.

Traces: Droppings often small, knobbly and mouse-like (5 mm by 2 mm).

QM

Giant White-tailed Rat
Uromys caudimaculatus

Identification: Enormous. Body length 330 mm; tail length 345 mm; weight 640 g. Grey to brown above, white below; tail 'hairless', last 100 mm (at least) white. Female, two pairs of teats.

Habitat and Range: Rainforest, closed woodland, swamps and mangroves. Tip of Cape York to Mt Elliot, Qld; New Guinea.

Notes: Common. Nocturnal; eats fruit, nuts, insects, bird eggs, small vertebrates, fungi. Nests in tree hollows.

Traces: Coconuts drilled and robbed of flesh; grinding sound of tough seeds being opened in canopy. Droppings like capsules (15 mm by 4 mm).

QM

Masked White-tailed Rat
Uromys hadrourus

Identification: Body length 175 mm; tail length 190 mm; weight 190 g. Light brown to reddish above, white below, dark eye-ring; tail-tip white for last 35 mm. Female, two pairs of teats.

Habitat and Range: Unfragmented rainforest. Endemic to TNQ; Thornton Peak, Mt Carbine and Atherton uplands, Qld.

Notes: Rare. Nocturnal; eats rainforest fruits and nuts, as well as insects.

Threats: Fragmentation of rainforest.

Traces: Droppings pointed at one end (6 mm by 3 mm).

M Trenerry

H & J Beste, Nature Focus

Prehensile-tailed Rat
Pogonomys sp.

Identification: Body length 140 mm; tail length 180 mm; weight 62 g. Grey-brown above, pure white below, black eye-ring; long prehensile tail. Female, three pairs of teats.

Habitat and Range: Rainforest. Iron Ra. (Cape York) to Townsville, Qld; probably New Guinea.

Similar Species: Long-tailed Pygmy Possum, which lacks chisel-like, upper incisors, has large clawless 'thumb' on hindfoot (see p. 339). Fawn-footed and Grassland Melomys (see p. 346–347).

Notes: Probably common, but rarely seen and never trapped. Nocturnal; eats leaves and fruits. Nests in tunnels on ground. Previously thought to be *P. mollipilosus*.

Traces: Spoil outside nesting tunnel entrance.

QM

Bush Rat
Rattus fuscipes

Identification: Body length 160 mm; tail length 150 mm; weight 120 g. Brown-grey. Tail ringed with bands of scales, tail length shorter than head-body length. Female, four pairs of teats.

Habitat and Range: Rainforest and thickly vegetated moist gullies and creekside verges. Cooktown to Mt Elliot, Rockhampton to south-east Qld; coastal southern WA, NSW, Vic., SA.

Notes: Nocturnal; eats insects as first choice, but anything else as well.

Traces: Messy feeder; leaves droppings and smelly urine on its dinner table or in dog's bowl. Often digs burrows alongside building footings. Droppings torpedo-shaped, usually pointed at one end (17 mm by 4 mm).

Cape York Rat
Rattus leucopus

Identification: Body length 180 mm; tail length 171 mm; weight 139 g. Brown above, lighter below. Female, three pairs of teats.

Habitat and Range: Rainforest. Tip of Cape York to Coen, Cooktown to Paluma, Qld; New Guinea.

Notes: Common. Nocturnal; eats mainly insects, but also fruit, seeds, fungi.

Traces: Strong 'ratty' smell, droppings as for Bush Rat (see p. 348).

QM

Swamp Rat
Rattus lutreolus

Identification: Body length 160 mm; tail length 110 mm; weight 120 g. Stocky with blackish-brown fur, shaggy rump, black feet, long claws; very short tail. Female, five pairs of teats.

Habitat and Range: Swamps, thick vegetation along creeks and dense vegetation outside rainforest. Atherton Tableland, Qld; coastal south-east Qld, NSW, Vic., SA, Tas.

Similar Species: Black phase of Ship Rat (see p. 351). Canefield Rat (see p. 350). Immature Swamp Rats might be confused with old individuals of Eastern Chestnut Mouse (see p. 344).

Notes: Uncommon; requires more specific habitat than most rats. Active day and night; eats reeds, swamp-grass stems, seeds.

Threats: Swamp reclamation.

Traces: Cuts trackways through reeds and sedges. Droppings large, coarsely granular (17 mm by 5 mm).

QM

QM

Canefield Rat
Rattus sordidus

Identification: Body length 165 mm; tail length 112 mm; weight 160 g. Grizzled dark grey-brown above, slightly lighter below; tail dark; light coloured soles of hindfeet. Female, five pairs of teats.

Habitat and Range: Tropical open forest and grassland, as well as cane fields. Tip of Cape York, eastern Qld to northern NSW; New Guinea.

Notes: Common. Nocturnal; eats sugarcane, seeds, vegetation and insects. Burrows, often in colonies. Irruptive breeding cycles.

Traces: Long, wide gashes at base of sugarcane. Droppings knobbly, pointed at one end (17 mm by 4 mm).

QM

Pale Field Rat
Rattus tunneyi

Identification: Body length 160 mm; tail length 135 mm; weight 125 g. Honey-coloured above, cream below. Bulging eyes. Tail shorter than head-body length. Female, five pairs of teats.

Habitat and Range: Grassy open forest near creeks and streams.

Notes: Common, attractive, gentle. Nocturnal; eats roots, grass stems and seeds.

Traces: Trackways through tussock grass. Droppings torpedo-shaped, usually pointed at one end (17 mm by 4 mm).

Introduced Mammals

House Mouse
Mus musculus

Identification: Body length 75 mm; tail length 80 mm; weight 15 g. Grey-brown. Small notch on inner side of upper incisors.

Habitat and Range: Australia-wide; world-wide.

Notes: Introduced from central Asia. Generally nocturnal.

Traces: Strong, musky urine smell. Droppings, pointed at one end (5 mm by 2 mm).

QM

Sewer Rat
Rattus norvegicus

Identification: Body length 240 mm; tail length 200 mm; weight 300 g. Black to white; generally brown on back, dirty white on belly. Shaggy with small ears that cannot be pulled forward to cover eyes; tail thick, scaly and light-coloured, when pulled forward just reaches eye. Female, six pairs of teats.

Habitat and Range: Common around human habitation. Worldwide.

Notes: Immigrant from China or Siberia. Nocturnal, non-climbing, burrowing.

Traces: Droppings large, pointed at one end (16 mm by 5 mm).

QM

Ship Rat
Rattus rattus

Identification: Body length 190 mm; tail length 230 mm; weight 240 g. Sleek-looking, any colour from black to pure white, but generally steel grey with white belly. Tail much longer than head-body length; ear folds forward to cover eye. Female, 5 pairs of teats.

Habitat and Range: Common around human habitation. Coastally, almost Australia-wide; worldwide.

Notes: Immigrant from south-east Asia. Nocturnal; accomplished climber.

Traces: Droppings blunt pellets (10 mm by 3 mm).

QM

Bruce Cowell

Dingo
Canis lupus dingo

Identification: Body length 100 cm; tail length 32 cm; weight 10–25 kg. Colour ranges from white through honey-ginger to black-and-tan.

Habitat and Range: Dry grassland through woodland to rainforest. Australia-wide; Asia.

Similar Species: Domestic dogs and first cross hybrids difficult to distinguish by external features.

Notes: Common. Pack animals, but may also hunt alone. Home range may be 10–40 sq km. Eats whatever is abundantly available from insects to large (often domestic) mammals.

Environmental Protection Agency

Red Fox
Vulpes vulpes

Identification: Body length 70 cm; tail length 40 cm; weight 5–8 kg. Orange-brown above, off-white below; bushy, white-tipped tail.

Habitat and Range: Occasionally seen in cleared patches around Tablelands and Cooktown, Qld; mainland southern Australia.

Notes: Uncommon. Nocturnal; usually solitary. Often guilty of killing binges on domestic animals, particularly poultry.

Traces: Fox holes (of surprisingly small diameter, around 15 cm) in sand, gravel, dirt banks; pungent 'tomcat' odour around droppings or den.

QM, Bruce Cowell

Cat
Felis catus

Identification: Body length 55 cm; tail length 30 cm; weight 3–6 kg. Domestic and feral populations have same colours.

Habitat and Range: Common throughout agricultural landscape. Australia-wide.

Notes: Usually nocturnal. Home range may be around 2–6 square km.

Traces: Unburied faeces on favoured trackways.

Rabbit
Oryctolagus cuniculus

Identification: Body length 40 cm; weight 1.5 kg, usually brown with reddish neck and white belly.

Habitat and Range: Abundant through Tablelands and in drier country; also along roads deep within rainforest (e.g. near Wallaman Falls), Qld. Australia-wide

Notes: Populations in tropics fluctuate dramatically; 10–25 young born per female per year.

Traces: Droppings smooth, pea-like; deposited in latrines around burrow entrances.

C Andrew Henley, Nature Focus

Brown Hare
Lepus capensis

Identification: Body length 60 cm; weight 4 kg; adults fawn to ginger-brown, very long ears, gangling appearance.

Habitat and Range: Absent from Wet Tropics; rare, patchy distribution further south (around Townsville, Ayr, Mackay). Common, south-eastern Qld, NSW, Vic., SA and Tas.

Notes: Mostly nocturnal; solitary, non-burrower. From 8–10 young born per female per year.

Traces: Smooth, pea-like droppings.

Environmental Protection Agency

Pig
Sus scrofa

Identification: Body length 120 cm; tail length 20 cm; weight up to 120 kg. Usually black, but any colour possible. 'Razor-back' male has thickened shoulders and well-developed, coarse, erectile mane.

Habitat and Range: Rainforest to open savannah. Qld, NSW, Vic., patchy distribution WA, northern NT.

Notes: Known reservoir for diseases such as Ross River Fever, Meliodosis, Brucellosis and Leptospirosis.

Traces: Mud-wallows; roughly 'ploughed' ground; igloo-like farrowing nests made of grass or other vegetation.

Bruce Cowell

DUGONG

Dugongs are large, gentle, long-lived marine mammals. Together with their Atlantic cousins, the manatees, they represent the Order of animals known as the Sirenia. This name relates to dugongs being the origin of the mermaid legend and the belief that, as sirens, they lured ancient mariners to a watery grave.

Dugongs are slow growers and slow breeders. They can live to 70 years, but they do not become sexually mature until they are 10–15 years old, and they have just one calf at intervals of 3 to 7 years. Their seagrass diet restricts them to shallow coastal waters, which they must share with humans. Consequently, their fate is increasingly being determined by human activities. The number of dugongs in the Great Barrier Reef region south of Cooktown has fallen by more than 50 per cent in recent years. Because of their very slow breeding rate, such a decline is extremely serious. The decline may even be greater than this as it may have commenced before monitoring started. For example, since the start of detailed aerial surveys in 1987 dugongs have been rare in the Cairns region, however, as the following quote shows, dugongs were once abundant at nearby Yarrabah.

An enquiry in 1952/3 had apparently concluded that [dugongs are] abundant locally and not being depleted by the large numbers being taken at nearby Yarraba

Settlement for Aborigines. At the time of our visit in 1956 some 200 were being taken by half a dozen fishermen from the Settlement, one (Police Sergeant John Maloney, our informant) having taken 64 in a single year. A herd of 100 had recently been seen… Shark nets [set for bather protection] at Cairns took 42 animals between 1964 and 1969…
(Bertram and Bertram, 1973. The modern Sirenia: their distribution and status).

Between 1969 and 1974, fifty-five dugongs died in shark nets. Since then, few have been caught, reflecting the loss of dugongs from the Cairns region.

Entanglement and drowning in gill nets set for barramundi, mackerel and other large fish appears to be a major threat to dugongs. In 1998 the Great Barrier Reef Marine Park Authority established a series of dugong sanctuaries within the marine park to further control netting.

Anthony Preen

Diane Yates, Nature Focus

Dugong
Dugong dugon

Identification: Length to 3 m; width to 1 m near mid-body; weight to more than 400 kg. Light brown to grey-brown on top, pale belly. No dorsal fin; large broad whale-like tail; large blunt head, with two nostrils.

Habitat and Range: Feeds almost exclusively on seagrasses, (favours *Halophila* and *Halodule* species). Can feed to depths of 30 m, but spends most time in water less than 10 m deep, where seagrasses are most common; often feeds in intertidal areas. Highly mobile, with home ranges of hundreds of thousands of square kilometres. Some tagged individuals move between preferred areas up to 700 km apart, but most are quite sedentary for periods of weeks to months. Coastal waters of tropical Indo-west Pacific, from Mozambique, south-east Africa, through Red Sea and Arabian Gulf to southern China, Vanuatu, New Caledonia. Northern Australia, from Shark Bay, WA, to Moreton Bay, south-eastern Qld.

Status: Populations in southern three-quarters of Great Barrier Reef Marine Park and Hervey Bay have declined severely in recent years. Populations off eastern Cape York (north of Cooktown) and in Torres Strait appear stable. Status of populations along Gulf of Carpentaria unknown, but anecdotal information suggests probable decline. Listed as Vulnerable to Extinction in Qld and internationally. Long-term survival prospects outside Australian area poor. Along TNQ coast, now generally rare around Cairns and Mackay. Most common in Townsville-Cardwell area, especially in Hinchinbrook dugong sanctuary.

Threats: Sharks may be important predators of calves, but not adults. Human activities — gill nets, indigenous hunting, boat strikes — are major threats. Habitat loss, through destruction of seagrass beds by coastal developments, or displacement of dugongs by high levels of boat traffic, is also of concern.

Notes: Surfaces briefly to breathe every 1–5 mins. Leaves serpentine feeding trails in seagrass meadows (10–20 cm wide and 1–10 m long).

ABOUT THE AUTHORS

Andrew Amey, PhD, is a Senior Technician (Vertebrates) at the Queensland Museum. His research interests are the biology of dragons and frogs. Identification of snakes is a prominent part of his work at the museum.

Chris Burwell, PhD, is a Curator (Insects) at the Queensland Museum. His main research interest is in the bees, wasps and ants, the Hymenoptera. He particularly enjoys unraveling the taxonomy and biology of minute parasitic wasps.

John Cann (OAM) is an international authority on Australian freshwater turtles and author of *Australian Freshwater Turtles*. John is an Honorary Consultant to the Queensland Musuem and is an advisor to the Tortoise and Turtle Specialist Group of the IUCN Species Survival Commission.

Lester Cannon, PhD, is a Senior Curator (Worms) at the Queensland Museum where he has been studying and writing about parasitic and free-living worms since 1976. Lester is especially interested in flatworms, good food, fine music and travel – though not necessarily in that order.

Patrick Couper is a Curator (Vertebrates) at the Queensland Museum. His research is on the taxonomy and zoogeography of Queensland's reptiles, especially skinks and leaf-tailed geckos.

Jeanette Covacevich, BA, MSc, is a Senior Curator (Vertebrates) at the Queensland Museum. She has had a long research interest in reptiles of Queensland. Snakes, particularly the potentially dangerous species, have been a special focus of her work.

Peter Davie, MSc, is a Senior Curator (Crustacea) at the Queensland Museum and is completing a PhD on crab taxonomy. Peter has written more than 45 scientific publications and contributed to

several popular books including *Wild Guide to Moreton Bay*. He is a past president of the Australian Marine Conservation Society.

Les Hall, PhD, has been studying bats for 35 years. He works at the University of Queensland, School of Veterinary Science. His research interests include a wide range of aspects involving bats and other animals.

John Hooper, PhD, is a Senior Curator (Sessile Invertebrates) at the Queensland Museum. He has published widely on the taxonomy and biogeography of Indo-West Pacific sponges. A major thrust of his present work involves investigating marine invertebrates for new chemical compounds with potential pharmaceutical use.

Heather Janetski, BAppSc, DipTeach, is a Technician (Vertebrates) at the Queensland Museum. Heather has experience in interpreting scientific information for the general public and has an interest in wildlife conservation issues.

Peter Johnson is a Technology Officer with the Queensland Parks and Wildlife Service who has specialised in mammal ecology, primarily macropods, since 1964. In 1971, Peter established the Captive Breeding Centre at Townsville where captive breeding of endangered macropods is still carried out.

Jeff Johnson has worked in the Ichthyology section of the Queensland Museum since 1977. He has accrued an extensive knowledge of Queensland's fish fauna. His current projects include the taxonomy of the family Haemulidae (sweetlips) and the biogeography of marine and estuarine fishes of Queensland.

Phil Lawless, BSc, is an Assistant Curator (Arachnology) at the Queensland Museum. Phil worked in the Crustacea and Social

History sections until 1991 when he settled in Arachnology.

Keith McDonald is a Chief Ranger with the Queensland Parks and Wildlife Service based in Atherton. His interests are the distribution, conservation and management of frogs, reptiles and earthworms, especially threatened species in the Tropics.

Geoff Monteith, PhD, is a Senior Curator (Insects) at the Queensland Museum. Geoff has a special interest in rainforest insects and has surveyed them extensively in Australia and overseas. He has also actively promoted public appreciation of insects through Museum displays and workshops.

Anthony Preen, PhD, has been studying dugongs from Moreton Bay, Hervey Bay, the Gulf of Carpentaria and the Arabian Gulf since 1985. His interests have covered many aspects of dugong ecology including movement, diet and the environmental factors affecting their distribution.

Robert Raven, PhD, is a Senior Curator (Arachnology) at the Queensland Museum and an international authority on Trapdoor, Funnel-web and Tarantula Spiders. He has named more than 250 new species from Australia, Africa, the Pacific and Thailand. Robert is also an authority on Redback Spiders.

Greg Richards lived and studied bats at Atherton with the CSIRO for seven years. He is now a wildlife consultant working mainly on bats throughout Australia.

Martin Schulz, PhD, studied bats in the Wet Tropics as part of his doctoral work. He is a wildlife consultant involved with a wide range of fauna including reptiles, amphibians, birds and bats.

John Short has worked in the Crustacea section of the Queensland Museum for 14 years. Through his collection responsibilities John has gained a detailed knowledge of the Queensland fauna. He is completing a PhD on the systematics and biogeography of Australian river prawns and has also published on the taxonomy of freshwater crayfish, crabs and shrimps.

John Stanisic, PhD, is a Senior Curator (Molluscs) at the Queensland Museum and is one of Australia's foremost experts on land snails. His main research interests are the distribution and taxonomy of land snails in eastern Australia, and their evolution in relation to the occurrence of rainforest and limestone outcrops.

Stephen Van Dyck, PhD, is a Curator (Vertebrates) at the Queensland Museum where he has worked since 1975. His research interests include studies of carnivorous marsupials in New Guinea and Australia and documentation of rare and endangered mammals of Queensland.

Ian Venables is an active member of the Queensland Ornithological Society, Royal Australasian Ornithologists Union, Australian Raptor Association, Australian Wader Study Group and several other groups. Ian is a guide and lecturer for many bird activities and has acted as an environmental consultant on birds for government and business.

INDEX OF SCIENTIFIC NAMES

INDEX OF COMMON NAMES